Bright Beginnings

מסכת

בבא מציעא

פרק שני - אלו מציאות

VOLUME I

GOLD FAMILY DEDICATION

אין העולם מתקיים אלא בשביל הבל תינוקות של בית רבן. שבת קיט:

The world is sustained in the merit of the Torah study of children (Shabbos 119B)

This groundbreaking project is dedicated in honor of the many thousands of young children whose learning will build the next generation of Torah, as they assume their roles as future leaders of Klal Yisroel.

We hope and pray that these Gemara Eilu Mitziyus Workbooks will provide them with the background and skills to begin their lifelong relationship with Hashem's Torah in an engaging and educationally sound manner.

לזכר נשמת

ר' ישראל שלום בן ר' בנימין צבי ע"ה

והאשה החשובה

מרת רחל בת ר' ישראל ע"ה

May their memories be blessed and may the enhanced Gemara learning of the countless tinokos shel bais rabban who will gain fluency and a love for learning through this unique workbook be a zechus for their neshamos .

Simi Gold
Dini & Mendy Gold
Shmuli, Diana, Chani & Avi

In loving memory of

Rabbi Chaim and Mrs. Chana Feuerman a"h

לזכר נשמת

הרב חיים יהושע בן ר' אברהם
אלטע חנה בת ר' אברהם

Family always came first to them. They gave their children, and later in life their grandchildren and great-grandchildren, every moment they had and were always "in the moment" when with us. They were an amazing couple, sharing every part of their public and personal lives as equal partners. They were extraordinarily respectful – to each other, to each of us, and to every person they interacted with.

They loved to learn and loved to transmit the knowledge they acquired to others. But mostly, they taught by personal example.

We are honored to partner with Rabbi Horowitz in this educational project from which our father derived much nachas, and we hope that the Torah learned from these pages will be a zechus for their neshamos.

Moishe and Malka Schreiber

Baruch and Ora Schreiber   Dovy and Hindy Schreiber   Nussy and Aliza Schreiber

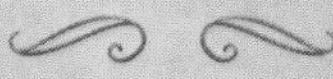

Rabbi Chaim Feuerman was my mentor, role model and rebbi for the past two decades and these lines cannot properly express my profound gratitude to him.

He was one of the wisest people I've ever met and a master at encouraging me to explore and self-discover, rather than be taught. He promoted independence, selflessly fading into the background, but always available to help.

I am eternally grateful for his friendship and candor, for his guidance and unwavering support.

Yakov Horowitz

RUTENBERG DEDICATION

This sefer/workbook is dedicated in honor of three men
who, each in his own way,
were instrumental in giving me my start in life.

My father

R' Aaron ben R' Moshe Rutenberg a"h

Rabbi Leibel Alevsky ylc"t

Executive Director, Chabad of Cleveland

Rabbi Shlomo Freifeld zt"l

Founder and Rosh Yeshiva, Yeshiva Shor Yashuv

Dr. Mark (Malachi Moshe Ben Aaron) Rutenberg

SCHERTZ DEDICATION

The Introduction to Gemara section
is dedicated to my childhood friend

Marc Schertz

לזכר נשמת **מנחם מנדל בן ר' משה** ע"ה

who tragically passed away
8 Menachem Av 5774 at the age of 48.

May the learning of thousands of Jewish children worldwide,
who benefit from these pages, be a Ze'chus for his Neshama.

Rabbi Yakov Horowitz

SUGYA DEDICATIONS

SUGYA #1 • SHIURIM 1-6

Dedicated to our mother, grandmother, and great grandmother,
the matriarch of our family

Evelyn Sokol

who is an inspiration to everyone she comes in contact with

Sora and Jerry Wolasky and family

SUGYA #2 • SHIURIM 7-9

In honor of our fathers

ר' שלום בן הרב יצחק מרדכי ע"ה
ר' וועלוול בן שלמה הלוי ע"ה

These great men did not have the benefit of formal Yeshiva Day school educations,
but nevertheless, greatly strived to learn Torah.

Dr. and Mrs. Joshua D. Gross & Family

SUGYA #3 • SHIURIM 10-11

Dedicated in honor of my father

Reb Aryeh Leib ben Reb Shlomo Berger ע"ה

who was a member of the Mirrer Kollel in Brooklyn for ten years in the 1960's
when Kollel learning was the exception rather than the rule.
He was scrupulous in setting aside significant time each day to learn Torah for his entire life.

May the learning of the many thousands of children
who benefit from this workbook be a zechus for his neshama.

Udi Horowitz

SUGYA DEDICATIONS

SUGYA #3 • SHIURIM 12-15

Dedicated by Michael and Estelle Stein *in loving memory of their parents*

Mendy & Shirley Stein a"h   Ephraim & Chaya Berger a"h

ר' מרדכי מנחם בן ר' זאב ע"ה ובת שבע בת ר' משה ע"ה

ר' אפרים בן ר' שמואל דוד ע"ה וחי' צפורה בת ר' יהודה לייב ע"ה

יהי זכרם ברוך

May their memories be for a blessing,
and may the enhanced learning of many thousands of Jewish children worldwide
who will gain fluency and a love for Torah learning from this workbook
be a zechus for their neshamos.

SUGYA #4 • SHIURIM 16-17

In loving memory of our grandfather

R' Moshe Avrohom ben R' Eliezer Zvi ע"ה

Yossie and Deena Eisenberger

SUGYA #5 • SHIURIM 18-19

In honor of our wonderful sons Zevi, Benny, and Ezra

We hope and pray that they will develop a genuine, lifelong love
for learning Hashem's Torah.

Dovid and Tamar Charnowitz

SUGYA #6 • SHUIRIM 20-23

Dedicated in loving memory of Our Grandparents ע"ה

Yudi and Chaya Sara Walden

INTRODUCTION

IN RESPONSE TO the many *menahalim*, heads of schools, *rebbeim*, and *talmidim* who requested it, we are delighted to present you with the introductory volume of our **Bright Beginnings *Gemara Eilu Mitziyus* Series,** including the *sugya*/topic of **"Yiush She'lo Mida'as."** Humbled by the overwhelming response of the Torah world to the release of our initial groundbreaking *Gemara Brachos* workbooks that in just four years, have already helped over 6,000 *talmidim*/students in 100 schools worldwide, we produced this new workbook to meet the needs of the many schools and students who begin their study of *Gemara* with *Eilu Mitziyus*.

"Yiush She'lo Mida'as" is the first extended *shakla v'tarya* (loosely, logical give-and-take) that beginner *Gemara* learners encounter. It also requirers them to compare and evaluate different scenarios of lost objects to properly ascertain the *halacha* for each of them. We invested a great deal of time, effort, and funding to create amazing visual tools – timelines, charts, and logical flowcharts – to help our beginner learners succeed and develop a lifelong love for learning.

Rabbi Aron Spivak lovingly authored both of the *Gemara Brachos* workbooks and this new *Gemara Eilu Metziyus* edition to introduce beginner learners to the beautiful and complex study of *Gemara*. Rabbi Spivak was a student in my eighth-grade classroom many years ago and I have watched him grow into a superstar *rebbi* with great pride and admiration. These workbooks are a testament to his knowledge, creativity, devotion, and ever-expanding skills.

Please note that we designed these workbooks to supplement the *Gemara*, not replace it. With that in mind, we recommend that students learn directly from a *Gemara* and use the workbook as a learning tool.

My dear friends Harry Skydell and Mark Karasick provided the initial seed money for Bright Beginnings. Over the past eighteen years, they were partners in our work with at-risk children and more recently our child safety/abuse prevention initiatives, by serving as chairmen of The Center for Jewish Family Life/Bright Beginnings. We are deeply grateful for their continued generous support and in awe of their tireless efforts for a seemingly endless list of Jewish causes.

On behalf of all those who will benefit from these pages, I would like to express our gratitude to my dear friends Mendy and Dini Gold for their generosity and vision in dedicating the Gold Family *Gemara Eilu Mitziyus* Series. May *Hashem* grant Mendy and Dini endless *nachas* from their beautiful family and success in all their endeavors.

I am deeply grateful to my dear friend and *Sfas Emes chavrusa*/study partner, Dr. Mark Rutenberg, for dedicating this first volume of the *Eilu Mitziyus* series, and for his interest in subsidizing the *"Yiush She'lo Mida'as"* section. I would also like to thank my dear friends Moishe and Malka Schreiber for their ongoing support of the Bright Beginnings *Chumash* and *Gemara* projects.

Producing creative Judaic studies materials like this workbook from initial concept to final product requires a very significant investment, and I ask those of you who may have the capacity to contribute development funds to Bright Beginnings or who would perhaps consider dedicating a future volume to kindly contact me at ryh@thebrightbeginnings.com. I also encourage you to email your comments, corrections and suggestions to publications@thebrightbeginnings.com to help us improve future workbooks in this series.

We are honored that Torah Umesorah distributes our Bright Beginnings *Gemara* and *Chumash* Series and I am deeply grateful to my dear friend Rabbi Dovid Bernstein, Director of Torah Umesorah's Aish Dos Training Institute, for including me in their three-year Senior Leadership Fellows (1997-1999).

We thank Mrs. Dena Peker and her talented and gifted staff at Dynagrafik Design Studio for their creative efforts in designing this beautiful workbooks, and Mr. Philip Weinreich of Noble Book Press for his assistance with its printing and binding. Mr. Tuvia Rotberg of Tuvia's Judaica in Monsey provided a great service to Jewish children worldwide by publishing *Gemara sefarim* (books) with punctuation to help ease the transition of beginner learners to Gemara and we thank him for graciously granting us permission to use his punctuated text in our workbooks.

This workbook would never have reached the finish line without the active participation of Mrs. Chaya Becker, administrative director of The Center for Jewish Family Life/Bright Beginnings, and I would like to express my deepest appreciation for all the incredible work she does.

May the enhanced learning generated by this workbook merit the memory of my father Reb Shlome Horowitz ע"ה, my mother Beile ע"ה, and of Reb Shlomo Nutovic ע"ה, the wonderful man who married her two years after my father's *petirah*. May their memories forever be blessed.

To our dear children and grandchildren, thank you for sharing me so graciously with the *klal* and for giving Mommy and me such unending *nachas* over the past thirty-nine years.

Over the past forty years, be"h, my wife Udi has been my full partner, confidant and closest friend, and she utilizes her incredible range of talents to help me actualize my dreams. May Hashem repay her with our greatest wish – that we grow old together and share *nachas* from our wonderful children and grandchildren.

Finally, and most importantly, I would like to humbly give thanks to Hashem for allowing me to, "dwell in His House," (*Tehillim* 27:4) and to teach His Torah for the past forty years. May it be His will that these pages bring us closer to actualize our dream of *V'chol banayich limudei Hashem* (*Yeshayahu* 54:13) that each and every one of our children become proud, committed and learned Jews.

Yakov Horowitz
Monsey, N.Y.

19 Sivan 5780
June 8, 2020

AUTHOR'S DEDICATION

This workbook is dedicated
in loving memory of my grandfather

יצחק שמואל בן יעקב משה ז"ל
Isaac Silverstein ז"ל

וְהָיָה הָאִישׁ הַהוּא תָּם וְיָשָׁר וִירֵא אֱלֹקִים וְסָר מֵרָע (איוב א:א)

That man was wholesome, just, G-d fearing, and shunned evil (Iyov 1:1).

He loved his family, had joy in every moment spent with us,
and was a living example of what it means to be a mentch.
He lived every day by the edict:

וּמָה ה' דּוֹרֵשׁ מִמְּךָ כִּי אִם עֲשׂוֹת מִשְׁפָּט וְאַהֲבַת חֶסֶד
וְהַצְנֵעַ לֶכֶת עִם-אֱלֹקֶיךָ (מיכה ו:ח)

And what does Hashem seek from you?
Only to do justice, love kindness, and walk humbly with your G-d (Micha 6:8).

ת. נ. צ. ב. ה.

A Letter to

MY FELLOW REBBEIM AND TEACHERS

סיון תש"פ

HOW FORTUNATE ARE WE who have the privilege of bringing our students into the world of learning גמרא. Whether our students are to become ראשי ישיבה or לומדי דף יומי, it is our hope that גמרא will be part of their lives for many years to come. Likewise, it is our hope that their future learning will be a source of joy, confidence, pride, and spiritual satisfaction. Our dedication, enthusiasm, and love will transmit the value of גמרא to the next generation.

We must remember that after they complete their short stay under our tutelage, our students may not have many more opportunities to develop the basic skills that are necessary to learn גמרא independently and confidently. This reality places a tremendous responsibility on us.

During the many years in which this work has been in development, I have been approached by countless fathers of students. These men, who were decades past their yeshiva years, remarked that their attitudes towards גמרא would be different in adulthood had they been provided with similar skill-building materials when they were in school. In short, it is up to us to make our students' first impression of גמרא a positive one.

When we were slaves in מצרים, we were able to cope with unimaginable levels of persecution and torment. However, the one point at which we threw up our hands was when we said "תֶּבֶן אֵין נִתָּן לַעֲבָדֶיךָ וּלְבֵנִים אֹמְרִים לָנוּ עֲשׂוּ" – "Straw is not being given to your servants, yet we are being told to make bricks." At that point, we felt the helplessness of one who is being set up to fail. This is a feeling from which we must shield our precious pupils. What is perhaps most frustrating for a student is being expected to succeed without having the skills or capability to do so. Conversely, a child faced with a task for which he knows the plan of action exudes a happiness that is palpable. If we hope to guide our students through the labor of love that is גמרא, we have to make sure that we are providing them with the tools and materials they will need to make their treasured "bricks."

This book is intended to serve as a tool to help you, the רבי/teacher, provide your students with the building blocks necessary to learn גמרא. This program will help you to break down the complexities of גמרא into bite-size pieces that your students will be able to absorb. It will also help them learn the mechanics of גמרא as well as develop a strong vocabulary of common גמרא words and jargon. Before long, they will feel pride and confidence in being able to decipher and tackle complex סוגיות one step at a time. With Hashem's help, you will guide them well on the first leg of a long and successful journey.

וִיהִי נֹעַם ה' אֱלֹקֵינוּ עָלֵינוּ וּמַעֲשֵׂה יָדֵינוּ כּוֹנְנָה עָלֵינוּ וּמַעֲשֵׂה יָדֵינוּ כּוֹנְנֵהוּ:

אהרן י. ספיוואק
Rabbi Aaron Spivak

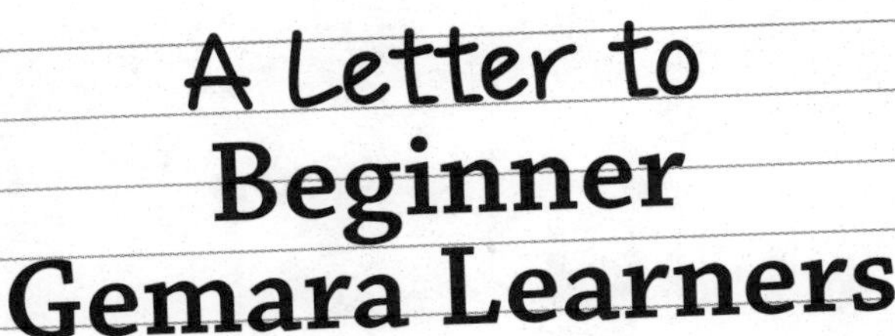

A Letter to Beginner Gemara Learners

Welcome to the world of learning גמרא. I hope that you will find it to be very enjoyable.

In order to be successful at learning גמרא, you will need many new skills, and be required to think in ways which you never had to think before. You will also have to become familiar with Aramaic, the language of גמרא. This book is designed to help you with all of this.

It is a lot of work, but if you take it one step at a time, you will get the hang of it. The skills that you will learn and develop in this workbook will help you with your learning for many years to come.

As you begin, keep in mind that every great תלמיד חכם started out at the same level that you are at right now. If you are determined and work hard, there is no telling how much you can accomplish!

Wishing you tremendous הצלחה in your learning,

Rabbi Aaron Spivak

Introduction to גמרא

LESSONS 1- 10

Introduction to גמרא

LESSON 1

VOCABULARY WORDS

1. **תַּנָא**
2. **אֲמוֹרָא**

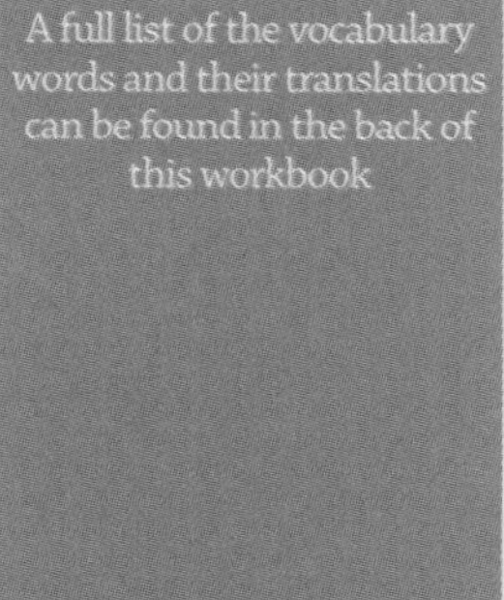

A full list of the vocabulary words and their translations can be found in the back of this workbook

Introduction

On שָׁבוּעוֹת in the year 2448 (from the creation of the world), מֹשֶׁה רַבֵּינוּ went up to הַר סִינַי and stayed there for 40 days. While he was there, Hashem taught him all of the הֲלָכוֹת of the תּוֹרָה. Hashem then had מֹשֶׁה write many of the הֲלָכוֹת in a סֵפֶר תּוֹרָה. This was the beginning of what we call תּוֹרָה שֶׁבִּכְתָב (Torah that was written). This part of the תּוֹרָה would be copied by hand many times, so that any member of the בְּנֵי יִשְׂרָאֵל could simply take a סֵפֶר תּוֹרָה and read what Hashem had said.

However, for some of the הֲלָכוֹת, Hashem instructed מֹשֶׁה to only write a hint in the תּוֹרָה שֶׁבִּכְתָב (such as an extra letter or word). For these הֲלָכוֹת, the actual הֲלָכָה would be part of תּוֹרָה שֶׁבְּעַל פֶּה (Torah that was taught orally).* This part of the תּוֹרָה was not written and could only be learned by listening when מֹשֶׁה (or one of his תַּלְמִידִים) taught it.

Additionally, there were still other הֲלָכוֹת that were not included in תּוֹרָה שֶׁבִּכְתָב at all (not even with a hint). These הֲלָכוֹת were called הֲלָכָה לְמֹשֶׁה מִסִּינַי.

*For example: Hashem taught מֹשֶׁה that just as a person must honor his parents, so too, he must honor his older brother. However, in תּוֹרָה שֶׁבִּכְתָב Hashem instructed מֹשֶׁה to only write "כַּבֵּד אֶת אָבִיךָ וְאֶת אִמֶּךָ – Honor your father and your mother." The הֲלָכָה of honoring an older brother remained in תּוֹרָה שֶׁבְּעַל פֶּה. Hashem had מֹשֶׁה write the word "אֶת" (which isn't really needed to understand the פָּסוּק) as a hint to the הֲלָכָה.

to גמרא

When מֹשֶׁה came down from הַר סִינַי, he began teaching the בְּנֵי יִשְׂרָאֵל all of the הֲלָכוֹת of the תּוֹרָה. He brought down the תּוֹרָה שֶׁבִּכְתַב in written form and taught them the תּוֹרָה שֶׁבְּעַל פֶּה.

At that time, מֹשֶׁה also began to make certain גְזֵירוֹת and תַּקָנוֹת (decrees and rules) about which Hashem did not command him. Hashem gave this ability to מֹשֶׁה and the חֲכָמִים. These laws are called הֲלָכוֹת מִדְרַבָּנָן. The חֲכָמִים of following generations added many more הֲלָכוֹת מִדְרַבָּנָן. These are also part of תּוֹרָה שֶׁבְּעַל פֶּה.

The הֲלָכוֹת of the תּוֹרָה can be divided into four categories:

1. הֲלָכוֹת taught to מֹשֶׁה and written in תּוֹרָה שֶׁבִּכְתַב
2. הֲלָכוֹת taught to מֹשֶׁה and hinted to (but not specifically written) in תּוֹרָה שֶׁבִּכְתַב
3. הֲלָכָה לְמֹשֶׁה מִסִּינַי – Taught to מֹשֶׁה but not included in תּוֹרָה שֶׁבִּכְתַב at all
4. הֲלָכוֹת מִדְרַבָּנָן – Instituted by the חֲכָמִים

תּוֹרָה שֶׁבְּעַל פֶּה is made up of the last three of these categories.

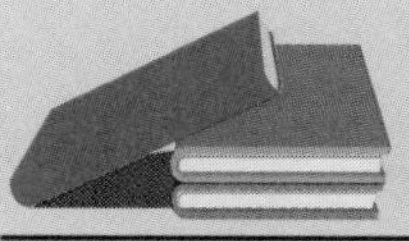

REVIEW QUESTIONS:

1. Who taught the תּוֹרָה to מֹשֶׁה רַבֵּינוּ?
2. What are the two parts of the תּוֹרָה called?
3. Which part (from question #2) was מֹשֶׁה taught on הַר סִינַי? (Trick question.☺)
4. What is תּוֹרָה שֶׁבִּכְתַב?
5. Which three types of הֲלָכוֹת make up תּוֹרָה שֶׁבְּעַל פֶּה?

Introduction to גמרא

LESSON 1 Review

KNOW YOUR FACTS:

1. To whom did ה׳ teach all of the הֲלָכוֹת of the תּוֹרָה? ______________________

2. Where did He teach the הֲלָכוֹת to him? ______________________

3. To whom did this person teach the הֲלָכוֹת when he came back from this place? ______
____

4. What is a הֲלָכָה לְמֹשֶׁה מִסִּינַי? ______________________

5. What is a הֲלָכָה מִדְּרַבָּנָן? ______________________

6. Which of the following are considered תּוֹרָה שֶׁבִּכְתַב (check all that apply)?
   - ☐ הֲלָכוֹת taught to מֹשֶׁה and written in the חוּמָשׁ
   - ☐ הֲלָכוֹת taught to מֹשֶׁה and hinted to in the חוּמָשׁ
   - ☐ הֲלָכָה לְמֹשֶׁה מִסִּינַי
   - ☐ הֲלָכוֹת מִדְּרַבָּנָן

7. Which of the following are considered תּוֹרָה שֶׁבְּעַל פֶּה (check all that apply)?
   - ☐ הֲלָכוֹת taught to מֹשֶׁה and written in the חוּמָשׁ
   - ☐ הֲלָכוֹת taught to מֹשֶׁה and hinted to in the חוּמָשׁ
   - ☐ הֲלָכָה לְמֹשֶׁה מִסִּינַי
   - ☐ הֲלָכוֹת מִדְּרַבָּנָן

8. Which of the following were taught by ה׳ (check all that apply)?
   - ☐ הֲלָכוֹת taught to מֹשֶׁה and written in the חוּמָשׁ
   - ☐ הֲלָכוֹת taught to מֹשֶׁה and hinted to in the חוּמָשׁ
   - ☐ הֲלָכָה לְמֹשֶׁה מִסִּינַי
   - ☐ הֲלָכוֹת מִדְּרַבָּנָן

MULTIPLE CHOICE:

	תּוֹרָה שֶׁבִּכְתָב		תּוֹרָה שֶׁבְּעַל פֶּה	Taught by Hashem		Originated from חֲכָמִים
הֲלָכוֹת taught to מֹשֶׁה and written in the חוּמָשׁ	☐	or	☐	☐	or	☐
הֲלָכוֹת taught to מֹשֶׁה and hinted to in the חוּמָשׁ	☐	or	☐	☐	or	☐
הֲלָכָה לְמֹשֶׁה מִסִּינַי	☐	or	☐	☐	or	☐
הֲלָכוֹת מִדְּרַבָּנָן	☐	or	☐	☐	or	☐

MATCHING:

_____ 1. The One Who taught מֹשֶׁה — א. ה׳

_____ 2. הֲלָכוֹת made by the חֲכָמִים — ב. הַר סִינַי

_____ 3. הֲלָכוֹת taught by ה׳ but not even hinted in the חוּמָשׁ — ג. הֲלָכָה לְמֹשֶׁה מִסִּינַי

_____ 4. The ones to whom מֹשֶׁה taught the תּוֹרָה — ד. מִדְּרַבָּנָן

_____ 5. The place where מֹשֶׁה learned the תּוֹרָה — ה. בְּנֵי יִשְׂרָאֵל

VOCABULARY REVIEW:

תַּנָּא ______________________________

אֲמוֹרָא ______________________________

Although מֹשֶׁה taught all of the הֲלָכוֹת to all of the בְּנֵי יִשְׂרָאֵל, he had one main תַּלְמִיד with whom he entrusted the task of teaching the תּוֹרָה after מֹשֶׁה was no longer living. This תַּלְמִיד was יְהוֹשֻׁעַ בִּן נוּן. If we keep in mind that תּוֹרָה שֶׁבְּעַל פֶּה was not written anywhere, we can begin to realize just how important יְהוֹשֻׁעַ's job really was. Any הֲלָכָה that would be forgotten would be extremely difficult to ever get back. However, יְהוֹשֻׁעַ proved worthy of his position and during his life לִימוּד הַתּוֹרָה flourished.

After יְהוֹשֻׁעַ was נִפְטַר, the job was left to פִּינְחָס בֶּן אֶלְעָזָר הַכֹּהֵן who, in turn, passed it on to the חֲכָמִים of the next generation. This began a chain which linked each generation back to הַר סִינַי. Each generation had one or two leaders who would lead the חֲכָמִים of their time in teaching תּוֹרָה to the בְּנֵי יִשְׂרָאֵל. They would teach the הֲלָכוֹת the way they had learned it from their רֶבִּי, going all the way back to מֹשֶׁה רַבֵּינוּ.

In those days, learning תּוֹרָה was very different than it is today. A child would learn with his father or a רֶבִּי and master all of the פְּסוּקִים of תּוֹרָה שֶׁבִּכְתָב between the ages of five and ten years old. Then, if he was lucky enough, he would continue learning תּוֹרָה and memorize הֲלָכוֹת until he was fifteen years old. If he had the privilege of continuing after that, he would begin to learn the underlying principles for the הֲלָכוֹת and how they are learned from the פְּסוּקִים (whether directly or from a hint).

There were no סְפָרִים in the בֵּית הַמִּדְרָשׁ other than סִפְרֵי תּוֹרָה (and perhaps the סְפָרִים of נְבִיאִים and כְּתוּבִים). When the רֶבִּי gave a שִׁיעוּר, he would teach everyone what he learned from his רֶבִּי and then they would review it until they knew it.

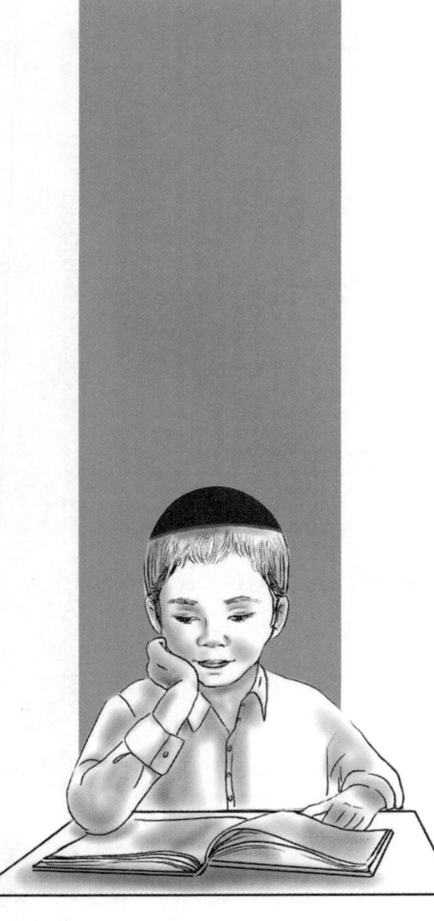

AGE:	LIMUD:
5 - 10	תּוֹרָה שֶׁבִּכְתָב of פְּסוּקִים
10 - 15	תּוֹרָה שֶׁבְּעַל פֶּה of הֲלָכוֹת
15+	Underlying principles of הֲלָכוֹת and how they are learned from פְּסוּקִים

This system worked well for many generations. This was how תּוֹרָה was learned when we came into אֶרֶץ יִשְׂרָאֵל, during the days of the שׁוֹפְטִים, through the first בֵּית הַמִּקְדָּשׁ, in גָלוּת בָּבֶל, and during the first half of the second בֵּית הַמִּקְדָּשׁ.

Towards the middle of the time of the second בֵּית הַמִּקְדָּשׁ, however, problems first began to arise.

The two גְּדוֹלֵי הַדּוֹר at that time were הִלֵּל and שַׁמַּאי. For the first time, they began to disagree about what the הֲלָכָה was in certain situations. Although the cases in which they had a מַחֲלוֹקֶת (disagreement) were limited, they each founded a יְשִׁיבָה (called בֵּית הִלֵּל and בֵּית שַׁמַּאי) and the יְשִׁיבוֹת had many more מַחֲלוֹקוֹת with each other over the years.

In the following generations, the Roman persecution made it more difficult for the חֲכָמִים to study with proper peace of mind. As a result, the disagreements increased. It was becoming more and more difficult to learn תּוֹרָה and have a clear picture of what the original הֲלָכָה was, as taught by מֹשֶׁה רַבֵּינוּ. This problem only became worse when the בֵּית הַמִּקְדָּשׁ was destroyed and the סַנְהֶדְרִין was exiled from יְרוּשָׁלַיִם (and finally disbanded altogether).

REVIEW QUESTIONS:

1. Who was the main תַּלְמִיד of מֹשֶׁה רַבֵּינוּ?
2. Why was יְהוֹשֻׁעַ's job so important?
3. How was תּוֹרָה learned in the early generations? What would it be like to learn in יְשִׁיבָה back then? How is it different from the way that you learn today?
4. What major change happened in the days of הִלֵּל and שַׁמַּאי? What impact did this have on those who learned תּוֹרָה? What happened in the years immediately following הִלֵּל and שַׁמַּאי?

Introduction to גמרא

LESSON 2 Review

KNOW YOUR FACTS:

1. Who was the main תַּלְמִיד of מֹשֶׁה רַבֵּינוּ? ______________________

2. What responsibility did this תַּלְמִיד have? ______________________

____

3. How was the תּוֹרָה transmitted to each future generation? ______________________

____

4. What would a child learn at each age?

   א. 5 yrs. old – 10 yrs. old ______________________

   ב. 10 yrs. old – 15 yrs. old ______________________

   ג. 15 yrs. old ______________________

5. Describe the main difference between the way that תּוֹרָה was learned in those days as opposed to the way we learn today. ______________________

____

____

6. What problem began to occur in the days of הִלֵּל and שַׁמַּאי? ______________________

____

7. What made this problem get worse? ______________________

____

MATCHING:

______	1. The main תַּלְמִיד of מֹשֶׁה רַבֵּינוּ	עָמוּד	א.
______	2. The main סֵפֶר they had	הֲלָכוֹת	ב.
______	3. What a child learned from 5 until 10	סֵפֶר תּוֹרָה	ג.
______	4. What a child learned from 10 until 15	דַּף	ד.
______	5. What a person learned from 15 and on	פְּסוּקִים	ה.
______	6. Began happening in the days of הִלֵּל וְשַׁמַּאי	יְהוֹשֻׁעַ בִּן נוּן	ו.
______	7. Problem got worse when they disbanded	תַּנָּא	ז.
______	8. One side of a page	סַנְהֶדְרִין	ח.
______	9. A full page (both sides)	אֲמוֹרָא	ט.
______	10. חָכָם from the מִשְׁנָה	מַחֲלוֹקֶת	י.
______	11. חָכָם from the גְמָרָא	**Underlying principles of הֲלָכוֹת**	יא.

VOCABULARY REVIEW:

אֲמוֹרָא ______________________________

שַׁקְלָא וְטַרְיָא ______________________________

דַּף ______________________________

תַּנָּא ______________________________

סוּגְיָא ______________________________

עָמוּד ______________________________

LESSON 3

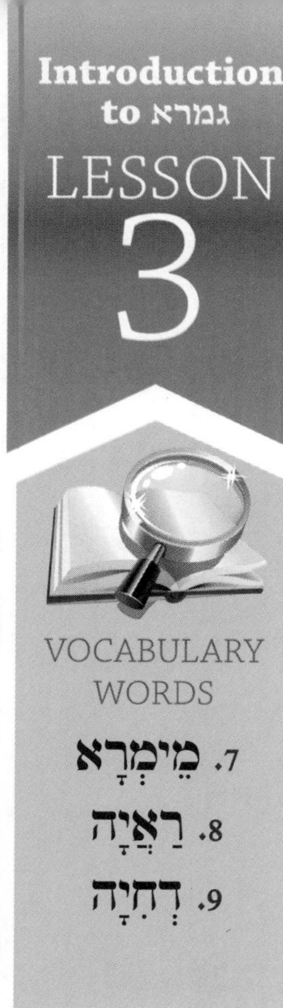

The future of תּוֹרָה looked like it was in trouble. As always, ה׳ saved us. This time, ה׳ sent the יְשׁוּעָה (salvation) through the hands of a great צַדִּיק named רַבִּי יְהוּדָה הַנָּשִׂיא. (Because of his greatness, he is sometimes just referred to as "רַבִּי".)

VOCABULARY WORDS

7. מֵימְרָא
8. רַאֲיָה
9. דְחִיָה

Although the תּוֹרָה שֶׁבְּעַל פֶּה was not supposed to be written down, רַבִּי יְהוּדָה הַנָּשִׂיא applied the פָּסוּק of "עֵת לַעֲשׂוֹת לַה׳ הֵפֵרוּ תּוֹרָתֶךָ" – "It is a time to do for Hashem so they have nullified your תּוֹרָה." This פָּסוּק means that at certain times of extreme need, a גָּדוֹל הַדּוֹר may violate a הֲלָכָה in order to save the generation from spiritual catastrophe. With this in mind, רַבִּי יְהוּדָה הַנָּשִׂיא wrote the מִשְׁנָה, which was a collection of the הֲלָכוֹת and other teachings that were taught by the חֲכָמִים from הִלֵּל and שַׁמַּאי until his own time. The חֲכָמִים from those generations became known as the "תַּנָּאִים".* Simply stated, הִלֵּל and שַׁמַּאי were the first תַּנָּאִים and רַבִּי יְהוּדָה הַנָּשִׂיא was the last.

*For the purpose of this work, we have defined the period of the תַּנָּאִים as having begun with הִלֵּל and שַׁמַּאי. It should be noted that there are those who use the term תַּנָּאִים to refer to a broader group of חֲכָמִים which began at an earlier time.

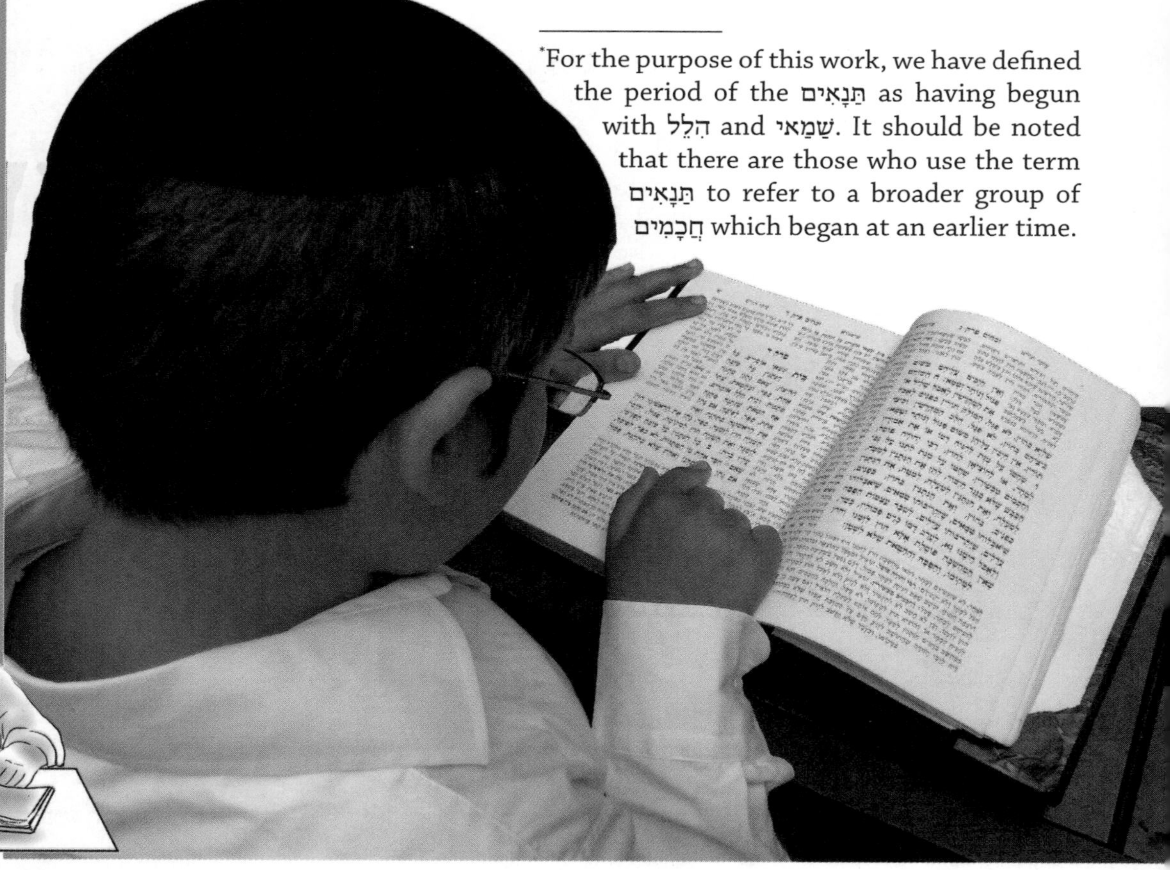

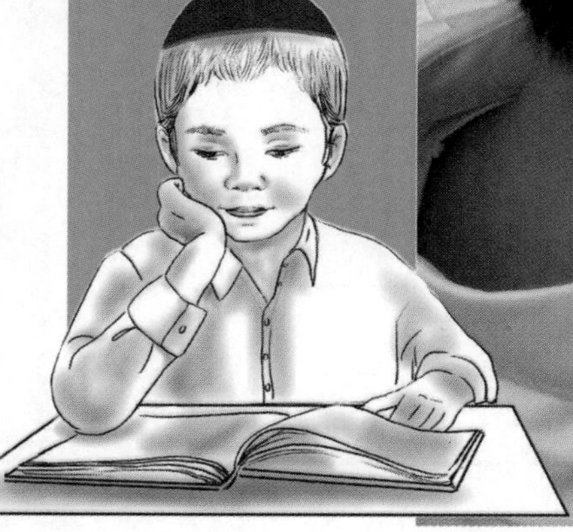

The מִשְׁנָה was divided into six sections called סְדָרִים. All of them together are known as the שִׁשָּׁה סִדְרֵי מִשְׁנָה:

זְרָעִים	The הֲלָכוֹת of planting and growing food
מוֹעֵד	The הֲלָכוֹת of שַׁבָּת and יָמִים טוֹבִים
נָשִׁים	The הֲלָכוֹת of marriage and divorce
נְזִיקִין	The הֲלָכוֹת of monetary issues and בֵּית דִין
קָדָשִׁים	The הֲלָכוֹת of the קָרְבָּנוֹת and the בֵּית הַמִקְדָּשׁ
טְהָרוֹת	The הֲלָכוֹת of טוּמְאָה and טַהֲרָה

Each סֵדֶר was then divided into מַסֶכְתּוֹת, each מַסֶכְתָּא was divided into פְּרָקִים (chapters), and each פֶּרֶק (chapter) was divided into מִשְׁנַיוֹת. For example, if a person wanted to find out what בְּרָכָה to make on fruit, he could look in סֵדֶר זְרָעִים, מַסֶכֶת בְּרָכוֹת, פֶּרֶק ו׳, מִשְׁנָה א׳.

REVIEW QUESTIONS:

1. What great problem was threatening the future of the תּוֹרָה?
2. Who did ה׳ send to save us from this problem?
3. What did he do to help the situation? Why was this a questionable thing to do? What reasoning did he have to explain why he could do this?
4. What is the מִשְׁנָה? Who wrote it?
5. Who were the תַּנָאִים? Who were the first ones? Who was the last one?
6. What are the שִׁשָּׁה סִדְרֵי מִשְׁנָה? What does each one discuss?
7. What is a מַסֶכְתָּא? How is each מַסֶכְתָּא divided up?

Introduction to גמרא

LESSON 3 Review

KNOW YOUR FACTS:

1. What great problem was threatening the future of the תּוֹרָה? ____________________

____

2. Who did ה׳ send to save us from this problem? ____________________

3. What did that person do to fix this problem? ____________________

____

4. Why were his actions considered questionable? ____________________

____

5. If so, why did he do this? ____________________

____

6. What are תַּנָּאִים? ____________________

7. Who were the first תַּנָּאִים? ____________________

8. Who was the last תַּנָּא? ____________________

9. Please describe the subject of each of the שִׁשָּׁה סִדְרֵי מִשְׁנָה:

א. זְרָעִים ____________________

ב. מוֹעֵד ____________________

ג. נָשִׁים ____________________

ד. נְזִיקִין ____________________

ה. קָדָשִׁים ____________________

ו. טְהָרוֹת ____________________

MATCHING:

_____	1. Laws of marriage and divorce	סֵדֶר נְזִיקִין	א.
_____	2. Laws of טוּמְאָה and טַהֲרָה	רַבִּי יְהוּדָה הַנָּשִׂיא	ב.
_____	3. Justification (why was it okay) to write down תּוֹרָה שֶׁבְּעַל פֶּה	סֵדֶר נָשִׁים	ג.
_____	4. Laws of planting and growing food	סֵדֶר זְרָעִים	ד.
_____	5. First תַּנָּאִים	סֵדֶר קָדָשִׁים	ה.
_____	6. Laws of the בֵּית הַמִּקְדָּשׁ and קָרְבָּנוֹת	הִלֵּל וְשַׁמַּאי	ו.
_____	7. Last תַּנָּא	סֵדֶר טְהָרוֹת	ז.
_____	8. Laws of שַׁבָּת and יוֹם טוֹב	עֵת לַעֲשׂוֹת לַה׳	ח.
_____	9. Laws of money and בֵּית דִּין	סֵדֶר מוֹעֵד	ט.
_____	10. First סֵפֶר of תּוֹרָה שֶׁבְּעַל פֶּה to be written	מִשְׁנָיוֹת	י.

VOCABULARY REVIEW:

מֵימְרָא ______________________________

רְאָיָה ______________________________

דְּחִיָּה ______________________________

סוּגְיָא ______________________________

אֲמוֹרָא ______________________________

שַׁקְלָא וְטַרְיָא ______________________________

Introduction to גמרא

LESSON 4

VOCABULARY WORDS

10. קֻשְׁיָא
11. תֵּירוּץ
12. שְׁאֵלָה
13. תְּשׁוּבָה

Rebbi Yehudah HaNassi had many great תַּלְמִידִים. Two of these תַּלְמִידִים were named רַב and שְׁמוּאֵל.* These two גְּדוֹלֵי הַדּוֹר (leaders of the generation) went to בָּבֶל to open יְשִׁיבוֹת for the people there. רַב opened a יְשִׁיבָה in the city of סוּרָא and שְׁמוּאֵל did the same in נְהַרְדְּעָא.

For the next few generations, people learned מִשְׁנָיוֹת. However, learning מִשְׁנָיוֹת alone was not enough. For although the מִשְׁנָיוֹת taught the הֲלָכוֹת, they did not include the reasons for the הֲלָכוֹת. They also didn't teach how these הֲלָכוֹת are learned from פְּסוּקִים. This part of the תּוֹרָה remained בְּעַל פֶּה, with each רֶבִּי teaching it to his תַּלְמִידִים. And just as it happened with the הֲלָכוֹת themselves, these reasons and sources began to become forgotten.

Once again, ה׳ sent the right people to save the situation. רַבִינָא and רַב אַשִׁי put together all of the teachings, beginning with רַב and שְׁמוּאֵל all the way to their own time. This collection of teachings was called "גְּמָרָא" or "תַּלְמוּד". (רַבִּי יוֹחָנָן had done something similar in אֶרֶץ יִשְׂרָאֵל

*This follows the opinion of the Rambam.

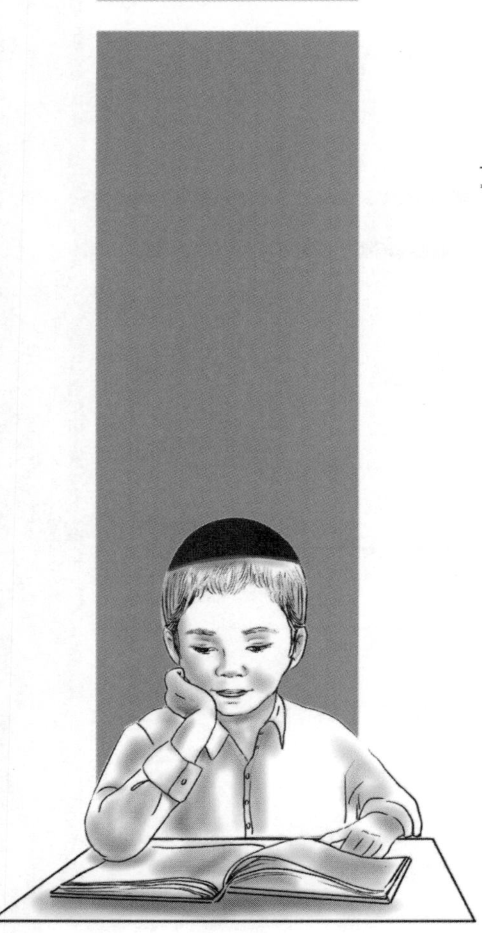

several generations earlier. To differentiate between the two works, the גְּמָרָא written in אֶרֶץ יִשְׂרָאֵל is called "תַּלְמוּד יְרוּשַׁלְמִי" and the one written in בָּבֶל is called "תַּלְמוּד בַּבְלִי". Our focus will be on the תַּלְמוּד בַּבְלִי.) The חֲכָמִים from these generations became known as the אֲמוֹרָאִים.

REVIEW QUESTIONS:

1. Which two תַּלְמִידִים did רַבִּי יְהוּדָה הַנָּשִׂיא send? Where did he send them?
2. What was the main thing that people learned in those days?
3. What did that סֵפֶר include? What didn't it include? How were these parts taught? What problem arose with that system?
4. Whom did ה' send to save us from this problem? What did they do to help?
5. Who were the אֲמוֹרָאִים? Who the first ones? Who were the last ones?
6. What is the difference between תַּלְמוּד בַּבְלִי and תַּלְמוּד יְרוּשַׁלְמִי? Which one is primary (the main one)?

Introduction to גמרא

LESSON 4 Review

KNOW YOUR FACTS:

1. Which תַּלְמִידִים did רַבִּי יְהוּדָה הַנָּשִׂיא send to בָּבֶל? ____________________

2. What part of תּוֹרָה שֶׁבְּעַל פֶּה was not included in the מִשְׁנָיוֹת? ____________________

3. What happened to this part of תּוֹרָה שֶׁבְּעַל פֶּה? ____________________

4. What is גְּמָרָא? ____________________

5. Who wrote the גְּמָרָא? א. תַּלְמוּד בַּבְלִי ____________________
   ב. תַּלְמוּד יְרוּשַׁלְמִי ____________________

6. Which גְּמָרָא do we focus on more? (Circle one) תַּלְמוּד יְרוּשַׁלְמִי תַּלְמוּד בַּבְלִי
   E.C. Why? ____________________

7. What are אֲמוֹרָאִים? ____________________

8. Who were the first אֲמוֹרָאִים? ____________________

9. Who were the last אֲמוֹרָאִים? ____________________

VOCABULARY REVIEW:

מֵימְרָא ____________________

דְּחִיָּה ____________________

רַאֲיָה ____________________

תַּנָּא ____________________

MATCHING:

______	1. A question asking for information	אֲמוֹרָאִים	א.
______	2. The first אֲמוֹרָאִים	תַּלְמוּד בַּבְלִי	ב.
______	3. חֲכָמִים of the גְמָרָא	תַּלְמוּד יְרוּשַׁלְמִי	ג.
______	4. A topic of discussion in the גְמָרָא	שְׁאֵלָה	ד.
______	5. The last אֲמוֹרָאִים	רַבִינָא וְרַב אַשִׁי	ה.
______	6. The back and forth discussion of the גְמָרָא	קֻשְׁיָא	ו.
______	7. Included in the גְמָרָא but not in the מִשְׁנָה	רַב וּשְׁמוּאֵל	ז.
______	8. גְמָרָא written by רַבִּי יוֹחָנָן	שַׁקְלָא וְטַרְיָא	ח.
______	9. A question that something does not make sense	סוּגְיָא	ט.
______	10. The main גְמָרָא	**Underlying principles of הֲלָכוֹת**	י.

VOCABULARY REVIEW:

קֻשְׁיָא ____

תֵּירוּץ ____

שְׁאֵלָה ____

תְּשׁוּבָה ____

Introduction to גמרא

LESSON 5

VOCABULARY WORDS

14. הֲוָה אַמִינָא
15. מַסְקָנָא
16. בְּרַיְיתָא
17. סְבָרָא

Before we start learning גְמָרָא we have to know how to "get around." In order to make learning easier, most גְמָרוֹת have an identical page layout. This means that if you look in your גְמָרָא at a certain word on a certain line on a certain page, almost anyone in the world will find the same word in that place. To make this possible, the גְמָרָא has a special page numbering system. Every page in גְמָרָא is called a דַף (בְּלַאט in Yiddish). Each דַף is numbered beginning with דַף ב. A דַף is one sheet of paper that is made up of two sides. Each side is called an עָמוּד. If you hold up a page in the גְמָרָא, the front side is called עָמוּד א and the back side is called עָמוּד ב. It seems simple enough, but be careful to remember that when your גְמָרָא is lying open, the first side you will read (the right-hand page) is עָמוּד ב and the second side (the left-hand page) is עָמוּד א. For example, in the picture above, the right-hand page is דַף כא עָמוּד ב and the left hand page is דַף כב עָמוּד א. The number of the דַף (using Hebrew letters) can be found on the top left corner of each עָמוּד א.

Most גמרות have regular numbers on top of עמוד ב'.
However, some גמרות have the דף and עמוד like this: כא:

בָּבָא מְצִיעָא פֶּרֶק שֵׁנִי אֵלּוּ מְצִיאוֹת 42

Very soon, we will start learning גְּמָרָא from the beginning of the second פֶּרֶק of מַסֶּכֶת בָּבָא מְצִיעָא. This פֶּרֶק begins in the middle of דַּף כא עַמוּד א. To make it easier to write, we abbreviate עַמוּד א with a "." and עַמוּד ב with ":". Therefore, if I wanted to write the same עַמוּד in short-hand, I could write "בָּבָא מְצִיעָא כא.".

To see if you understand this all, open your גְּמָרָא בָּבָא מְצִיעָא to לא:. If the first word on the page is "אֲבָל", you've got it!

REVIEW QUESTIONS:

1. What is a דַּף? What is a בְּלַאט? What is an עַמוּד?
2. What is the difference between עַמוּד א and עַמוּד ב?
3. How do I know which דַּף and עַמוּד I am learning?
4. I looked in my notes and it said the following: "בָּבָא מְצִיעָא כט."
   What does that mean?
5. What is the first דַּף in each מַסֶּכְתָּא?

Introduction to גמרא

LESSON 5 Review

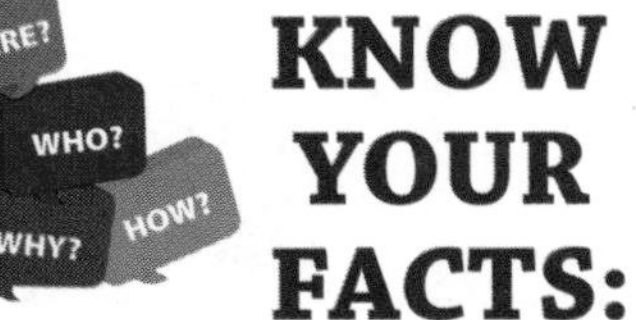

KNOW YOUR FACTS:

1. What is a דַּף? ______________________________

2. What is a בְּלַאט? ______________________________

3. What is an עַמוּד? ______________________________

4. How do I know which דַּף I am learning? ______________________________

____

5. The first side of each דַּף is called ______________________________

The second side of each דַּף is called ______________________________

6.

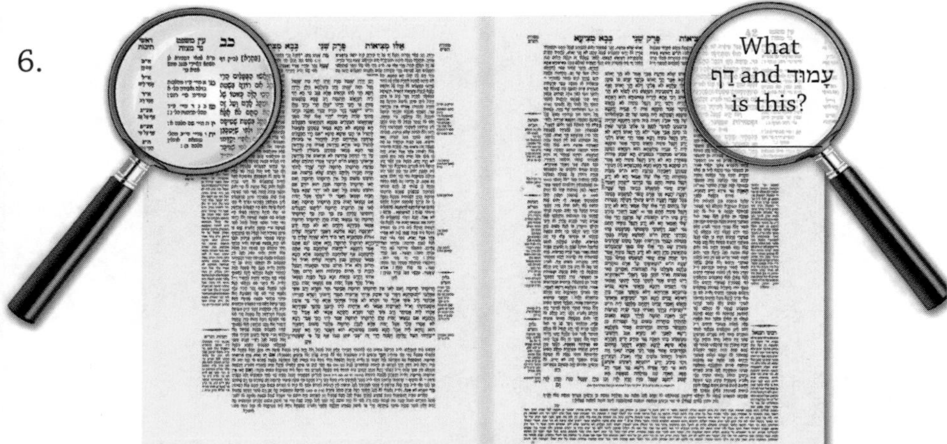

7. What do the following abbreviations mean?

א. קִידוּשִׁין לה. ______________________________

ב. זְבָחִים ב: ______________________________

ג. בָּבָא בַּתְרָא קמג. ______________________________

8. Please abbreviate the following:

א. מַסֶּכֶת עֲרָכִין דַּף יג עָמוּד ב ______________________________

ב. מַסֶּכֶת תְּמוּרָה דַּף כ עָמוּד א ______________________________

ג. מַסֶּכֶת כְּתוּבּוֹת דַּף קב עָמוּד ב ______________________________

TRUE OR FALSE:
(Circle T or F)

1. 

דַּף and בְּלַאט are the same thing.

2. 

There are two דַּף on every עָמוּד.

3. 

מַסֶּכֶת בְּרָכוֹת דַּף לא עָמוּד ב means בְּרָכוֹת לא:.

4. 

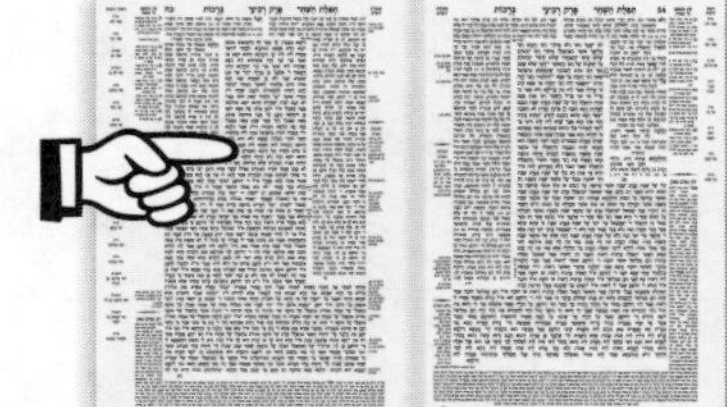
The hand is pointing to עָמוּד ב.

5. 

For שַׁבָּת דַּף מג עָמוּד ב I would write שַׁבָּת מג:.

6. 

The first page of גְּמָרָא is דַּף א.

7. 

To know which דַּף I am learning, I look at the top of עָמוּד א.

8. 

Every דַּף has עָמוּד א and עָמוּד ב.

9. 

Most גְּמָרוֹת have the same page layout.

10. 

The second פֶּרֶק of מַסֶּכֶת בָּבָא מְצִיעָא begins in the middle of דַּף כב עָמוּד א.

VOCABULARY REVIEW:

הֲוָה אַמִינָא ____________________

מַסְקָנָא ____________________

בְּרַיְיתָא ____________________

סְבָרָא ____________________

קַשְׁיָא ____________________

תֵּירוּץ ____________________

שְׁאֵלָה ____________________

תְּשׁוּבָה ____________________

עָמוּד ____________________

Once you start to learn גְּמָרָא, you will notice that the style of גְּמָרָא is extremely different than the style of מִשְׁנָיוֹת. Most מִשְׁנָיוֹת list הֲלָכוֹת without any discussion. Most of the גְּמָרָא, on the other hand, is nothing but discussions. In one discussion, the גְּמָרָא will be trying to figure out what the הֲלָכָה would be in a particular situation, and in another discussion, the גְּמָרָא might be trying to understand why the מִשְׁנָה said a certain הֲלָכָה. The one thing that these sections of גְּמָרָא have in common is that they are all discussions. Each topic of discussion is called a סוּגְיָא. In fact, once you start learning גְּמָרָא, you might be asked (either by a friend, relative, or anyone in shul), "What סוּגְיָא are you learning?" What the person means to say is, "What is the גְּמָרָא (that you are learning) discussing?"

There are times, though, while learning גְּמָרָא that you will see straight הֲלָכוֹת with no discussion. This will usually be in one of two cases. One possibility is that you are learning a מִשְׁנָה. Every גְּמָרָא begins with a מִשְׁנָה because, after all, the גְּמָרָא is just the explanation of the מִשְׁנָה. The other possibility is that you are learning a בְּרַיְיתָא. I can hear you asking, "What is a בְּרַיְיתָא?" I'm glad you asked!

When רֶבִּי was putting together the מִשְׁנָיוֹת, it was not possible for him to collect each and every teaching of each and every תַּנָּא. Some things had to be left out. Any teaching of a תַּנָּא that was not included in a מִשְׁנָה is called a בְּרַיְיתָא. It is very common for the גְּמָרָא to teach and quote בְּרַיְיתוֹת.

A בְּרַיְיתָא is very useful because of the following rule: An אֲמוֹרָא is not allowed to argue with a תַּנָא. The אֲמוֹרָאִים must accept any teaching of a תַּנָא whether that teaching is in a מִשְׁנָה or a בְּרַיְיתָא. If an אֲמוֹרָא says something and we then find a teaching of a תַּנָא that says the same thing, it is considered a רְאָיָה for the אֲמוֹרָא. After all, a תַּנָא agrees with him.

However, if an אֲמוֹרָא says something and we then find a teaching of a תַּנָא that says the opposite, the statement of the אֲמוֹרָא is considered to be disproven and is rejected. We cannot simply say that it is a מַחֲלוֹקֶת between the תַּנָא and the אֲמוֹרָא. The אֲמוֹרָא is forced to take back what he had said and accept the words of the תַּנָא.

There are two ways that the אֲמוֹרָא can avoid being disproven. First, he can explain that he is not really arguing against the תַּנָא because he was discussing a different situation than the תַּנָא. Secondly, if the אֲמוֹרָא can find a teaching of a different תַּנָא that teaches the same thing that he himself had taught, he can hold like that other תַּנָא. The אֲמוֹרָא would not be disproven for arguing with a תַּנָא, because it was the תַּנָאִים who were doing the arguing. The אֲמוֹרָא was simply stating which of the two תַּנָאִים he held like, which is perfectly fine.

An אֲמוֹרָא makes a statement.

A בְּרַיְיתָא teaches that a תַּנָא had said the opposite from what the אֲמוֹרָא taught. This is a problem for the אֲמוֹרָא.

The אֲמוֹרָא has two options to deal with the problem.

OPTION 1

The אֲמוֹרָא has a second בְּרַיְיתָא which supports his teaching.

OPTION 2

The אֲמוֹרָא explains that the בְּרַיְיתָא was talking about a different case.

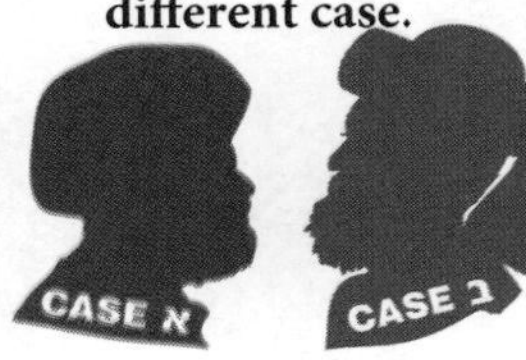

Consider the following (made up) example:

Imagine that an אֲמוֹרָא made the following statement: "The correct בְּרָכָה to make on potato chips is שֶׁהַכֹּל נִהְיֶה בִּדְבָרוֹ."

However, we then find a מִשְׁנָה that says that the correct בְּרָכָה to make on potato chips is בּוֹרֵא פְּרִי הָאֲדָמָה.

This is a problem for the אֲמוֹרָא. Since a תַּנָּא has taught differently, he will be forced to retract his statement and agree that we say הָאֲדָמָה on potato chips. However, the אֲמוֹרָא may be able to defend himself. If he were to find a בְּרַיְיתָא that taught that we should say שֶׁהַכֹּל before eating potato chips, the אֲמוֹרָא would no longer be stuck. He can simply say that he is agreeing with the תַּנָּא of the בְּרַיְיתָא. It is that תַּנָּא (and not himself) who is arguing with the מִשְׁנָה. It is certainly acceptable for an אֲמוֹרָא to choose the תַּנָּא with whom he agrees.

However, if no such בְּרַיְיתָא existed, the אֲמוֹרָא would have to use a different approach. He could explain that the מִשְׁנָה was talking about potato chips which were made from slices of potatoes. Because they are whole pieces of a vegetable, the correct בְּרָכָה is בּוֹרֵא פְּרִי הָאֲדָמָה. The אֲמוֹרָא then explains that he himself was discussing the type of potato chips which were made from powdered potatoes. These chips contain no whole pieces of vegetable and therefore get the בְּרָכָה of שֶׁהַכֹּל. This way, the אֲמוֹרָא has successfully defended his teaching. He has shown that he is not arguing with the תַּנָא, rather, he is discussing a different case.

Chips made from powdered potatoes and pressed in a mold (all chips are the exact same shape and size).

Chips made from slices of potatoes (each chip is a unique shape and size).

REVIEW QUESTIONS:

1. What is the main difference in style between מִשְׁנַיוֹת and גְמָרָא?
2. What is a סוּגְיָא?
3. What are the two types of teachings of תַּנָאִים?
4. What is a בְּרַיְיתָא? How is it different from a מִשְׁנָה?
5. Why is it so important to know when something is the statement of a תַּנָא?
6. What restriction is there on an אֲמוֹרָא?
7. What are two ways that an אֲמוֹרָא can defend himself if it seems that he is arguing with a תַּנָא?

Introduction to גמרא

LESSON 6 Review

KNOW YOUR FACTS:

1. How is the style of גְּמָרָא different from that of מִשְׁנָיוֹת? ______________________

____

2. A discussion of topic in the גְּמָרָא is called a ______________________ .

3. A teaching of a תַּנָּא can either be a ______________ or a ______________ .

4. With whom can an אֲמוֹרָא not argue? ______________________

5. If it seems that an אֲמוֹרָא is arguing with a __________, he can defend himself by finding another ______________ with whom he agrees.

6. Another defense would be to explain that he was not really arguing because he was talking about ______________________

____ .

VOCABULARY REVIEW:

הֵיכָא ______________	דַּף ______________
הֲוָה אַמִינָא ______________	סְבָרָא ______________
הָכִי ______________	הֵיכִי ______________
מַסְקָנָא ______________	בְּרַיְיתָא ______________
הָתָם ______________	הָכָא ______________

MULTIPLE CHOICE:

A) facts	B) discussion	מִשְׁנַיוֹת:
A) facts	B) discussion	בְּרַיְיתָא:
A) facts	B) discussion	גְמָרָא:

TRUE OR FALSE:
(Circle T or F)

1. T F Every teaching of a תַּנָא is found in a מִשְׁנָה.

2. T F A בְּרַיְיתָא is a teaching of a תַּנָא.

3. T F An אֲמוֹרָא may may teach something that goes against the teaching of a תַּנָא if there is another תַּנָא that supports him.

4. T F A תַּנָא may not argue with a בְּרַיְיתָא.

5. T F If we find a תַּנָא who said the same thing as an אֲמוֹרָא, it is a רַאֲיָה for the אֲמוֹרָא.

6. T F If there is a מַחֲלוֹקֶת between two תַּנָאִים, an אֲמוֹרָא is not allowed to choose to agree with one of them.

As we learned in lesson 6, גְמָרָא is made up of סוּגְיוֹת (discussions). In this lesson, we will begin to learn more about the nature of these discussions.

A סוּגְיָא is made up of שַׁקְלָא וְטַרְיָא, which literally means "give and take." However, the words "שַׁקְלָא וְטַרְיָא" really refer to the back and forth debating and discussing that goes on in a סוּגְיָא. Each part of the שַׁקְלָא וְטַרְיָא makes one point in the discussion. In this book, we will call each of these points a "step."

In this book, we will have eight different types of steps. We will now briefly describe each one (three of them in this lesson and five more in Lesson 8):

מימרא

A STATEMENT – Very often a סוּגְיָא will start with a statement made by a תַּנָא (in a מִשְׁנָה or בְּרַיְיתָא) or an אֲמוֹרָא. The statement might also be telling us about a מַחֲלוֹקֶת. This statement is not asking a question, answering a question, or proving anything. It is simply telling us a fact (usually a הֲלָכָה). This מֵימְרָא will likely be the topic of our סוּגְיָא. The גְמָרָא will then use the next steps to either prove that the statement is correct, ask a question that the statement seems to be wrong, or discuss it in some other way.

Illustration by Gadi Pollack for Beth Medrash Govoha © 2012

A QUESTION THAT SOMETHING SEEMS TO MAKE NO SENSE – A קֻשְׁיָא is the גְּמָרָא's way of attacking a מֵימְרָא or anything else that may have been said. When learning a קֻשְׁיָא we must know what it is that we are attacking. Which statement are we challenging? Whatever it is that seems to make no sense is called "the target." That is the thing that the קֻשְׁיָא seeks to prove wrong. Once we know the target, we then need to understand how the גְּמָרָא is challenging it. What reason does the גְּמָרָא have for claiming that the statement makes no sense? This part of the קֻשְׁיָא is what we call "the attack." The two main types of attacks are:

a. Using logic to show that the statement makes no sense

b. Quoting the words of a תַּנָא (in a מִשְׁנָה or בְּרַיְיתָא) that says differently than the אֲמוֹרָא. Remember, an אֲמוֹרָא may not argue with a תַּנָא. If his words go against the words of a תַּנָא, he is considered to have been proven wrong.

AN ANSWER – In a תֵּירוּץ we defend the original statement (the target of the קֻשְׁיָא) and show that it DOES make sense. There are many ways that this can be done. As we learn some תֵּירוּצִים, you will see how some of them work. However, there is one thing that all תֵּירוּצִים have in common.

In order to answer a קֻשְׁיָא, we need to find something that the גְּמָרָא had been assuming incorrectly. We call this incorrect assumption the **הֲוָה אַמִינָא**. The הֲוָה אַמִינָא is what led us to have the קֻשְׁיָא in the first place. The גְּמָרָא then provides the conclusion that corrects the mistaken assumption. We call this conclusion the **מַסְקָנָא**. With the new understanding that the **מַסְקָנָא** provides, we no longer have a קֻשְׁיָא.

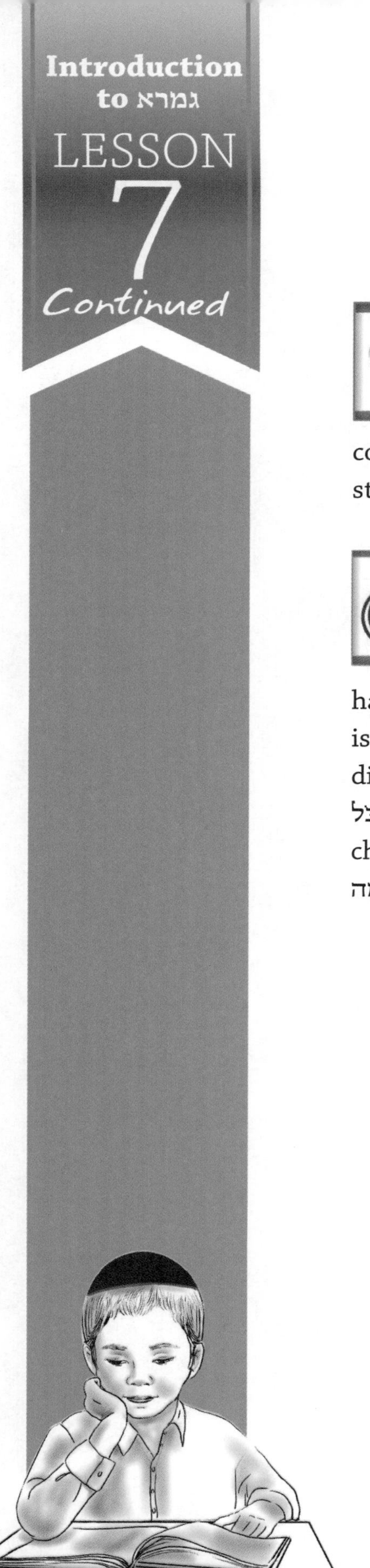

To understand this all, let's go back to the example that we gave in lesson 6.

STEP 1

An אֲמוֹרָא made the following statement: "The correct בְּרָכָה to make on potato chips is שֶׁהַכֹּל נִהְיֶה בִּדְבָרוֹ." That statement is a מֵימְרָא and would be the first step of our סוּגְיָא.

STEP 2

In the second step of our סוּגְיָא, we said that we have a מִשְׁנָה that says that the correct בְּרָכָה to make on potato chips is בּוֹרֵא פְּרִי הָאֲדָמָה. This is a קֻשְׁיָא on the אֲמוֹרָא. Since a תַּנָא has taught differently, it no longer makes sense to say that the right בְּרָכָה is שֶׁהַכֹּל. In this קֻשְׁיָא, the target is the teaching of the אֲמוֹרָא that potato chips are שֶׁהַכֹּל. Our attack is the מִשְׁנָה that teaches us to say הָאֲדָמָה.

STEP 3

Step three of the סוּגְיָא is a תֵּירוּץ. The אֲמוֹרָא explained that the מִשְׁנָה was talking about potato chips which were made from slices of potatoes, for which the correct בְּרָכָה is בּוֹרֵא פְּרִי הָאֲדָמָה. On the other hand, the אֲמוֹרָא himself was discussing the type of potato chips which were made from powdered potatoes which get the בְּרָכָה of שֶׁהַכֹּל. The אֲמוֹרָא has defended his teaching by showing that he is not arguing with the תַּנָא, rather, he is discussing a different case. In this תֵּירוּץ, we are showing that the קֻשְׁיָא was based on a הֲוָה אַמִינָא. We had been assuming that the אֲמוֹרָא and the מִשְׁנָה were talking about the same type of potato chips. This הֲוָה אַמִינָא was corrected with a מַסְקָנָא that they were talking about different types of chips. With this new understanding, the קֻשְׁיָא disappears.

REVIEW QUESTIONS:

1. What is שַׁקְלָא וְטַרְיָא?
2. What is a STEP?
3. What is a מֵימְרָא?
4. Which is a קֻשְׁיָא? What two things do I need to know in order to understand the קֻשְׁיָא?
5. Which is a תֵּירוּץ? What two things do I need to know in order to understand the תֵּירוּץ?

Introduction to גמרא

LESSON 7 Review

KNOW YOUR FACTS:

1. What is שַׁקְלָא וְטַרְיָא? ______________________________

2. What do we call one piece of שַׁקְלָא וְטַרְיָא? ______________________________

3. A statement which simply teaches us a fact is called a ______________________ .

4. To understand a קֻשְׁיָא, we must know the target and the attack.

   The target is ______________________________

   and the attack is ______________________________ .

5. The תֵּירוּץ explains that we only had a קֻשְׁיָא based on our wrong ______________________ . The תֵּירוּץ then provides us with the ______________________ that corrects it.

VOCABULARY REVIEW:

הָכִי ______________________________

דָמִי ______________________________

הָכָא ______________________________

הֵיכָא ______________________________

הָתָם ______________________________

הֵיכִי ______________________________

הֵיכִי דָמִי ______________________________

נַמִי ______________________________

TRUE OR FALSE:
(Circle T or F)

1.   שַׁקְלָא וְטַרְיָא literally means “up and down.”

2.  Each piece of שַׁקְלָא וְטַרְיָא is called a “step”.

3.  A הֲוָה אַמִינָא is a type of step.

4.  Every תֵּירוּץ has a target and attack.

5.   A מַסְקָנָא corrects our הֲוָה אַמִינָא.

6.  We only have a קֻשְׁיָא because of an incorrect assumption (הֲוָה אַמִינָא).

E.C. EXTRA CREDIT

Make up a סוּגְיָא of your own with the following three steps:

1. 

____

____

2. 

____

____

3. 
____

____

In Lesson 7, you were introduced to מֵימְרוֹת (statements that begin discussions), קֻשְׁיוֹת (questions that challenge מֵימְרוֹת), and תֵּירוּצִים (answers that defend the target). In this שִׁיעוּר, we will learn about some other types of steps of שַׁקְלָא וְטַרְיָא.

4.

A PROOF – Sometimes, the גְּמָרָא will seek to prove that something which was said is correct. This is called a רַאֲיָה. To understand a רַאֲיָה, we need to know two things. First of all, what is it that we are trying to prove? We need to know which statement we are trying to claim must be correct. We will call this "the object." Secondly, we need to know how it is that we are proving it. What is our reasoning for being sure that the statement is right? We will call this "the support."

There are two main types of רַאֲיוֹת:

a. Using logic to show that the statement must be true

b. Quoting the words of a תַּנָּא (in a מִשְׁנָה or בְּרַיְיתָא) that says the same thing as an אֲמוֹרָא. If a תַּנָּא had said the same thing, no other אֲמוֹרָא can argue against it.

You might notice that these are similar to the two types of קֻשְׁיוֹת that we learned about in Lesson 7.

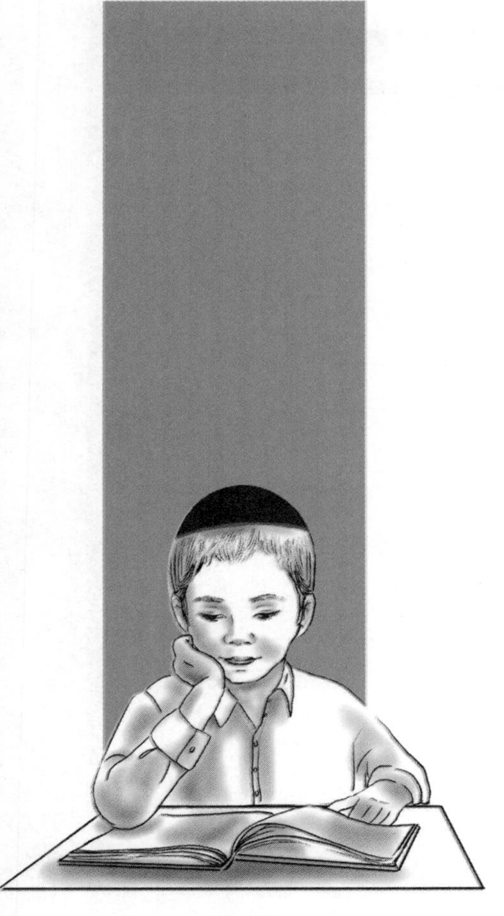

5. דחיה

A REJECTION OF A רַאֲיָה - Not every רַאֲיָה is as solid as we thought it was when it was first presented. There are times when the גְמָרָא is able to show that what was thought to be a good support does not actually prove the object to be correct. This is called a דְחִיָה. A דְחִיָה is very similar to a תֵּירוּץ. It is also made up of a הֲוָה אַמִינָא and מַסְקָנָא. The גְמָרָא will explain that the proof was based on an incorrect assumption. The גְמָרָא then gives us the correct conclusion which leaves us without a proof at all.

6. שאלה

A QUESTION WHICH ASKS FOR INFORMATION - Often, the גְמָרָא will not be attacking or proving something which was said before. Instead, it will be asking a question about something which was not yet taught. This is called a שְׁאֵלָה. Most of the time, a שְׁאֵלָה will be asking about what the הֲלָכָה would be in a specific case.

7. תשובה

A RESPONSE TO A שְׁאֵלָה - When **the גְמָרָא provides the answer to the שְׁאֵלָה** it is called the תְּשׁוּבָה. Sometimes, the תְּשׁוּבָה will be a direct answer. Other times, the גְמָרָא will simply quote a source which provides the information we wanted. This is helpful because it provides a source for the answer to our question.

A CONCLUSION - When the גְּמָרָא gives a final decision about something, we call it a מַסְקָנָא. If we have a discussion about what the הֲלָכָה would be in particular case, the גְּמָרָא might give us a final פְּסַק הֲלָכָה (halachic ruling). Another type of מַסְקָנָא might be to declare that a particular רַאֲיָה successfully proves its point. A מַסְקָנָא might tell us that we do not have an answer to our question.

It is important to know the difference between a מַסְקָנָא which gives a final decision (and is a step in the שַׁקְלָא וְטַרְיָא) and the type of מַסְקָנָא which corrects a הֲוָה אַמִינָא (and is not its own step - it is part of a תֵּירוּץ). Although we use the word מַסְקָנָא for both, they are different things.

To make sure this is clear, let's continue our "סוּגְיָא" about potato chips. If you remember, we had three steps so far. If you don't remember them, take a quick moment to review them (on pages 30-31).

STEP 4

The גְּמָרָא proves that the אֲמוֹרָא is correct by quoting a בְּרַיְיתָא. In the בְּרַיְיתָא, a תַּנָא teaches that the בְּרָכָה for chips is שֶׁהַכֹּל. This בְּרַיְיתָא is a proof to the אֲמוֹרָא because it teaches the same הֲלָכָה as he had said. The **object** of the רַאֲיָה is the original statement made by the אֲמוֹרָא about the בְּרָכָה on potato chips. The **support** is the בְּרַיְיתָא which seems to teach the same הֲלָכָה.

Illustration by Gadi Pollack for Beth Medrash Govoha © 2012

STEP 5

דחיה

The גְּמָרָא rejects the רַאֲיָה by explaining that we were making an incorrect assumption. Our הֲוָה אַמִינָא was that when the בְּרַיְיתָא said that the בְּרָכָה for chips is שֶׁהַכֹּל, it was talking about potato chips. The מַסְקָנָא, however, is that the בְּרַיְיתָא was speaking about chocolate chips, which everyone agrees have the בְּרָכָה of שֶׁהַכֹּל. Therefore, the בְּרַיְיתָא is not a רַאֲיָה at all in our discussion of potato chips.

Seemed like a good proof.

No longer seems like a good proof.

ראיה

STEP 6

The גְּמָרָא tries one more time to prove the אֲמוֹרָא correct. This time, it quotes a (different) בְּרַיְיתָא that is a bit more specific. This בְּרַיְיתָא says that when potato chips are made from slices of potato chips the correct בְּרָכָה is הָאֲדָמָה, but those made from powdered potatoes are שֶׁהַכֹּל. This בְּרַיְיתָא proves that the אֲמוֹרָא's statement is correct (the way we explained it in Step #3). Once again, the object of the רַאֲיָה is the statement about the בְּרָכָה on potato chips and the support is the בְּרַיְיתָא.

שאלה

STEP 7

The גְּמָרָא then asks what the correct בְּרָכָה would be for corn chips. This question is not challenging anything that we said before. It is simply asking for more information that is important for us to know.

What בְּרָכָה?

תשובה

STEP 8

The גְּמָרָא answers the שְׁאֵלָה by quoting yet another בְּרַיְיתָא that teaches that if corn chips are made from pressed (flattened) whole kernels of corn, the בְּרָכָה is הָאֲדָמָה. However, if the chips are made from milled (ground-up) corn, the correct בְּרָכָה is שֶׁהַכֹּל. This בְּרַיְיתָא clearly provides the information that we wanted to know and answers our שְׁאֵלָה.

STEP 9

In the conclusion of our סוּגְיָא, the גְּמָרָא states that the הֲלָכָה is that any chips which are made from whole pieces of a vegetable have the בְּרָכָה of הָאֲדָמָה, and those chips which are made from vegetables that have been ground into powder have the בְּרָכָה of שֶׁהַכֹּל. This statement concludes the discussion.

Please remember that this "סוּגְיָא" has been completely made up. Therefore, keep in mind the following:

1. Not all סוּגְיוֹת have the same number or order of steps. Even though our example סוּגְיָא had nine steps, actual סוּגְיוֹת can have far fewer or far more steps. You might learn a סוּגְיָא that has only two steps followed by another one with thirty-two steps. Furthermore, the order of steps can be any combination of the eight types of steps we have discussed.

2. The statements and בְּרַיְיתוֹת which were quoted are not real. Therefore, it is important to not rely on this "סוּגְיָא" for actual הֲלָכָה. If you are unsure of the correct בְּרָכָה to make on a food (chips included), ask your rebbe, rav, or parent.

REVIEW QUESTIONS:

1. What is a רַאֲיָה? What two things do I need to know in order to understand the רַאֲיָה? What are two common types of רַאֲיוֹת?
2. What is a דְחִיָה? What two things do I need to know in order to understand the דְחִיָה?
3. What is a שְׁאֵלָה? How is it different from a קַשְׁיָא?
4. What is a תְּשׁוּבָה?
5. What is a מַסְקָנָא (the type of step)? How is it different from the מַסְקָנָא that corrects a הֲוָה אַמִינָא?

Introduction to גמרא

LESSON 8 Review

KNOW YOUR FACTS:

1. To understand a רַאֲיָה, we must know the object and the support.

   The object is ____________________ and the support is ____________________.

2. A דְחִיָּה explains that we only had a רַאֲיָה based on our wrong ____________________.

   The דְחִיָּה then provides us with the ____________________ that corrects it.

3. A שְׁאֵלָה is a question that ____________________.

   This is different than a קֻשְׁיָא, which is a question that ____________________.

4. What is a תְּשׁוּבָה? ____________________.

5. The conclusion of a סוּגְיָא is called the ____________________.

VOCABULARY REVIEW:

דָמִי ____________________

טוּבָא ____________________

הֵיכִי דָמִי ____________________

הֵיכָא ____________________

בָּצִיר ____________________

דְ ____________________

MATCHING:

Match each item to the type of step it is.

______	1. I can prove that I am right because ...	מֵימְרָא	א.
______	2. What is the הֲלָכָה if ...?	קֻשְׁיָא	ב.
______	3. The גְּמָרָא ends off by saying that the הֲלָכָה is ...	תֵּירוּץ	ג.
______	4. It's not a רַאֲיָה because the בְּרַיְיתָא really meant ...	רַאֲיָה	ד.
______	5. It's not a קֻשְׁיָא because the בְּרַיְיתָא really meant ...	דְחִיָּה	ה.
______	6. The סוּגְיָא begins by telling us ...	שְׁאֵלָה	ו.
______	7. The answer to your שְׁאֵלָה is ...	תְּשׁוּבָה	ז.
______	8. How can you say ...? We have a בְּרַיְיתָא that says ...!	מַסְקָנָא	ח.

E.C. EXTRA CREDIT

Write your own (made up) סוּגְיָא with at least five steps. Make sure to write what type of step each one is.

STEP 1 ______________________________

____

STEP 2 ______________________________

____

STEP 3 ______________________________

____

STEP 4 ______________________________

____

STEP 5 ______________________________

____

When we begin learning גְּמָרָא (after only two more lessons!), we will be learning a מַסֶכְתָּא called **בָּבָא מְצִיעָא**. The name of this מַסֶכְתָּא means "[The] middle gate." This might sound like a strange name for a מַסֶכְתָּא. After all, it doesn't really discuss gates. Also, what is it the middle gate of?

Let's explain. When רַבִּי יְהוּדָה הַנָּשִׂיא was putting together סֵדֶר נְזִיקִין, he started with a מַסֶכְתָּא that was also called נְזִיקִין, which had thirty פְּרָקִים.

However, רֶבִּי decided that this מַסֶכְתָּא was too long and needed to be divided. He then split the מַסֶכְתָּא into three smaller מַסֶכְתּוֹת, each one with ten פְּרָקִים. He called each of these smaller מַסֶכְתּוֹת a "gate." The first one was called בָּבָא קַמָּא (The First Gate), the second one בָּבָא מְצִיעָא (The Middle Gate), and last one was called בָּבָא בַּתְרָא (The Last Gate). As we said, we will be learning בָּבָא מְצִיעָא.

However, we will not be learning the beginning of the מַסֶכְתָּא. Instead, we will be learning the second פֶּרֶק, which begins on .דַף כא. In גְמָרָא, each פֶּרֶק has a name (in addition to its number). The name of a פֶּרֶק is usually taken from the first words of the פֶּרֶק. The name of the second פֶּרֶק of מַסֶכֶת בָּבָא מְצִיעָא is:

אֵלוּ מְצִיאוֹת

פֶּרֶק אֵלוּ מְצִיאוֹת discusses the הֲלָכוֹת of what a person must do when he finds something that some else has lost. In short, the topic of our פֶּרֶק is found objects. Something that someone has lost is called an **אֲבֵידָה** (plural is אֲבֵידוֹת) and something that someone has found is called a **מְצִיאָה** (plural is מְצִיאוֹת).

When someone finds something that someone else had lost, there are times when he may keep it. The הֲלָכָה is that these מְצִיאוֹת are **שֶׁלוֹ** (his). There are other times when he must announce what he has found, so that the owner can claim it. The הֲלָכָה regarding these מְצִיאוֹת is that the finder is **חַיָּיב לְהַכְרִיז** (obligated to announce).

The heading on every עַמּוּד of our פֶּרֶק, showing the name of the מַסֶכְתָּא as well as the name and number of the פֶּרֶק.

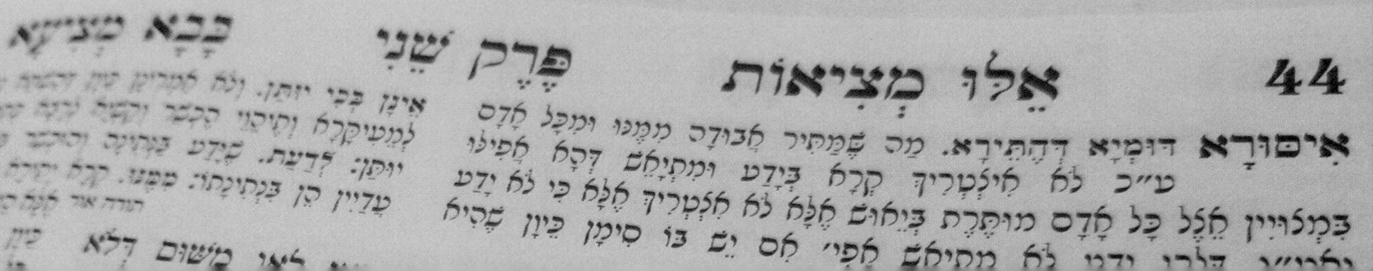

The thing that determines whether or not a person may keep the מְצִיאָה is if the owner has given up hope of getting it back. Giving up hope is known as **יֵאוּשׁ**. When a person has given up hope, we say that he was **מְיָאֵשׁ**. If the owner has been מְיָאֵשׁ on his אֲבֵידָה before the other person has even found it, the finder may keep it. If, however, when the finder finds the object, the owner still has hope of getting it back (he was not מְיָאֵשׁ), the finder may not keep it. Instead, the finder must announce what he has found so that the owner can claim it.

By now, you might be wondering how the finder can possibly know if the owner has given up hope of getting back his אֲבֵידָה. After all, he doesn't even know who the owner is! The answer to this question is that if it seems reasonable for the owner to get back his object, the finder must assume that he has not been מְיָאֵשׁ. However, if it is not at all likely that the owner could get back his object, we may assume that he has given up hope and the finder may keep the object.

Let's consider some examples:

Imagine that you found a notebook in the school lunchroom. You look at it and see that the owner has drawn a picture of a סֵפֶר תּוֹרָה on the cover. For a moment, let's put ourselves in the mind of the owner. He is probably waiting for someone to announce that a notebook has been found. He will be ready to tell the finder that the notebook is his. He will be able to prove that it is his by saying that the notebook has a hand-drawn picture of a סֵפֶר תּוֹרָה on the cover. The picture is a unique sign that he can give to show that it is his. Such a sign is called a **סִימָן**. In this case, the owner will not be מְיָאֵשׁ because he knows that he has a סִימָן which he can give to the finder. In this case, the הֲלָכָה is that you would be חַיָּיב לְהַכְרִיז. You would have to announce that you found a notebook so that the owner can describe his סִימָן and get back his אֲבֵידָה.

The הֲלָכָה would be different if you found a plain black pen (the type that you buy in a pack of twelve) on the sidewalk. The pen has no name on it and no markings of any kind. Because this type of pen is so common and has no

סִימָן, the owner will have no way of proving that it is his and he will therefore be מְיָאֵשׁ. The הֲלָכָה is that the pen is שֶׁלוֹ, meaning that the finder may keep it.

However, there are times when a person will be מְיָאֵשׁ even if he does have a סִימָן. Imagine that you had a really nice pair of headphones. On the side of the headphones you painted a blue stripe. This would be a good סִימָן in case you ever lost them. Unfortunately, you lost the headphones in middle of a very busy city. This is the type of city that has millions of people (if you have ever been to Manhattan you may know what I mean). It is not likely that the finder of the headphones

will be the type of person who is interested in returning them to you. It is much more probable that he will be happy to keep these great headphones for himself. Furthermore, even if he does want to return them, he will have no way of announcing his find to the whole city. In this case, you would probably be מְיָאֵשׁ because the chances of getting back your headphones are not very good. The finder may therefore keep the headphones even though they have a סִימָן.

This example illustrates a very important point:

יֵאוּשׁ is the thing that determines whether a מְצִיאָה is שֶׁלוֹ or if the finder is חַיָּיב לְהַכְרִיז.
It is not the סִימָן that determines this.

The importance of the סִימָן is that it very often, it will determine whether or not the owner was מְיָאֵשׁ. However, the סִימָן alone does not mean that the finder is חַיָּיב לְהַכְרִיז.

Now that we understand some of the basic terms and rules about מְצִיאוֹת, we will be ready to learn the מִשְׁנָה in the next lesson.

REVIEW QUESTIONS:

1. What מַסֶּכְתָּא will we be learning? What does the name of the מַסֶּכְתָּא mean? Why does it have this name?
2. What number פֶּרֶק will we be learning? What is the name of the פֶּרֶק? What is the topic of the פֶּרֶק? On what דַּף and עָמוּד does the פֶּרֶק begin?
3. What is an אֲבֵידָה? What is a מְצִיאָה?
4. What does it mean when something is שֶׁלוֹ? What does it mean when something is חַיָּיב לְהַכְרִיז?
5. What is יֵאוּשׁ? Explain what we mean when we say "the owner was מְיָאֵשׁ."
6. What is a סִימָן? Why is a סִימָן important?

Introduction to גמרא

LESSON 9 Review

KNOW YOUR FACTS:

1. What מַסֶכְתָּא will we be learning? ______________________

2. What number פֶּרֶק will we be learning? ______________________

3. What is the name of the פֶּרֶק? ______________________

4. What is the topic of the פֶּרֶק? ______________________

5. On what דַף and עָמוּד does the פֶּרֶק begin? ______________________

6. Define the following terms:

א. אֲבֵידָה ______________________

ב. מְצִיאָה ______________________

ג. יֵאוּשׁ ______________________

ד. סִימָן ______________________

ה. שֶׁלוֹ ______________________

ו. חַיָּיב לְהַכְרִיז ______________________

VOCABULARY REVIEW:

נַמִי ______________ טִירְחָא ______________

עַסְקִינַן ______________ הָתָם ______________

טוּבָא ______________ נָפִישׁ ______________

בָּצִיר ______________ אֲמוֹרָא ______________

MATCHING:

____ 1. The name of our פֶּרֶק

____ 2. The topic of our פֶּרֶק

____ 3. The דַּף and עָמוּד on which our פֶּרֶק begins

____ 4. Large מַסֶכְתָּא which was divided into three parts

____ 5. When a person gives up hope of getting back his object

____ 6. The number of our פֶּרֶק

____ 7. The הֲלָכָה that means that the finder can keep the object

____ 8. The middle gate

____ 9. Something that might prevent a person from being מְיָאֵשׁ

____ 10. The הֲלָכָה that means that the finder must announce what he found

א. נְזִיקִין

ב. בָּבָא מְצִיעָא

ג. אֵלּוּ מְצִיאוֹת

ד. אֲבֵידוֹת וּמְצִיאוֹת

ה. שֵׁנִי

ו. כא.

ז. מְיָאֵשׁ

ח. סִימָן

ט. חַיָּיב לְהַכְרִיז

י. שֶׁלוֹ

As we have explained, the גְּמָרָא discusses the הֲלָכוֹת that are taught in the מִשְׁנָה. Therefore, in this final lesson, before we begin the גְּמָרָא, we will learn the מִשְׁנָה that our סוּגְיָא will be discussing.

The מִשְׁנָה introduces the topic of the פֶּרֶק by letting us know about the two types of found objects (the ones that the finder may keep and the those that the finder must announce).

These found objects	אֵלּוּ מְצִיאוֹת
are his [to keep]	שֶׁלּוֹ
and these [found objects]	וְאֵלּוּ
he is obligated* to announce.	חַיָּיב לְהַכְרִיז

The מִשְׁנָה has told us that there will be two lists of found objects. The first list (which will be in our מִשְׁנָה at the start of the פֶּרֶק) describes the type of found objects that one mey keep. Next, the מִשְׁנָה will list the type of found objects which must be announced. However, that list will not be presented until the next מִשְׁנָה (which will be almost four דַּפִּים of גְּמָרָא later).

Now, the מִשְׁנָה will introduce the first list (the list of objects that the finder may keep):

These found objects are his [to keep]:	אֵלּוּ מְצִיאוֹת שֶׁלּוֹ
[If] he found	מָצָא
(1) scattered produce,	פֵּירוֹת מְפוּזָּרִין

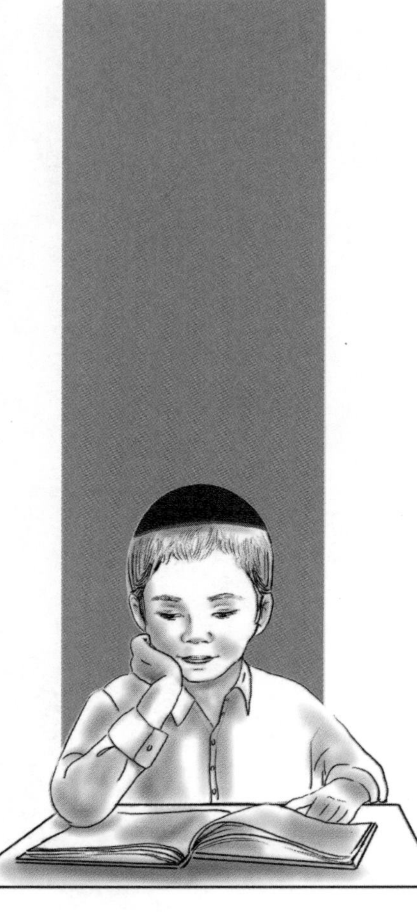

The first item on the list is scattered produce. The word that the מִשְׁנָה uses for produce is פֵּירוֹת. You are probably used to translating this word as "fruit." However, the מִשְׁנָה is using it to mean kernels of grain. (Scientifically speaking, the

*The word "obligated" means that someone must do something.

grain kernel is the fruit of the grain plant.) Our מִשְׁנָה teaches that if someone found kernels of grain scattered on the ground, he may keep the grain for himself. The גְמָרָא will discuss why this is so.

(2) scattered money (coins),	מָעוֹת מְפוּזָּרוֹת

Similarly, if someone found coins scattered on the ground, he may keep them. This is because there is no סִימָן on the coins themselves. Also, because the coins were scattered, there is no סִימָן in the way that they were arranged. Therefore, the owner will be מְיָאֵשׁ.

(3) bundles [of grain stalks]	כְּרִיכוֹת
in the public domain,	בִּרְשׁוּת הָרַבִּים

The term רְשׁוּת הָרַבִּים (which is best translated as "public domain") refers to any place where anyone may go without needing permission. This includes the street, sidewalk, or any similar place. If bundles of grain stalks are found in this type of area, the finder may keep them. Although it is possible that the bundles had a סִימָן tied to them, the owner will assume that in a רְשׁוּת הָרַבִּים his bundles will be stepped on enough to make the סִימָן fall off. He will therefore be מְיָאֵשׁ.

(4) and circles of pressed figs,	וְעִיגּוּלֵי דְּבֵילָה

When figs were grown in order to sell them, it was most common to press them into round, flat discs. They would then be packaged and sold.

(You can still find them sold this way in the supermarket nowadays!) Since this is the way that everyone makes them, there is no סִימָן, so the owner will be מְיָאֵשׁ.

(5) loaves [of bread] of a baker,	כִּכָּרוֹת שֶׁל נַחְתּוֹם

When a baker makes bread, he makes many loaves which all look the same. The loaves are then sold to many different people. Therefore, the loaves have no סִימָן. The owner will be מְיָאֵשׁ and the finder may keep them.

(6) strings of fish,	מַחְרוֹזוֹת שֶׁל דָּגִים
(7) and cuts (pieces) of meat,	וַחֲתִיכוֹת שֶׁל בָּשָׂר

Strings of fish all look the same. Although there are different types of cuts of meat, all cuts of a specific type look similar. For example, all rib steaks or all briskets look similar. The owner will be מְיָאֵשׁ because there is no סִימָן, so the finder may keep them.

(8) and shearings of wool	וְגִיזֵּי צֶמֶר
which were bought from their country,	הַלְּקוּחִין מִמְּדִינָתָן

Wool is the fur of a sheep. Cutting the wool off the sheep is called shearing. After the wool is sheared, it is made into a bundle. Each country had a unique way of bundling wool. However, within one country, all the wool looked the same. The wool would then be sent to a craftsman who would color and process it. If someone finds wool

which is still bundled and has not yet been processed, it is recognizable as coming from that specific country , so it is called wool which was "bought from its country." As we have explained, all such bundles look the same and have no סִימָן. That is why the מִשְׁנָה teaches that this type of wool may be kept by the finder. However, if the wool is found after it was given to the craftsman to color and process, it would have a סִימָן because of the unique way in which it was made.

(9) and bundles of combed flax,	וַאֲנִיצֵי פִשְׁתָּן

Flax is a plant which can be broken down to get fibers. The fibers can then be spun into threads known as linen. However, before the fibers are spun, they are made into bundles. Since all the bundles look the same, they have no סִימָן. The owner will be מְיָאֵשׁ and the bundles may be kept by the finder.

(10) and tongues of purple wool,	וּלְשׁוֹנוֹת שֶׁל אַרְגָּמָן

We learned earlier that wool which has not been processed may be kept by the finder. On the other hand, wool which has been processed may not be kept by the finder. However, there is one type of processed wool which the finder may keep. It was very common for wool to be dyed purple and combed into long strips. These were called "tongues of purple wool." Because these were so common, the dyeing and combing were not considered to be a סִימָן and the owner would be מְיָאֵשׁ.

The מִשְׁנָה now teaches the הֲלָכָה for these ten types of מְצִיאוֹת:

these are his [to keep],	הֲרֵי אֵלּוּ שֶׁלּוֹ
these are the words of רַבִּי מֵאִיר.	דִּבְרֵי רַבִּי מֵאִיר

רַבִּי מֵאִיר teaches us that these ten מְצִיאוֹת (and others that are just like them) may be kept by the finder because they have no סִימָן. However, רַבִּי יְהוּדָה הַנָּשִׂיא argues and says that even these מְצִיאוֹת may have a סִימָן in certain situations:

רַבִּי יְהוּדָה says,	רַבִּי יְהוּדָה אוֹמֵר
any [found object] that has something unusual in it	כָּל שֶׁיֵּשׁ בּוֹ שִׁינּוּי
[the finder] is obligated to announce.	חַיָּיב לְהַכְרִיז
How so?	כֵּיצַד
If he found a circle [of pressed figs]	מָצָא עִגּוּל
and [there was] pottery inside it	וּבְתוֹכוֹ חֶרֶס
[or] a loaf [of bread]	כִּכָּר
and [there was] money inside it.	וּבְתוֹכוֹ מָעוֹת

רַבִּי יְהוּדָה teaches that if a common item has something uncommon about it (like pottery in a circle of figs or coins in a loaf of bread), they must be announced.

The cases that רַבִּי יְהוּדָה lists seem so unusual that they certainly seem to have a סִימָן. It is hard to imagine why רַבִּי מֵאִיר argues and says that they do not have a סִימָן. The גְּמָרָא will explain what exactly רַבִּי מֵאִיר is arguing about. (However, we will not be learning that גְּמָרָא for a while, so you will have to be patient.)

The מִשְׁנָה ends with one more הֲלָכָה:

רַבִּי שִׁמְעוֹן בֶּן אֶלְעָזָר says,	רַבִּי שִׁמְעוֹן בֶּן אֶלְעָזָר אוֹמֵר
any כֵּלִים* (vessels) which are אַנְפּוּרְיָא	כָּל כְּלֵי אַנְפּוּרְיָא
[the finder] is not obligated to announce.	אֵין חַיָּיב לְהַכְרִיז

רַבִּי שִׁמְעוֹן בֶּן אֶלְעָזָר teaches us that when a person finds a כֵּלִי which is אַנְפּוּרְיָא, he may keep it.

If you're wondering what it means for כֵּלִים to be אַנְפּוּרְיָא, you're not alone. However, you will once again have to be patient and wait for the גְּמָרָא to explain this term.

Now that we have learned the מִשְׁנָה, you can work to master it. Knowing this one מִשְׁנָה thoroughly will help you tremendously for all of the גְּמָרָא that we will be learning for quite some time!

---

* A כֵּלִי (plural: כֵּלִים) is an object that a person uses. This includes dishes, pots, clothing, some types of furniture, and many other items. (If you want a detailed understanding of what is considered a כֵּלִי, you can learn מַסֶּכֶת כֵּלִים in סֵדֶר טְהָרוֹת.)

REVIEW QUESTIONS:

1. Why are we learning a מִשְׁנָה now? Why can't we go straight to the גְּמָרָא?
2. In which מַסֶכְתָּא and פֶּרֶק can this מִשְׁנָה be found?
3. What type of found objects are listed in this מִשְׁנָה?
4. What type of found objects are listed in the next מִשְׁנָה?
5. What are some of the found objects listed in this מִשְׁנָה? What is the הֲלָכָה when someone finds them? Why?
6. What הֲלָכָה does רַבִּי יְהוּדָה teach? What do we not understand about this הֲלָכָה? When will this be made clear?
7. What הֲלָכָה does רַבִּי שִׁמְעוֹן בֶּן אֶלְעָזָר teach? What do we not understand about this הֲלָכָה? When will this be made clear?

Introduction to גמרא

LESSON 10 Review

KNOW YOUR FACTS:

1. This מִשְׁנָה is found in ______________ מַסֶּכֶת ______________ פֶּרֶק.
2. Please **underline** the topic of our פֶּרֶק.
3. Please (circle) the title of the list in our מִשְׁנָה.
4. Please [1]number the items on the list.
5. What is the הֲלָכָה about the items on our list? ______________
6. רַבִּי יְהוּדָה teaches that if a found object has something ______________, the הֲלָכָה is that the finder ______________.
7. When learning רַבִּי יְהוּדָה's rule, we did not understand ______________ ______________.
8. רַבִּי שִׁמְעוֹן בֶּן אֶלְעָזָר teaches that if a found object has something ______________, the הֲלָכָה is that the finder ______________.
9. When learning רַבִּי שִׁמְעוֹן בֶּן אֶלְעָזָר's rule, we did not understand ______________.

אֵלּוּ מְצִיאוֹת שֶׁלּוֹ וְאֵלּוּ חַיָּיב לְהַכְרִיז אֵלּוּ
מְצִיאוֹת שֶׁלּוֹ ᵃמָצָא פֵּירוֹת מְפוּזָּרִין
ᵇמָעוֹת מְפוּזָּרוֹת ᶜכְּרִיכוֹת בִּרְשׁוּת הָרַבִּים
ᵈוְעִגּוּלֵי דְבֵילָה כִּכָּרוֹת שֶׁל נַחְתּוֹם *מַחְרוֹזוֹת
שֶׁל דָּגִים וַחֲתִיכוֹת שֶׁל בָּשָׂר וְגִיזֵּי צֶמֶר
הַלְּקוּחִין מִמְּדִינָתָן וַאֲנִיצֵי פִשְׁתָּן וּלְשׁוֹנוֹת
שֶׁל אַרְגָּמָן הֲרֵי אֵלּוּ שֶׁלּוֹ *דִּבְרֵי רַבִּי מֵאִיר
ר' יְהוּדָה אוֹמֵר *כָּל שֶׁיֵּשׁ בּוֹ שִׁינּוּי חַיָּיב
לְהַכְרִיז כֵּיצַד ᵉמָצָא עִגּוּל וּבְתוֹכוֹ חֶרֶס
כִּכָּר וּבְתוֹכוֹ מָעוֹת רַבִּי שִׁמְעוֹן בֶּן אֶלְעָזָר
אוֹמֵר כָּל כְּלֵי אַנְפּוּרְיָא אֵין חַיָּיב לְהַכְרִיז:

VOCABULARY REVIEW:

______________	שְׁקִיל	______________	טִירְחָא
______________	בָּצִיר	______________	אָתִי
______________	סוּגְיָא	______________	הָכִי
______________	נְפִישׁ	______________	טוּבָא
______________	הָדַר	______________	עַסְקִינַן

 |

MATCHING:

Match the following items with their pictures:

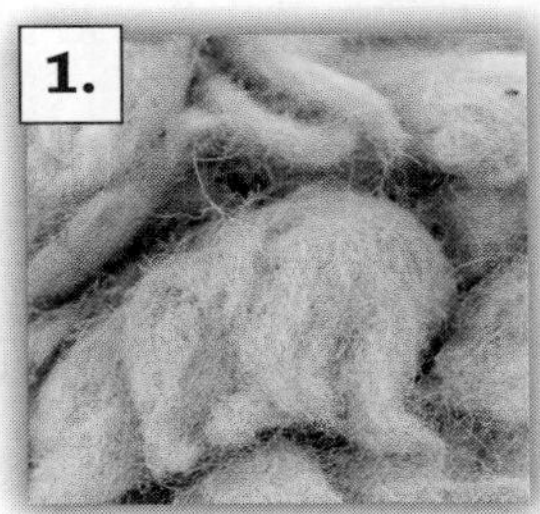

1.

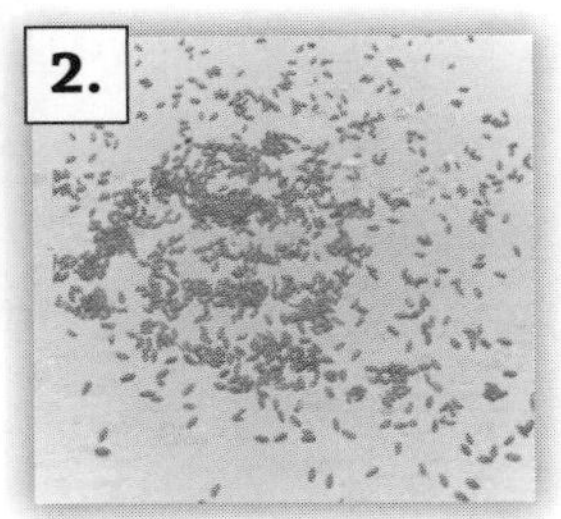

2.

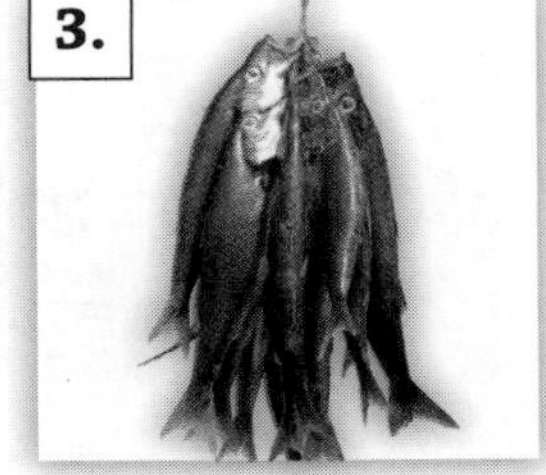

3.

4.

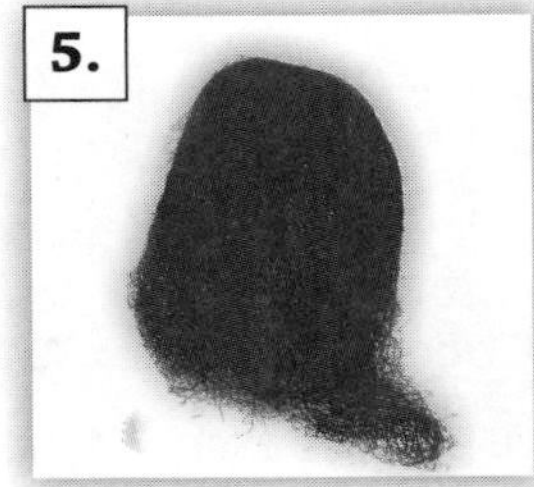

5.

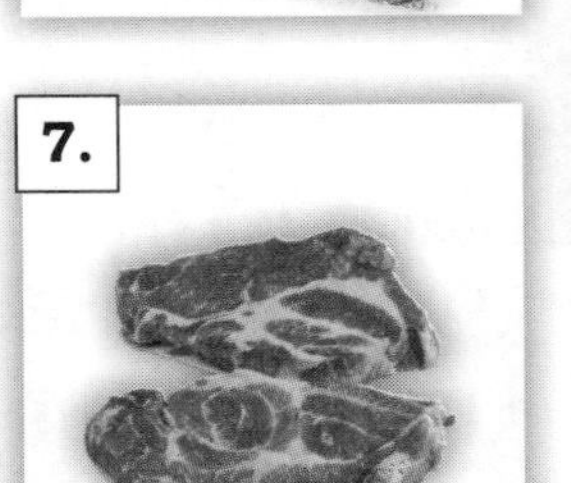

6.

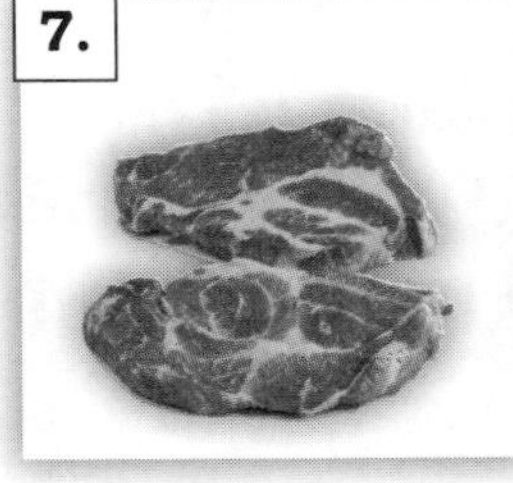

7.

8.

9.

10.

___ א. כְּרִיכוֹת בִּרְשׁוּת הָרַבִּים

___ ב. לְשׁוֹנוֹת שֶׁל אַרְגָּמָן

___ ג. גִּיזֵי צֶמֶר הַלְּקוּחִין מִמְּדִינָתָן

___ ד. פֵּירוֹת מְפוּזָּרִין

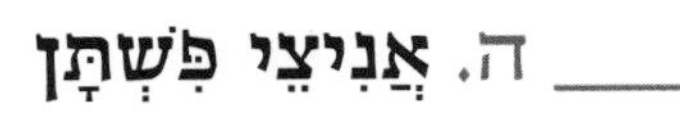

___ ה. אֲנִיצֵי פִּשְׁתָּן

___ ו. מָעוֹת מְפוּזָּרוֹת

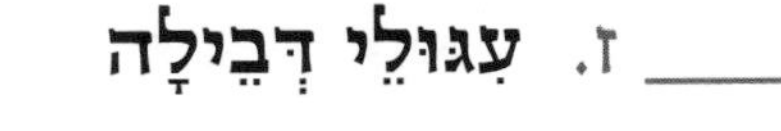

___ ז. עִגּוּלֵי דְבֵילָה

___ ח. כִּכָּרוֹת שֶׁל נַחְתּוֹם

___ ט. מַחְרוֹזוֹת שֶׁל דָּגִים

___ י. חֲתִיכוֹת שֶׁל בָּשָׂר

UNIT REVIEW

Please put the letter of the correct choice on each blank line.

Lesson 1

_____ taught מֹשֶׁה _____ of the הֲלָכוֹת of the תּוֹרָה on _____. Some הֲלָכוֹת were written down. These הֲלָכוֹת are _____. Other הֲלָכוֹת were only written with _____. Some other הֲלָכוֹת were not written at all and are called _____. Additionally, מֹשֶׁה and the _____ of later generations made other rules which are called _____. These last three types of הֲלָכוֹת are known as _____.

א. **הֲלָכָה לְמֹשֶׁה מִסִּינַי**
ב. **הֲלָכוֹת מִדְּרַבָּנָן**
ג. **ה׳**
ד. **תּוֹרָה שֶׁבִּכְתָב**
ה. **הַר סִינַי**
ו. **חֲכָמִים**
ז. **hints**
ח. **תּוֹרָה שֶׁבְּעַל פֶּה**
ט. **all**

Lesson 2

The main תַּלְמִיד of מֹשֶׁה רַבֵּינוּ was _____. His job was incredibly important because the תּוֹרָה שֶׁבְּעַל פֶּה was not _____. Each generation had _____ who would ensure that the תּוֹרָה was passed down to the next generation.

In those days, when a child was between five and ten years old, he would learn all of the _____ of the תּוֹרָה. Between the ages of ten and fifteen, he would learn all of the _____ of the תּוֹרָה. From fifteen years old and on, he would learn the _____ of the הֲלָכוֹת and the way that they are learned out from פְּסוּקִים.

Towards the middle of the time of the second _____, there began to be _____ about the הֲלָכוֹת that ה׳ had taught to _____. The חֲכָמִים who began to disagree were named _____ and _____. The situation became worse when the _____ left יְרוּשָׁלַיִם and later was disbanded.

א. **written down**
ב. **הֲלָכוֹת**
ג. **בֵּית הַמִּקְדָּשׁ**
ד. **הִלֵּל**
ה. **יְהוֹשֻׁעַ בִּן נוּן**
ו. **פְּסוּקִים**
ז. **חֲכָמִים**
ח. **סַנְהֶדְרִין**
ט. **מַחֲלוֹקוֹת**
י. **underlying principles**
י. **underlying principles**
יא. **מֹשֶׁה רַבֵּינוּ**
יב. **שַׁמַּאי**

(Hint: One answer is used twice!)

In order to save ____ from being forgotten, ה׳ sent ____ (his full name). The great צַדִּיק was also known as ____.

He applied the פָּסוּק of ____ to mean that because of the extreme situation, he should do something that is not normally allowed. What he did was write down the teachings of the ____. This was the group of חֲכָמִים beginning with ____ and ending with ____.

The סֵפֶר that he wrote was called ____. It was made up of the following six ____:

______ The הֲלָכוֹת of planting and growing food

______ The הֲלָכוֹת of שַׁבָּת and יָמִים טוֹבִים

______ The הֲלָכוֹת of marriage and divorce

______ The הֲלָכוֹת of monetary issues and בֵּית דִין

______ The הֲלָכוֹת of the קָרְבָּנוֹת and the בֵּית הַמִּקְדָּשׁ

______ The הֲלָכוֹת of טוּמְאָה and טַהֲרָה

א. סְדָרִים	ח. סֵדֶר טְהָרוֹת
ב. רַבִּי	ט. הִלֵּל וְשַׁמַּאי
ג. סֵדֶר נְזִיקִין	י. סֵדֶר מוֹעֵד
ד. תּוֹרָה שֶׁבְּעַל פֶּה	יא. תַּנָּאִים
ה. סֵדֶר זְרָעִים	יב. סֵדֶר קָדָשִׁים
ו. עֵת לַעֲשׂוֹת לַה׳ הֵפֵרוּ תוֹרָתֶךָ	יג. מִשְׁנָיוֹת
ז. רַבִּי יְהוּדָה הַנָּשִׂיא	יד. סֵדֶר נָשִׁים

(Hint: Four answers are used twice!)

רַבִּי יְהוּדָה הַנָּשִׂיא had two תַּלְמִידִים named ______ and __________. These two opened יְשִׁיבוֹת in the country of ___________.

Over time, the __________________ of the הֲלָכוֹת began to be forgotten. In order to save the situation, ה׳ sent ______________ and ______________. They wrote a סֵפֶר called ____________. This סֵפֶר included the teachings and discussions of the חֲכָמִים from ___________ and ____________ all the way down to ______________ and ______________. These חֲכָמִים were known as the ______________. Because they lived in בָּבֶל, their version of this סֵפֶר was called____________. Several generations earlier, ______________ wrote another version called __________________.

א. רַב אַשִׁי

ב. בָּבֶל

ג. רַבִינָא

ד. underlying principles

ה. רַבִּי יוֹחָנָן

ו. רַב

ז. גְמָרָא

ח. תַּלְמוּד בַּבְלִי

ט. שְׁמוּאֵל

י. תַּלְמוּד יְרוּשַׁלְמִי

יא. אֲמוֹרָאִים

For each question, circle the letter of the correct choice:

1. In order to make learning גְּמָרָא easier, almost every גְּמָרָא that is printed:
   a. has the English translation printed in the back.
   b. has the same page layout.
   c. uses a twelve-point font size.
   d. all of the above

2. Each full page (with two sides) is called
   a. a דַּף
   b. a בְּלַאט
   c. both a and b
   d. an עָמוּד
   e. none of the above

3. The first דַּף in each מַסֶּכְתָּא is called
   a. דַּף א
   b. דַּף 1
   c. דַּף רִאשׁוֹן
   d. none of the above

4. One side of a page is called
   a. a דַּף
   b. a בְּלַאט
   c. both a and b
   d. an עָמוּד
   e. none of the above

5. The two עַמּוּדִים of every page are called
   a. עָמוּד א and עָמוּד ב
   b. עָמוּד 1 and עָמוּד 2
   c. עָמוּד רִאשׁוֹן and עָמוּד שֵׁנִי
   d. none of the above

6. The abbreviations for the two עַמּוּדִים are
   a. "-" and "--"
   b. "-" and "="
   c. "." and ".."
   d. "." and ":"
   e. none of the above

In גְּמָרָא, each discussion is called a __________. Often, the גְּמָרָא will teach and quote the teachings of the ______________. These will either be in a ____________ or in a ________________.

These are important because if something was taught by a תַּנָא, an ___________ may not argue.

א. סוּגְיָא **ב. בְּרַיְיתָא** **ג. אֲמוֹרָא** **ד. תַּנָאִים** **ה. מִשְׁנָה**

For each question, choose the correct type of step:
(hint: all choices are used twice)

א. מֵימְרָא	ב. קֻשְׁיָא	ג. תֵּירוּץ	ד. רַאֲיָה
ה. דְחִיָּה	ו. שְׁאֵלָה	ז. תְּשׁוּבָה	ח. מַסְקָנָא

_____ 1. Which type of step asks for information?

_____ 2. Which type of step attacks a מֵימְרָא?

_____ 3. Which type of step simply tells us information?

_____ 4. Which type of step proves something which an אֲמוֹרָא had said?

_____ 5. Which type of step gives a final conclusion?

_____ 6. Which type of step shows that we don't actually have a good proof?

_____ 7. Which type of step defends the אֲמוֹרָא from an attack?

_____ 8. Which type of step supplies the information that was asked for?

_____ _____ 9. Which two types of steps explain that we had an incorrect assumption (הֲוָה אַמִינָא) and corrects it with a מַסְקָנָא?

_____ 10. Which type of step is very often the beginning of a סוּגְיָא?

_____ _____ 11. Which two types of steps use logic or the words of a תַּנָא?

_____ 12. Which type of step usually asks about what the הֲלָכָה is in a specific situation?

_____ 13. Which type of step might give a final פְּסַק הֲלָכָה?

_____ 14. Which type of step will often quote a source?

Lesson 9

The name of the מַסֶּכְתָּא that we will be learning is ________________. We will be learning the second פֶּרֶק of the מַסֶּכְתָּא which is called ________________. The פֶּרֶק discusses the הֲלָכוֹת of lost objects (which are called __________) and found objects (which are called ___________).

Sometimes, the finder may keep the item that he found. In such a situation, we say that the object is _________. In other situations, the finder must call out what he found. In those situations, the finder is ________________.

The הֲלָכָה is based on whether or not the owner has been __________. The owner is less likely to give up hope if his object has a ____________. However, the sign on the object is not what actually determines the הֲלָכָה. The thing that determines the הֲלָכָה is _______________.

א. אֵלּוּ מְצִיאוֹת ג. יֵאוּשׁ ה. חַיָּיב לְהַכְרִיז ז. בָּבָא מְצִיעָא ט. סִימָן

ב. מְצִיאוֹת ד. שֶׁלּוֹ ו. אֲבֵידוֹת ח. מְיָאֵשׁ

Lesson 10

1. Before beginning the גְמָרָא, we learned the _______.
2. Please read and translate the מִשְׁנָה. ⟶
3. The מִשְׁנָה tells us that there are two lists of ________. The first list (found in this מִשְׁנָה) is a list of מְצִיאוֹת which are _________. In the next מִשְׁנָה, we will have a list of מְצִיאוֹת for which the owner is ___________.
4. רַבִּי יְהוּדָה teaches us that any object which has a _______ (something unique), may be kept by the finder.
5. רַבִּי שִׁמְעוֹן בֶּן אֶלְעָזָר teaches us that any כֵּלִים which are _________________ may be kept by the finder. However, we will have to wait for the _________ to explain what that word means.

אֵלּוּ מְצִיאוֹת שֶׁלּוֹ וְאֵלּוּ חַיָּיב לְהַכְרִיז אֵלּוּ מְצִיאוֹת שֶׁלּוֹ [ה]מָצָא פֵּירוֹת מְפוּזָּרִין [ו]מָעוֹת מְפוּזָּרוֹת [ז]כְּרִיכוֹת בִּרְשׁוּת הָרַבִּים [ח]וְעִגּוּלֵי דְבֵילָה כִּכָּרוֹת שֶׁל נַחְתּוֹם *מַחְרוֹזוֹת שֶׁל דָּגִים וַחֲתִיכוֹת שֶׁל בָּשָׂר וְגִיזֵּי צֶמֶר הַלְּקוּחִין מִמְּדִינָתָן וַאֲנִיצֵי פִשְׁתָּן וּלְשׁוֹנוֹת שֶׁל אַרְגָּמָן הֲרֵי אֵלּוּ שֶׁלּוֹ *דִּבְרֵי רַבִּי מֵאִיר ר׳ יְהוּדָה אוֹמֵר *כָּל שֶׁיֵּשׁ בּוֹ שִׁינּוּי חַיָּיב לְהַכְרִיז כֵּיצַד [ט]מָצָא עִגּוּל וּבְתוֹכוֹ חֶרֶס כִּכָּר וּבְתוֹכוֹ מָעוֹת רַבִּי שִׁמְעוֹן בֶּן אֶלְעָזָר אוֹמֵר כָּל כְּלֵי אַנְפּוֹרְיָא אֵין חַיָּיב לְהַכְרִיז:

א. שֶׁלּוֹ ב. מִשְׁנָה ג. מְצִיאוֹת ד. גְמָרָא ה. שִׁינּוּי ו. חַיָּיב לְהַכְרִיז ז. אַנְפּוֹרְיָא

Congratulations!
YOU ARE NOW
READY TO START
LEARNING
גמרא

מסכת
בבא מציעא

פרק שני
אלו מציאות

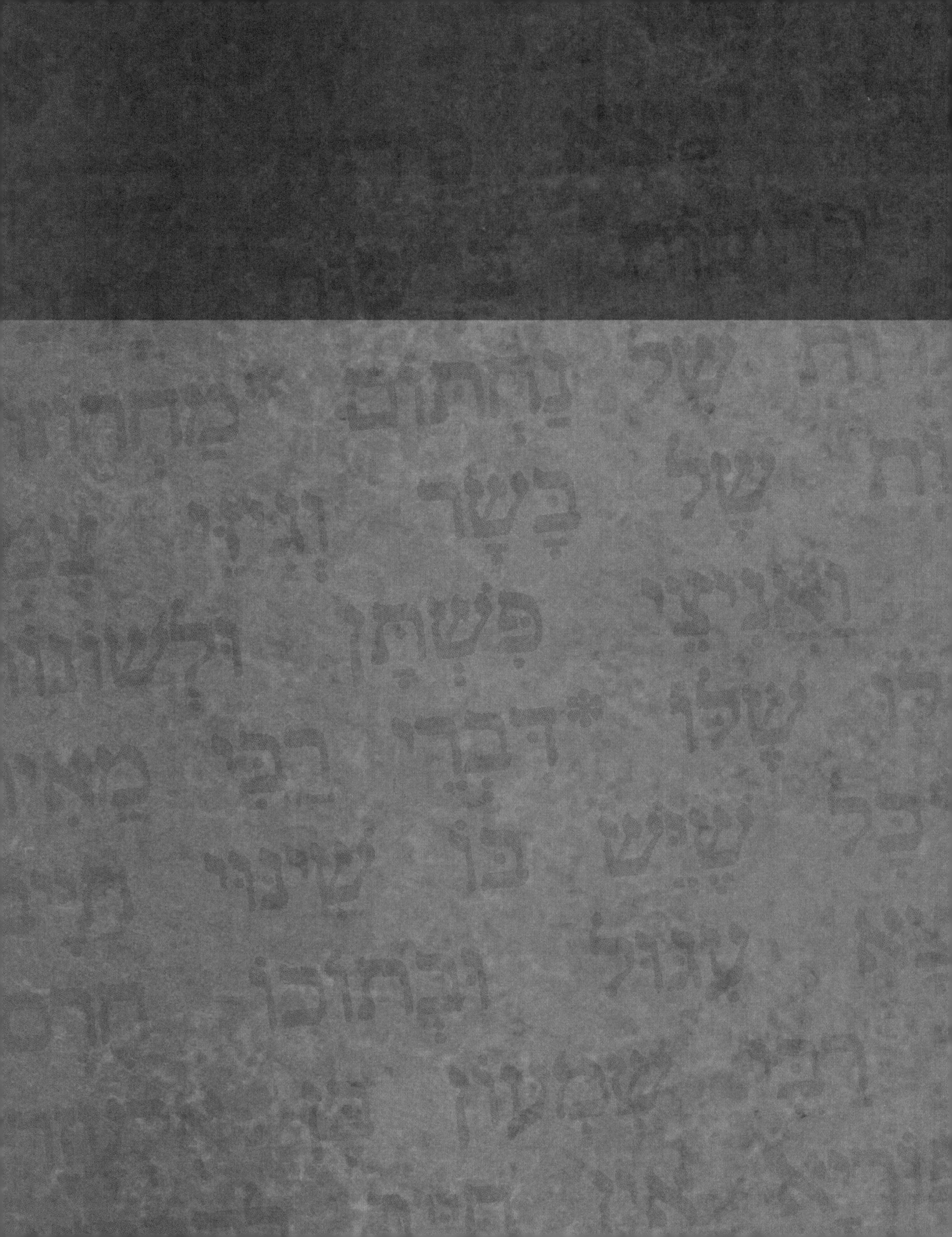

סוגיא א׳

שיעורים
א׳ - ו׳

שיעור א

.כא lines 12-13

VOCABULARY WORDS

35. לְהוּ

36. לֵיהּ

37. לָן

A full list of the vocabulary words and their translations can be found in the back of this workbook

STEP 1

In the first step of our סוּגְיָא, the גְּמָרָא quotes the first הֲלָכָה of our מִשְׁנָה. This begins a discussion of that הֲלָכָה. Because this step is a statement which is not asking, answering, or proving anything, it is a מֵימְרָא.

[If] he found scattered produce [he may keep it].	**מָצָא פֵּירוֹת מְפוּזָּרִין**

The first הֲלָכָה that the מִשְׁנָה taught is that one who finds scattered produce may keep it. The גְּמָרָא is now ready to discuss this הֲלָכָה.

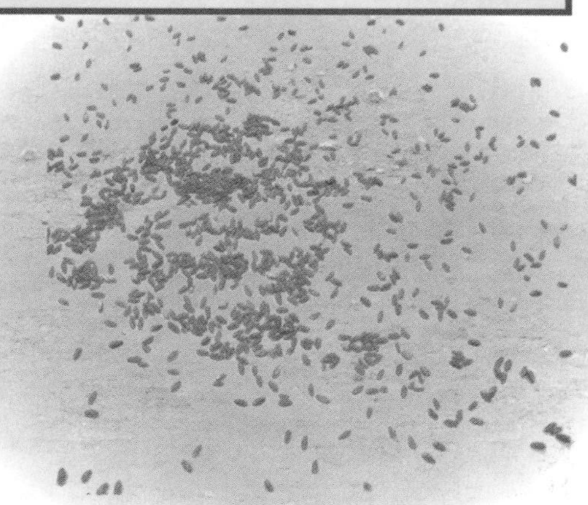

STEP 2

The גְּמָרָא asks a שְׁאֵלָה in order to clarify the מֵימְרָא:

And how much [does it have to be scattered in order for the owner to be able to keep it]?	וְכַמָּה

The גְּמָרָא wants to clarify what the מִשְׁנָה meant when it said that the produce is scattered. This is important to know because if the produce is not scattered, but rather it is gathered in a pile, the finder would have to announce it and would not be able to keep it*. Therefore, we need an exact definition of what is considered scattered and what is considered piled. (Otherwise, the הֲלָכָה of the מִשְׁנָה would not have a true meaning. Each person would be left to decide for himself whether the produce is scattered enough for him to keep or not.)

*The גְּמָרָא explains the reason for this on דַּף כה עָמוּד א.

פֵּירוֹת מְפוּזָּרִין – וְכַמָּה?

STEP 3

In order to understand the answer that the גְּמָרָא will give, we must remember that in the times of the גְּמָרָא, they measured things with different units than we have today. For example, when we want to measure a distance, we might measure in inches, feet, and miles (or, depending on your country, you might use centimeters, meters, and kilometers). However, in the times of the גְּמָרָא, they would measure using טְפָחִים and אַמּוֹת, and for large distances they would use מִיל.* Similarly, they had different ways of measuring volume (how much space something takes up). Instead of cup, quart, and gallon, they used קַב and סְאָה, and for larger amounts they used אֵיפָה.** In order to define the meaning of "scattered," the גְּמָרָא will use units that are no longer common. But don't worry, we will describe these units after we learn the answer of the גְּמָרָא:

רַבִּי יִצְחָק said,	א"ר (אָמַר רַבִּי) יִצְחָק
One קַב [of produce]	קַב
[spread out] in [an area of] four אַמּוֹת [by four אַמּוֹת].	בְּאַרְבַּע אַמּוֹת

A קַב is a measure of volume. There are many שִׁיטוֹת (opinions) about the exact amount that a קַב would be, using today's measures. However, all of the שִׁיטוֹת are in the range of a half-gallon or two liters. So, to understand what a קַב of produce is, imagine a two liter bottle of soda or half-gallon container of milk filled with

אלו מציאות
פרק שני
בבא מציעא

*A טֶפַח is the size of an average man's fist. An אַמָּה equals six טְפָחִים. A מִיל is equal to 2,000 אַמּוֹת.
**A קַב is equal to 24 בֵּיצִים (eggs). A סְאָה equals six קַבִּין. One אֵיפָה is equal to 3 סְאִין.

wheat kernels. This a good way to get the basic idea (but not the exact amount) of what we are talking about.

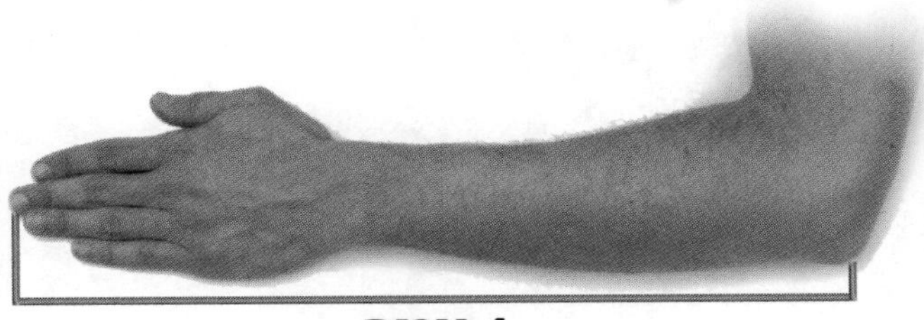
1 אַמָּה

An אַמָּה is a measure of distance. It is the length of an averaged-sized man's arm from the elbow to the tip of the middle finger. Again, there are different שִׁיטוֹת as to exactly how long an אַמָּה is (because of the fact that all men's arms are different lengths, as well as other factors which go into the calculation). The opinions range from between one and a half feet to two feet.

In order to keep things simple, we will use the שִׁיטָה of two feet. This means that four אַמּוֹת by four אַמּוֹת is a square that is approximately eight feet long and eight feet wide.

רַבִּי יִצְחָק tells us that in order for produce to be considered scattered, it must be a קַב of kernels (or less) in an area of four אַמּוֹת by four אַמּוֹת (or more). However, if there was more than a קַב of kernels in the four אַמָּה square, the produce would not be considered scattered and the finder would have to announce it. Similarly, if a קַב of kernels was found in an area that was smaller than a four אַמָּה square, it would also not be considered scattered and the finder would have to announce it.*

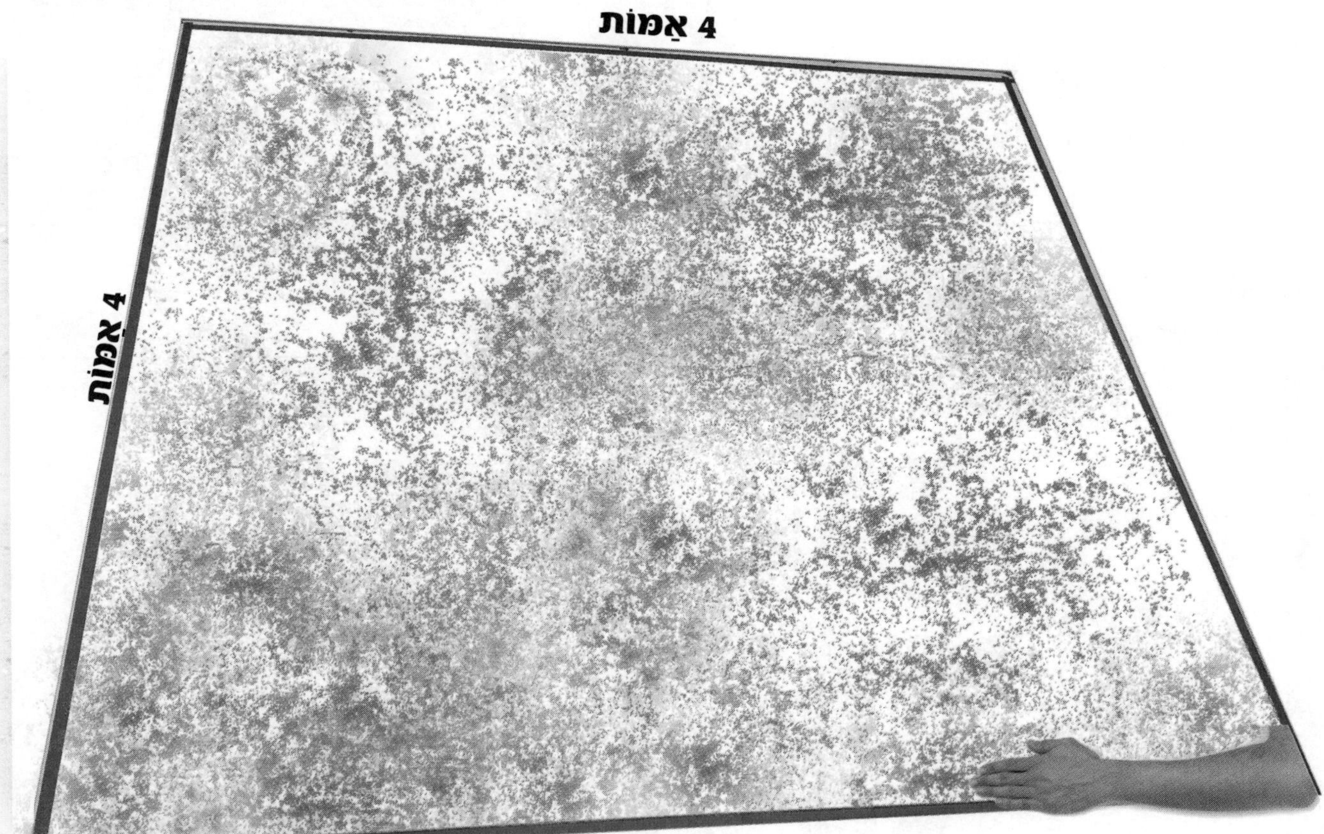

A קַב of grain spread out in an area of four אַמּוֹת by four אַמּוֹת. We included a picture of an arm (אַמָּה) in the lower right corner to make the actual size easier to visualize.

*Again, the גְּמָרָא explains the reason for this on דַּף כה עָמוּד א.

שיעור א Review

PUT IT ALL TOGETHER:

1. Read, translate and explain the following גְּמָרָא.

אֵלּוּ מְצִיאוֹת שֶׁלּוֹ וְאֵלּוּ חַיָּיב לְהַכְרִיז אֵלּוּ
מְצִיאוֹת שֶׁלּוֹ מָצָא פֵּירוֹת מְפוּזָּרִין
מָעוֹת מְפוּזָּרוֹת כְּרִיכוֹת בִּרְשׁוּת הָרַבִּים
וְעִגּוּלֵי דְבֵילָה כִּכְּרוֹת שֶׁל נַחְתּוֹם *מַחְרוֹזוֹת
שֶׁל דָּגִים וַחֲתִיכוֹת שֶׁל בָּשָׂר וְגִיזֵּי צֶמֶר
הַלְּקוּחִין מִמְּדִינָתָן וַאֲנִיצֵי פִשְׁתָּן וּלְשׁוֹנוֹת
שֶׁל אַרְגָּמָן הֲרֵי אֵלּוּ שֶׁלּוֹ *דִּבְרֵי רַבִּי מֵאִיר
ר' יְהוּדָה אוֹמֵר *כָּל שֶׁיֵּשׁ בּוֹ שִׁינּוּי חַיָּיב
לְהַכְרִיז כֵּיצַד מָצָא עִגּוּל וּבְתוֹכוֹ חֶרֶס
כִּכָּר וּבְתוֹכוֹ מָעוֹת רַבִּי שִׁמְעוֹן בֶּן אֶלְעָזָר
אוֹמֵר כָּל כְּלֵי אַנְפּוֹרְיָא אֵין חַיָּיב לְהַכְרִיז:
**גמ' מָצָא פֵּירוֹת מְפוּזָּרִין וְכַמָּה א"ר יִצְחָק קַב
בְּאַרְבַּע אַמּוֹת**

2. What הֲלָכָה does the גְּמָרָא quote from our מִשְׁנָה? ______________________

3. What does the גְּמָרָא ask about this הֲלָכָה? ______________________

4. Why is this important for us to know? ______________________

5. Why is this question called a שְׁאֵלָה and not a קֻשְׁיָא? ______________________

6. What is the answer to the גְּמָרָא's question? ______________________

7. For each of the following cases, circle the appropriate הֲלָכָה: חַיָּיב לְהַכְרִיז or שֶׁלּוֹ:

- A קַב of kernels in a space of four אַמּוֹת by four אַמּוֹת
- A קַב and a half of kernels in a space of four אַמּוֹת by four אַמּוֹת
- A קַב of kernels in a space of three אַמּוֹת by three אַמּוֹת
- Three-quarters of a קַב of kernels in a space of four אַמּוֹת by four אַמּוֹת
- A קַב of kernels in a space of five אַמּוֹת by five אַמּוֹת

IDENTIFY THE STEPS:

BE SURE TO INCLUDE EVERY WORD.

גמ׳ מָצָא פֵּירוֹת מְפוּזָּרִין וְכַמָּה א״ר יִצְחָק קַב בְּאַרְבַּע אַמּוֹת

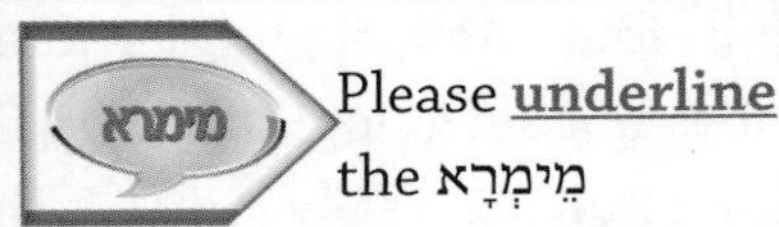

Please underline the מֵימְרָא

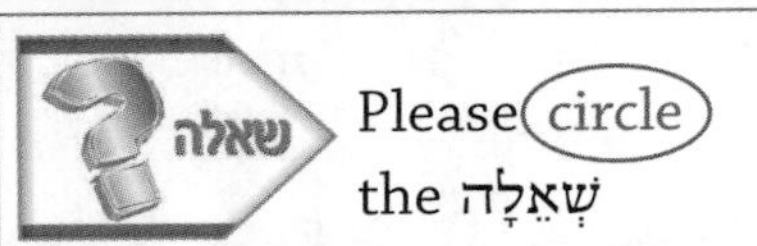

Please circle the שְׁאֵלָה

Please [bracket] the תְּשׁוּבָה

VOCABULARY REVIEW:

לֵיהּ ____________	שָׁקִיל ____________
הָדַר ____________	לָן ____________
לְהוּ ____________	אָתִי ____________

MATCHING:

____	1. Step 1 of the סוּגְיָא is a ______	א. אַרְבַּע אַמּוֹת
____	2. Step 2 of the סוּגְיָא is a ______	ב. רַבִּי יִצְחָק
____	3. Step 3 of the סוּגְיָא is a ______	ג. שְׁאֵלָה
____	4. The מִשְׁנָה says that you may keep it	ד. מֵימְרָא
____	5. The גְּמָרָא's question about the הֲלָכָה	ה. קַב
____	6. He answered our שְׁאֵלָה	ו. תְּשׁוּבָה
____	7. How scattered is considered scattered	ז. קַב בְּאַרְבַּע אַמּוֹת
____	8. A measure of volume	ח. וְכַמָּה
____	9. A measure of length	ט. פֵּירוֹת מְפוּזָּרִין

STEP 4

In שִׁיעוּר א׳ we learned that רַבִּי יִצְחָק said that if a קַב of grain is scattered in four אַמּוֹת, the finder may keep it. On the other hand, if there is more than a קַב in four אַמּוֹת, the finder must announce it. The גְּמָרָא now asks that this does not seem logical. After all, why should the amount of grain or the space that it's in really matter? The only thing that should matter is whether or not the owner has been מְיָאֵשׁ (given up hope)! We can tell whether the owner has been מְיָאֵשׁ or not by the way that the grain is laying on the ground, as the גְּמָרָא will explain:

_______________?	הֵיכִי דָּמֵי
If [it looks] the way [it would look if it had] fallen [accidentally],	אִי דֶּרֶךְ נְפִילָה
[then] even ________ [than a קַב]	אֲפִילּוּ טוּבָא
[should] _______ [be שֶׁלּוֹ];	נַמִּי
and if [it looks] the way [it would look if it had] been placed [on purpose by the owner],	וְאִי דֶּרֶךְ הִינּוּחַ
[then] even ______ than this (less than a קַב)	אֲפִילּוּ בָּצִיר מֵהָכֵי
[should] _______ not [be שֶׁלּוֹ]!?	נַמִּי לֹא

If the grain looks like it had fallen, then we can assume that the owner does not know where it is and that he has been מְיָאֵשׁ. Therefore, the finder should be able to keep it regardless of how much grain there was. On the other hand, if the grain looks like the owner had put it down, then we can assume that the owner put it where it is and plans to come back for it (and was certainly not מְיָאֵשׁ). Therefore, the finder should not be able to keep it regardless of how little grain there was. Why, then, did רַבִּי יִצְחָק say that the הֲלָכָה depends on the amount of grain and the space in which it is found?

In this קֻשְׁיָא, the target is the statement of רַבִּי יִצְחָק that the הֲלָכָה depends on whether there is more or less than a קַב in four אַמּוֹת. The attack is the logical argument that the הֲלָכָה should depend on whether or not it looks like the owner was מְיָאֵשׁ.

CANNOT BE THE SITUATION DESCRIBED BY רַבִּי יִצְחָק

CANNOT BE THE SITUATION DESCRIBED BY רַבִּי יִצְחָק

רַבִּי

דֶּרֶךְ הִינּוּחַ

GRAIN WHICH HAS BEEN PLACED

Finder may NOT keep it no matter how little there is.

דֶּרֶךְ נְפִילָה

GRAIN WHICH HAS FALLEN

Finder may keep it no matter how much there is.

THERE DOESN'T SEEM TO BE ANY SITUATION IN WHICH רַבִּי יִצְחָק'S RULE CAN APPLY!?

שיעור ב
כא. lines 13-20
Continued

STEP 5

The גְּמָרָא answers that we were making an incorrect assumption – a הֲוָה אַמִינָא – which needs to be corrected with a מַסְקָנָא. Our הֲוָה אַמִינָא was that when the מִשְׁנָה mentioned "scattered produce" it meant that someone found the grain in a random place where the owner may not know where it is. If that was the case, then the only thing that should matter is whether or not the owner was מְיָאֵשׁ. The מַסְקָנָא will teach us that that is not the case of our מִשְׁנָה:

רַב עוּקְבָא בַּר חָמָא said,	א"ר (אָמַר רַב) עוּקְבָא בַּר חָמָא
With the gathering	בְּמַכְנַשְׁתָּא
of the threshing floor	דְּבֵי דָּרֵי
____________________ (talking about).	עַסְקִינַן

רַב עוּקְבָא בַּר חָמָא explains that when the מִשְׁנָה said that someone found פֵּירוֹת מְפוּזָּרִין, it doesn't mean that he found grain which had been lost someplace. Rather, it is referring to grain which had been knowingly left behind.

One of the steps of processing grain is called threshing. This is when the outer shell of the kernel (the husk) is broken open so that the inner part (the grain) can be taken out. Nowadays, we have special machines that do this. However, before these machines were invented, threshing was done by putting all of the grain on the ground in a special area called "the threshing floor." Then, either animals would stomp on it or the farmer would beat it with sticks. Once the grain has been removed, the grain can be collected and brought to the silo (the storage building).

THRESHING FLOOR (ALONI)IN GREECE, ETHNOGRAPHIC MU
IN ANO MERIA ON FOLEGANDROS, 15M664
30 JUNE 2015, 17:48:09 AUTHOR

Hopefully, the farmer has had a good year and there is too much grain for him to bring in one trip to the silo. Instead, he will take as much as he can to the silo, and if there is still enough grain left at the threshing floor, he will go back for another load. However, there will come a point when there is too little grain left for it to be worth it for him to go back.

רַב עוּקְבָא בַּר חָמָא explains that when the מִשְׁנָה said that a person found scattered produce, it meant that he found grain on the threshing floor. The question is not whether the owner knows where the grain is; of course he does. The question is whether the owner plans to come back for the grain, or if he decided to just leave it behind. He might intend to make another trip to take it. On the other hand, he might have decided to leave the remaining grain behind because it is not worth the effort of collecting it. This will depend on how much grain was left behind (on the threshing floor) and how much bother will be involved in gathering it.

The גְּמָרָא will now explain the rule that רַבִּי יִצְחָק taught us:

A קַב in four אַמּוֹת [by four אַמּוֹת],	קַב בְּאַרְבַּע אַמּוֹת
______ is a lot of bother [to collect the kernels],	דְּנָפִישׁ טִרְחַיְיהוּ
a person will not ______	לֹא טָרַח אִינִישׁ
and will not come back (return)	וְלֹא הָדַר אָתֵי
and ______ them,	וְשָׁקִיל לְהוּ
[rather,] he will make them הֶפְקֵר (ownerless and free to be taken).	אַפְקוּרֵי מַפְקַר לְהוּ
[However, if the kernels are in] ______ than this (space of four אַמּוֹת),	בָּצִיר מֵהָכֵי
he will bother	טָרַח
and come back (return)	וְהָדַר אָתֵי
and ______ them,	וְשָׁקִיל לְהוּ
and he will not make them הֶפְקֵר.	וְלֹא מַפְקַר לְהוּ

We now understand the rule of רַבִּי יִצְחָק. Because the owner knows where the grain is, the הֲלָכָה depends on whether we assume the owner will come back to get it or whether we assume that the owner will not consider it worth the bother.

רַבִּי יִצְחָק tells us that if a קַב of grain is spread out in an area of four אַמּוֹת by four אַמּוֹת, the effort involved in gathering it is not worth it. Therefore, the owner will make it הֶפְקֵר and the finder may keep it. However, if the קַב is spread out in an area of less than four אַמּוֹת by four אַמּוֹת, the owner will consider it worthwhile to spend the time to gather it. Therefore, the owner will not make it הֶפְקֵר and the finder may not take it.

אלו מציאות
פרק שני
בבא מציעא

"There is more than a קַב in 4 אַמּוֹת remaining on the threshing floor. I'll trouble myself to go back and get it."

"There is **not** more than a קַב in 4 אַמּוֹת remaining on the threshing floor. I won't trouble myself to go back and get it."

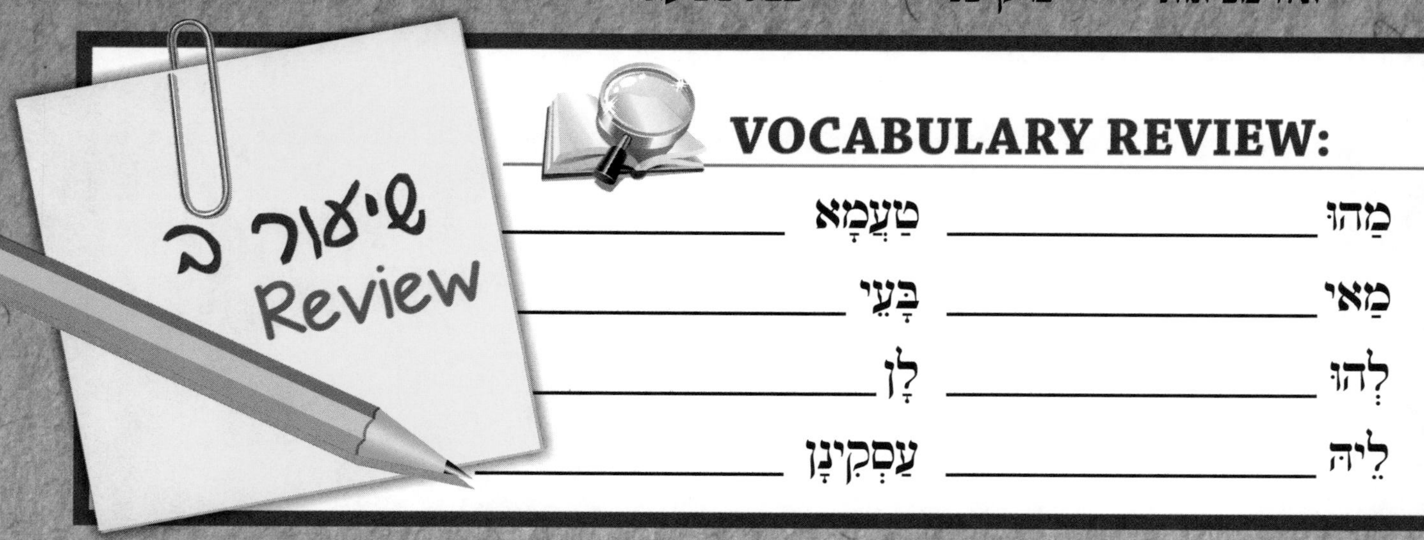

PUT IT ALL TOGETHER:

הֵיכִי דָּמֵי אִי דֶּרֶךְ נְפִילָה
אֲפִילּוּ טוּבָא נַמִּי וְאִי דֶּרֶךְ הִינּוּחַ אֲפִילּוּ
בָּצִיר מֵהָכֵי נַמִּי לֹא א"ר עוּקְבָא בַּר חָמָא
בְּמַכְנַשְׁתָּא דְּבֵי דָּרֵי עַסְקִינָן קַב בְּאַרְבַּע
אַמּוֹת דְּנָפִישׁ טִרְחַיְיהוּ לֹא טָרַח אִינִישׁ וְלֹא
הָדַר אָתֵי וְשָׁקִיל לְהוּ אַפְקוּרֵי מַפְקַר לְהוּ
בָּצִיר מֵהָכֵי טָרַח וְהָדַר אָתֵי וְשָׁקִיל לְהוּ וְלֹא
מַפְקַר לְהוּ

1. Read, translate and explain the following גְּמָרָא.

2. What rule did רַבִּי יִצְחָק teach (in שִׁיעוּר א׳)? ______________________

____

3. What הֲוָה אַמִּינָא did we have about the case that רַבִּי יִצְחָק discussed? ______________________

____

4. What קֻשְׁיָא did we ask because of our assumption? ______________________

____

5. What is our מַסְקָנָא about the case that רַבִּי יִצְחָק discussed? ______________________

____

6. Explain why the קֻשְׁיָא is no longer a problem based on this מַסְקָנָא. ______________________

____

____

7. Explain the reasoning of רַבִּי יִצְחָק's rule. ______________________

____

____

IDENTIFY THE STEPS:
BE SURE TO INCLUDE EVERY WORD.

Please underline the קֻשְׁיָא

Please [bracket] the תֵּירוּץ

הֵיכִי דָּמֵי אִי דֶּרֶךְ נְפִילָה
אֲפִילּוּ טוּבָא נַמִּי וְאִי דֶּרֶךְ הִינּוּחַ אֲפִילּוּ
בָּצִיר מֵהָכֵי נַמִּי לֹא א״ר עוּקְבָא בַּר חָמָא
בְּמַכְנַשְׁתָּא דְּבֵי דָּרֵי עַסְקִינַן קַב בְּאַרְבַּע
אַמּוֹת דְּנָפִישׁ טִרְחַיְיהוּ לֹא טָרַח אִינִישׁ וְלֹא
הָדַר אָתֵי וְשָׁקִיל לְהוּ אַפְקוּרֵי מַפְקַר לְהוּ
בָּצִיר מֵהָכֵי טָרַח וְהָדַר אָתֵי וְשָׁקִיל לְהוּ וְלֹא
מַפְקַר לְהוּ

MATCHING:

_____ 1. Step 4 of the סוּגְיָא is a ________

_____ 2. Step 5 of the סוּגְיָא is a ________

_____ 3. Grain that is found in a random place may be kept if it is _______

_____ 4. Grain that is found in a random place may not be kept if it is _______

_____ 5. Where we assumed the grain (mentioned in the מִשְׁנָה) was found

_____ 6. Where the grain (mentioned in the מִשְׁנָה) was really found

_____ 7. His statement was the target of our קֻשְׁיָא

_____ 8. Why the owner will not come back for a קַב in four אַמּוֹת

_____ 9. When the owner will bother and come back for the grain

_____ 10. When the owner will not bother and come back for the grain

א. רַבִּי יִצְחָק

ב. תֵּירוּץ

ג. קַב בְּאַרְבַּע אַמּוֹת

ד. קֻשְׁיָא

ה. בְּמַכְנַשְׁתָּא דְּבֵי דָּרֵי

ו. דֶּרֶךְ נְפִילָה

ז. A random place

ח. דֶּרֶךְ הִינּוּחַ

ט. בָּצִיר מֵהָכֵי

י. דְּנָפִישׁ טִרְחַיְיהוּ

The סוגיא to this point

שיעורים א-ב

NUMBER THE STEPS:

PLACE A SMALL NUMBER BY THE BEGINNING OF EACH STEP

(example: מָצָא פֵּירוֹת[1])

אֵלּוּ מְצִיאוֹת שֶׁלּוֹ וְאֵלּוּ חַיָּיב לְהַכְרִיז אֵלּוּ מְצִיאוֹת שֶׁלּוֹ [ג]מָצָא פֵּירוֹת מְפוּזָּרִין [ד]מָעוֹת מְפוּזָּרוֹת [ו]כְּרִיכוֹת בִּרְשׁוּת הָרַבִּים [ח]וְעִגּוּלֵי דְבֵילָה כִּכָּרוֹת שֶׁל נַחְתּוֹם *מַחֲרוֹזוֹת שֶׁל דָּגִים וַחֲתִיכוֹת שֶׁל בָּשָׂר וְגִיזֵּי צֶמֶר הַלְּקוּחִין מִמְּדִינָתָן וַאֲנִיצֵי פִשְׁתָּן וּלְשׁוֹנוֹת שֶׁל אַרְגָּמָן הֲרֵי אֵלּוּ שֶׁלּוֹ *דִּבְרֵי רַבִּי מֵאִיר ר' יְהוּדָה אוֹמֵר *כָּל שֶׁיֵּשׁ בּוֹ שִׁינּוּי חַיָּיב לְהַכְרִיז כֵּיצַד [ט]מָצָא עִגּוּל וּבְתוֹכוֹ חֶרֶס כִּכָּר וּבְתוֹכוֹ מָעוֹת רַבִּי שִׁמְעוֹן בֶּן אֶלְעָזָר אוֹמֵר כָּל כְּלֵי אַנְפּוֹרְיָא אֵין חַיָּיב לְהַכְרִיז:

גמ' מָצָא פֵּירוֹת מְפוּזָּרִין וְכַמָּה א"ר יִצְחָק קַב בְּאַרְבַּע אַמּוֹת הֵיכִי דָּמֵי אִי דֶּרֶךְ נְפִילָה [י]אֲפִילּוּ טוּבָא נַמִּי וְאִי דֶּרֶךְ הִינּוּחַ [כ]אֲפִילּוּ בָּצִיר מֵהָכֵי נַמִּי לֹא א"ר עוּקְבָא בַּר חָמָא [ל]בְּמַכְנַשְׁתָּא דְבֵי דָרֵי עָסְקִינָן [מ]קַב בְּאַרְבַּע אַמּוֹת דְּנָפִישׁ טִרְחַיְיהוּ לֹא טָרַח אִינִישׁ וְלֹא הָדַר אָתֵי וְשָׁקֵיל לְהוּ אַפְקוּרֵי מַפְקַר לְהוּ בָּצִיר מֵהָכֵי טָרַח וְהָדַר אָתֵי וְשָׁקֵיל לְהוּ וְלֹא מַפְקַר לְהוּ

VOCABULARY REVIEW:

לְהוּ ____________________ מַהוּ ____________________

טַעֲמָא ____________________ בָּעֵי ____________________

מַאי ____________________ נָפִישׁ ____________________

לֵיהּ ____________________ הָדַר ____________________

לָן ____________________ שָׁקִיל ____________________

LABEL AND SUMMARIZE:

For each step, write what type of step it is and a brief explanation.

If someone finds scattered produce, he may keep it.	STEP 1 מֵימְרָא
	STEP 2
	STEP 3
	STEP 4
	STEP 5

STEP 6

In our first two שִׁיעוּרִים we have clarified the הֲלָכָה in the מִשְׁנָה that פֵּירוֹת מְפוּזָּרִין may be kept by the finder. We now know that the מִשְׁנָה was discussing a case of grain that was found on the threshing floor. We also know that the amount of grain which is considered scattered is one קַב in an area of four אַמּוֹת by four אַמּוֹת. In this case, the owner will not consider it worth the effort to come back and collect the grain. Rather, he will make it הֶפְקֵר and the finder may keep it.

In each of next four שִׁיעוּרִים, the גְּמָרָא will ask a שְׁאֵלָה that deals with a case that is slightly different than a קַב of grain in four אַמּוֹת. For each of these four cases, the גְּמָרָא will give a סְבָרָא (logical reason) why the הֲלָכָה should be the same as a קַב in four אַמּוֹת [the finder may keep it] and another סְבָרָא why the הֲלָכָה should be different [the finder may not keep it].

רַבִּי יִרְמְיָה asked [a שְׁאֵלָה]:	בָּעֵי רַבִּי יִרְמְיָה
[If someone found] half of a קַב [of grain]	חֲצִי קַב
in [an area of] two אַמּוֹת*,	בִּשְׁתֵּי אַמּוֹת
____________________?	מַהוּ

רַבִּי יִרְמְיָה asks about a case where there was half the amount of grain [half of a קַב] in half of the space [two אַמּוֹת]*.

*תּוֹסְפוֹת give two possible ways to understand this גְּמָרָא. The גְּמָרָא either means that the half קַב was found in an area of two אַמּוֹת by two אַמּוֹת or the intent is that the area is two אַמּוֹת by four אַמּוֹת. See תּוֹסְפוֹת for a rationale for each פְּשַׁט.

Is the הֲלָכָה the same as it is in a case of a קַב in four אַמּוֹת, or does the fact that it is half of the amount in half of the space change things? רַבִּי יִרְמְיָה will now give us a סְבָרָא for each of the two possibilities.

First, he tells us the סְבָרָא why the הֲלָכָה would be different in this case and the finder may not keep it:

[In the case of] a קַב [of kernels] in four אַמּוֹת,	קַב בְּאַרְבַּע אַמּוֹת
________ is the ________ [that the owner will make them הֶפְקֵר and the finder may keep them]?	טַעְמָא מַאי
[It is] __________	מִשּׁוּם
there is ________ of bother [to collect them].	דְּנָפִישׁ טִרְחַיְיהוּ
[But] half of a קַב [of kernels] in two אַמּוֹת,	חֲצִי קַב בִּשְׁתֵּי אַמּוֹת
_________	כֵּיוָן
there is not ________ of bother [to collect them],	דְּלָא נָפִישׁ טִרְחַיְיהוּ
he will not make them הֶפְקֵר [so the finder may not take them].	לָא מַפְקַר לְהוּ

If the main reason that the owner will not come back to get a קַב in four אַמּוֹת is because collecting it is too much of a bother, he might feel differently about half of a קַב in two אַמּוֹת. Because it is much less bother to collect it, perhaps he will come back for it. Therefore, the finder should not be allowed to keep it.

Now, רַבִּי יִרְמְיָה will explain a סְבָרָא why the הֲלָכָה about half of a קַב in two אַמּוֹת should be the same as a קַב in four אַמּוֹת:

Or ________, [in the case of a קַב in four אַמּוֹת, the owner will make them הֶפְקֵר and the finder may keep them]	אוֹ דִּלְמָא
____________	מִשּׁוּם
[a קַב of kernels] is not valuable [enough to go back for them];	דְּלָא חֲשִׁיבֵי
and half of a קַב in two אַמּוֹת	וַחֲצִי קַב בִּשְׁתֵּי אַמּוֹת
__________	כֵּיוָן
they are [certainly] not valuable	דְּלָא חֲשִׁיבֵי
he will make them הֶפְקֵר [and the finder may keep them].	מַפְקַר לְהוּ

אלו מציאות
פרק שני
בבא מציעא

It is possible that the reason that the owner will not come back for a קַב in four אַמּוֹת has nothing to do with how much bother it is to collect it. Rather, he makes it הֶפְקֵר because it is simply not valuable enough to be worth going back for. If this is so, he will certainly not consider it worth his time to go back for half of a קַב. For this reason, we can understand why the הֲלָכָה might be that the finder might be allowed to keep half of a קַב in two אַמּוֹת.

We now understand the why רַבִּי יִרְמְיָה had a שְׁאֵלָה about this case:

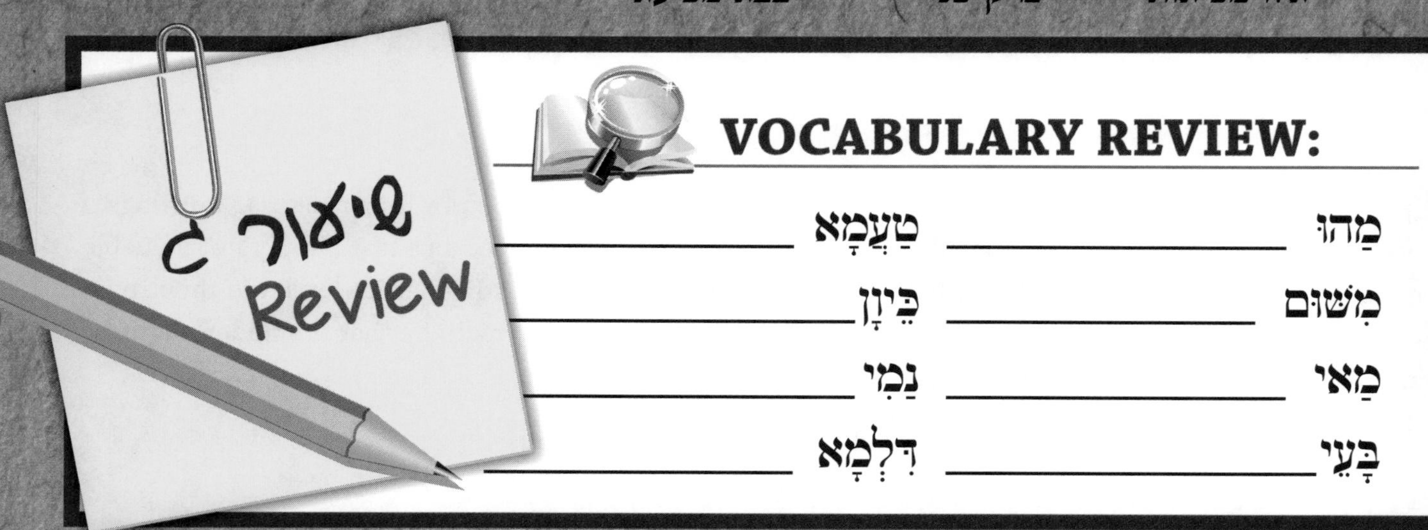

VOCABULARY REVIEW:

מַהוּ ________________ טַעְמָא ________________

מִשּׁוּם ________________ כֵּיוָן ________________

מַאי ________________ נַמִּי ________________

בָּעֵי ________________ דִּלְמָא ________________

PUT IT ALL TOGETHER:

בָּעֵי רַבִּי יִרְמְיָה חֲצִי קַב בִּשְׁתֵּי
אַמּוֹת מַהוּ קַב בְּאַרְבַּע אַמּוֹת טַעְמָא מַאי
מִשּׁוּם דִּנְפִישׁ טִרְחַיְיהוּ חֲצִי קַב בִּשְׁתֵּי אַמּוֹת
כֵּיוָן דְּלָא נְפִישׁ טִרְחַיְיהוּ לָא מַפְקַר לְהוּ אוֹ
דִּלְמָא מִשּׁוּם דְּלָא חֲשִׁיבֵי *וַחֲצִי קַב בִּשְׁתֵּי
אַמּוֹת כֵּיוָן דְּלָא חֲשִׁיבֵי מַפְקַר לְהוּ

1. Read, translate and explain the following גְּמָרָא.

2. Who is asking a שְׁאֵלָה? ________________

3. What is the case of his שְׁאֵלָה? ____________

____

4. What is the הֲלָכָה about a קַב in four אַמּוֹת? ________________________________

____

5. Which of the following is a bigger bother to collect? (circle one)

קַב בְּאַרְבַּע אַמּוֹת   חֲצִי קַב בִּשְׁתֵּי אַמּוֹת

6. Which of the following is more valuable? (circle one)

קַב בְּאַרְבַּע אַמּוֹת   חֲצִי קַב בִּשְׁתֵּי אַמּוֹת

7. What is the סְבָרָא to say that the case of our שְׁאֵלָה should have the same הֲלָכָה as a קַב in four אַמּוֹת? ________________________________

8. What is the סְבָרָא to say that the case of our שְׁאֵלָה should not have the same הֲלָכָה as a קַב in four אַמּוֹת? ________________________

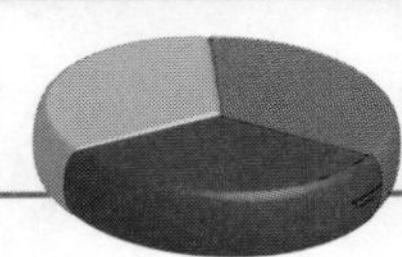

TAKE IT APART:

בָּעֵי רַבִּי יִרְמְיָה חֲצִי קַב בִּשְׁתֵּי
אַמּוֹת מַהוּ קַב בְּאַרְבַּע אַמּוֹת טַעֲמָא מַאי
מִשּׁוּם דְּנָפִישׁ טִרְחַיְיהוּ חֲצִי קַב בִּשְׁתֵּי אַמּוֹת
כֵּיוָן דְּלָא נָפִישׁ טִרְחַיְיהוּ לָא מַפְקַר לְהוּ אוֹ
דִּלְמָא מִשּׁוּם דְּלָא חֲשִׁיבֵי *וַחֲצִי קַב בִּשְׁתֵּי
אַמּוֹת כֵּיוָן דְּלָא חֲשִׁיבֵי מַפְקַר לְהוּ

What type of step is this?

____

MATCHING:

_____ 1. Step 6 of the סוּגְיָא is a ________

_____ 2. "because"

_____ 3. He asked a שְׁאֵלָה

_____ 4. "since"

_____ 5. What happens to a קַב בְּאַרְבַּע אַמּוֹת

_____ 6. The case of the שְׁאֵלָה

_____ 7. Why this case might have the same הֲלָכָה as קַב בְּאַרְבַּע אַמּוֹת

_____ 8. Why this case might NOT have the same הֲלָכָה as קַב בְּאַרְבַּע אַמּוֹת

א. דְּלָא חֲשִׁיבֵי

ב. רַבִּי יִרְמְיָה

ג. מַפְקַר לְהוּ

ד. "מִשּׁוּם"

ה. חֲצִי קַב בִּשְׁתֵּי אַמּוֹת

ו. שְׁאֵלָה

ז. דְּלָא נָפִישׁ טִרְחַיְיהוּ

ח. "כֵּיוָן"

VOCABULARY WORDS

45. כָּל שֶׁכֵּן

46. טְפֵי

STEP 7

In שִׁיעוּר ג׳ we learned that רַבִּי יִרְמִיָה asked a שְׁאֵלָה. However, before the גְּמָרָא has a chance to respond, רַבִּי יִרְמִיָה asks another (similar) שְׁאֵלָה. Once again, רַבִּי יִרְמִיָה is asking about a case that is similar to a קַב of grain in four אַמּוֹת but is different enough that the הֲלָכָה might not be the same. In שִׁיעוּר ג׳ the שְׁאֵלָה was about half of a קַב in two אַמּוֹת. In that case, it was less bother to collect it but also less valuable. In this שִׁיעוּר, the שְׁאֵלָה is the opposite.

[If someone found] two קַבִּים* [of kernels]	קַבַּיִים
in [an area of] eight אַמּוֹת**,	בִּשְׁמוֹנֶה אַמּוֹת
____________________?	מַהוּ

Again, the שְׁאֵלָה presents a case with two possible הֲלָכוֹת.

We know that in the מִשְׁנָה's case (one קַב in four אַמּוֹת), the הֲלָכָה is that the finder may keep it. When there are two קַבִּים in eight אַמּוֹת, the case might be similar enough to the מִשְׁנָה's case for the הֲלָכָה to be the same. On the other hand, it is possible that the case is different enough from the מִשְׁנָה's case, and the הֲלָכָה would not be the same; rather, the finder may not keep it.

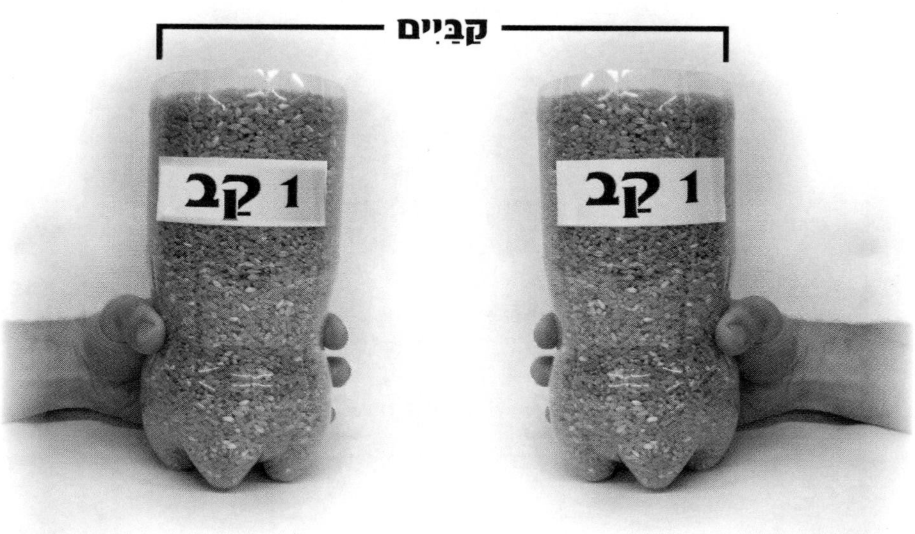

* קַבִּים is the plural of קַב.

** Again, the רִאשׁוֹנִים disagree whether this means eight אַמּוֹת by four אַמּוֹת or eight אַמּוֹת by eight אַמּוֹת.

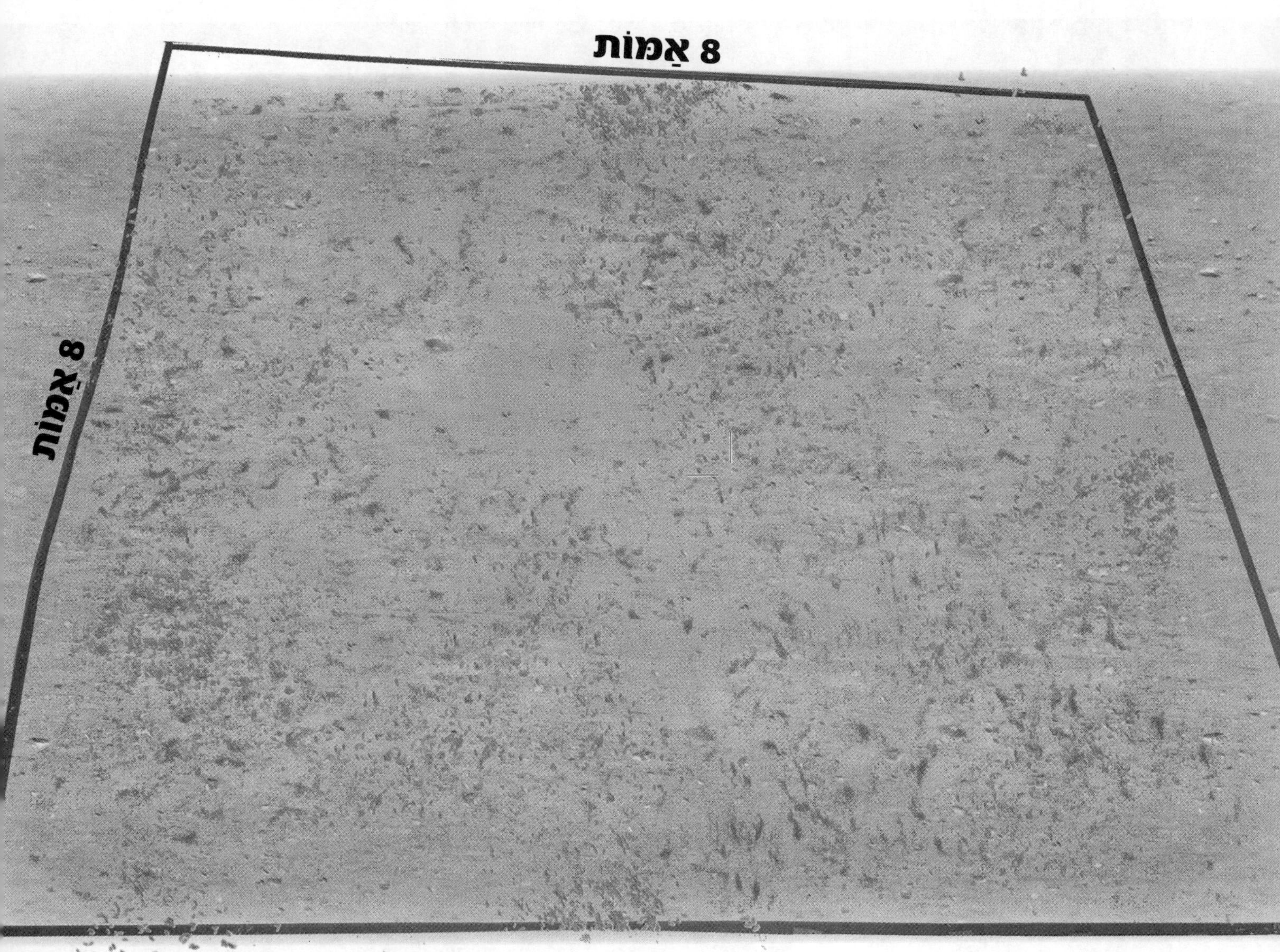
8 אַמּוֹת
8 אַמּוֹת

First, the גְּמָרָא will explain why the הֲלָכָה of two קַבִּים in eight אַמּוֹת might be the same as when there is one קַב in four אַמּוֹת:

קַב בְּאַרְבַּע אַמּוֹת	[In the case of] a קַב [of kernels] in four אַמּוֹת,
טַעֲמָא מַאי	________ is the __________ [that the owner will make them הֶפְקֵר and the finder may keep them]?
מִשּׁוּם דִּנְפִישׁ טִרְחַיְיהוּ	[It is] _________ there is __________ of bother [to collect them],
וְכ"ש (וְכָל שֶׁכֵּן)	and _____________
קַבַּיִים בִּשְׁמוֹנֶה אַמּוֹת	[in the case of] two קַבִּים in eight אַמּוֹת,
כֵּיוָן דִּנְפִישָׁא טִרְחַיְיהוּ	________ there is ________ of bother [to collect them]
טְפֵי	[even] ________ [so],
מַפְקַר לְהוּ	he will make them הֶפְקֵר [so the finder may take them].

Two קַבִּים in eight אַמּוֹת involves even more bother to collect than one קַב in four אַמּוֹת. If the owner will not come back for one קַב because it is too much bother, he will certainly not come back for two קַבִּים in eight אַמּוֹת.

However, there is another possible way to understand the הֲלָכָה of one קַב in four אַמּוֹת:

אוֹ דִּלְמָא	Or ___________, [in the case of a קַב in four אַמּוֹת, the owner will make them הֶפְקֵר and the finder may keep them]
מִשּׁוּם דְּלָא חֲשִׁיבֵי	__________ [a קַב of kernels] is not valuable [enough for the owner to go back];
וְקַבַּיִים בִּשְׁמוֹנֶה אַמּוֹת	and two קַבִּים in eight אַמּוֹת
כֵּיוָן דַּחֲשִׁיבֵי	________ they are valuable
לָא מַפְקַר לְהוּ	he will not make them הֶפְקֵר [and the finder may not keep them].

Perhaps, the only reason that the owner does not come back for a קַב in four אַמּוֹת is because one קַב is not valuable enough for it to be worthwhile. Two קַבִּים , on the other hand, might be worth the effort of coming back.

אלו מציאות
פרק שני
בבא מציעא

1 KAV
IN 4 AMOS
OWNER WILL
NOT COME BACK.
4 אמות
4 אמות
סברא #1
טירחא
סברא #2
VALUE
MORE טירחא:
OWNER WILL NOT
COME BACK.
Finder may
keep it.
MORE VALUE:
OWNER WILL
COME BACK.
Finder may NOT
keep it.
8 אמות
8 אמות
2 KAV IN 8 AMOS

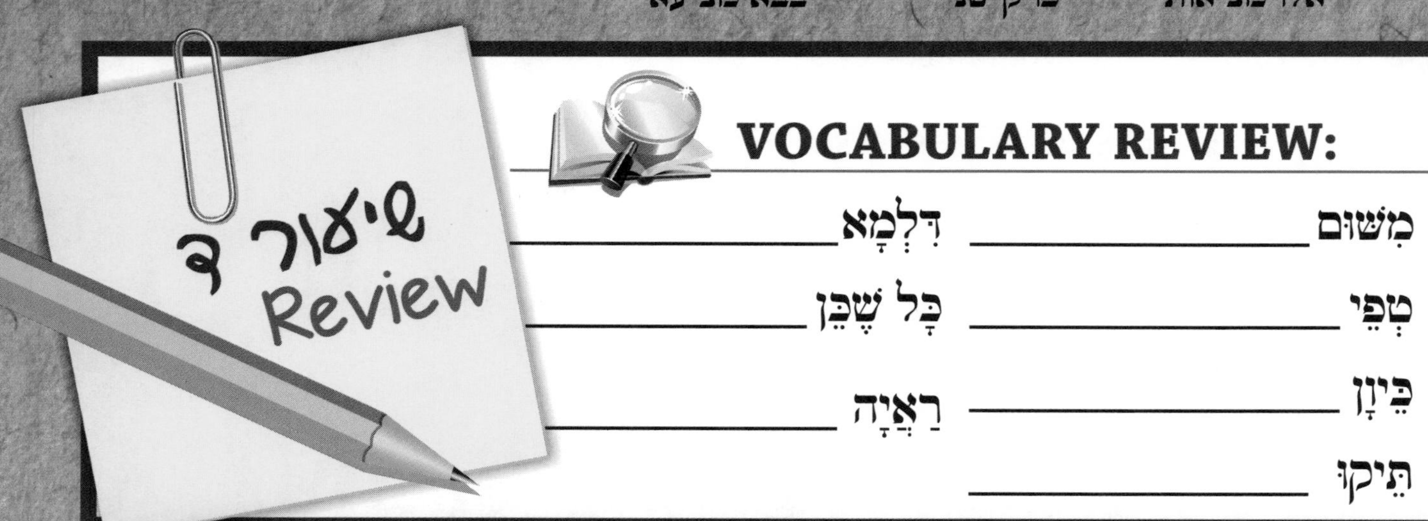

VOCABULARY REVIEW:

מִשּׁוּם ____________ דִּלְמָא ____________

טְפֵי ____________ כָּל שֶׁכֵּן ____________

כֵּיוָן ____________ רַאֲיָה ____________

תֵּיקוּ ____________

PUT IT ALL TOGETHER:

קַבַּיִים
בִּשְׁמוֹנֶה אַמּוֹת מַהוּ קַב בְּאַרְבַּע אַמּוֹת טַעֲמָא מַאי מִשּׁוּם דְּנָפִישׁ טִרְחַיְיהוּ וְכ״ש קַבַּיִים בִּשְׁמוֹנֶה אַמּוֹת כֵּיוָן דִּנְפִישָׁא טִרְחַיְיהוּ טְפֵי מַפְקַר לְהוּ אוֹ דִּלְמָא מִשּׁוּם דְּלָא חֲשִׁיבֵי וְקַבַּיִים בִּשְׁמוֹנֶה אַמּוֹת כֵּיוָן דַּחֲשִׁיבֵי לָא מַפְקַר לְהוּ

1. Read, translate and explain the following גְּמָרָא.

2. Who is asking the שְׁאֵלָה in this שִׁיעוּר? ____________

3. What is the case of his שְׁאֵלָה in this שִׁיעוּר? ____________

4. What is the הֲלָכָה about a קַב in four אַמּוֹת? ____________

5. Which of the following is a bigger bother to collect? (circle one)

קַב בְּאַרְבַּע אַמּוֹת   קַבַּיִים בִּשְׁמוֹנֶה אַמּוֹת

6. Which of the following is more valuable? (circle one)

קַב בְּאַרְבַּע אַמּוֹת   קַבַּיִים בִּשְׁמוֹנֶה אַמּוֹת

7. What is the סְבָרָא to say that the case of our שְׁאֵלָה should have the same הֲלָכָה as a קַב in four אַמּוֹת? ____________

8. What is the סְבָרָא to say that the case of our שְׁאֵלָה should not have the same הֲלָכָה as a קַב in four אַמּוֹת? ____________

IDENTIFY THE STEPS:

BE SURE TO INCLUDE EVERY WORD.

קַבַּיִים
בִּשְׁמוֹנֶה אַמּוֹת מַהוּ קַב בְּאַרְבַּע אַמּוֹת
טַעְמָא מַאי מִשּׁוּם דְּנָפִישׁ טִרְחַיְיהוּ וְכ"ש
קַבַּיִים בִּשְׁמוֹנֶה אַמּוֹת כֵּיוָן דִּנְפִישָׁא טִרְחַיְיהוּ
טְפֵי מַפְקַר לְהוּ אוֹ דִּלְמָא מִשּׁוּם דְּלֹא חֲשִׁיבֵי
וְקַבַּיִים בִּשְׁמוֹנֶה אַמּוֹת כֵּיוָן דַּחֲשִׁיבֵי לֹא
מַפְקַר לְהוּ

What type of step is this?

____

MATCHING:

_____ 1. Step 7 of the סוּגְיָא is a ________

_____ 2. What happens to a קַב בְּאַרְבַּע אַמּוֹת

_____ 3. He asked a שְׁאֵלָה

_____ 4. The case of the שְׁאֵלָה

_____ 5. Why this case might have the same הֲלָכָה as קַב בְּאַרְבַּע אַמּוֹת

_____ 6. Why this case might NOT have the same הֲלָכָה as קַב בְּאַרְבַּע אַמּוֹת

א. מַפְקַר לְהוּ

ב. שְׁאֵלָה

ג. מִשּׁוּם דְּנָפִישׁ טִרְחַיְיהוּ

ד. מִשּׁוּם דַּחֲשִׁיבֵי

ה. קַבַּיִים בִּשְׁמוֹנֶה אַמּוֹת

ו. רַבִּי יִרְמְיָה

The סוגיא to this point

שיעורים א-ד

NUMBER THE STEPS:

PLACE A SMALL NUMBER AT THE BEGINNING OF EACH STEP (example: מָצָא פֵּירוֹת[1])

אֵלּוּ מְצִיאוֹת שֶׁלּוֹ וְאֵלּוּ חַיָּיב לְהַכְרִיז אֵלּוּ
מְצִיאוֹת שֶׁלּוֹ אמָצָא פֵּירוֹת מְפוּזָּרִין
במָעוֹת מְפוּזָּרוֹת גכְּרִיכוֹת בִּרְשׁוּת הָרַבִּים
דוְעִגּוּלֵי דְבֵילָה כִּכָּרוֹת שֶׁל נַחְתּוֹם *מַחְרוֹזוֹת
שֶׁל דָּגִים וַחֲתִיכוֹת שֶׁל בָּשָׂר וְגִיזֵּי צֶמֶר
הַלְּקוּחִין מִמְּדִינָתָן וַאֲנִיצֵי פִשְׁתָּן וּלְשׁוֹנוֹת
שֶׁל אַרְגָּמָן הֲרֵי אֵלּוּ שֶׁלּוֹ *דִּבְרֵי רַבִּי מֵאִיר
ר' יְהוּדָה אוֹמֵר *כָּל שֶׁיֵּשׁ בּוֹ שִׁינּוּי חַיָּיב
לְהַכְרִיז כֵּיצַד טמָצָא עִגּוּל וּבְתוֹכוֹ חֶרֶס
כִּכָּר וּבְתוֹכוֹ מָעוֹת רַבִּי שִׁמְעוֹן בֶּן אֶלְעָזָר
אוֹמֵר כָּל כְּלֵי אַנְפּוֹרְיָא אֵין חַיָּיב לְהַכְרִיז:

גמ' מָצָא פֵּירוֹת מְפוּזָּרִין וְכַמָּה א"ר יִצְחָק קַב
בְּאַרְבַּע אַמּוֹת הֵיכִי דָּמֵי אִי דֶּרֶךְ נְפִילָה
יאֲפִילּוּ טוּבָא נַמִּי וְאִי דֶּרֶךְ הִינּוּחַ כאֲפִילּוּ
בָּצִיר מֵהָכֵי נַמִּי לָא א"ר עוּקְבָא בַּר חָמָא
לבְּמַכְנַשְׁתָּא דְּבֵי דָּרֵי עָסְקִינָן מקַב בְּאַרְבַּע
אַמּוֹת דְּנָפִישׁ טִרְחַיְיהוּ לָא טָרַח אִינִישׁ וְלָא
הָדַר אָתֵי וְשָׁקֵיל לְהוּ אַפְקוּרֵי מַפְקַר לְהוּ
בָּצִיר מֵהָכֵי טָרַח וְהָדַר אָתֵי וְשָׁקֵיל לְהוּ וְלָא
מַפְקַר לְהוּ בָּעֵי רַבִּי יִרְמְיָה חֲצִי קַב בִּשְׁתֵּי
אַמּוֹת מַהוּ קַב בְּאַרְבַּע אַמּוֹת טַעְמָא מַאי
מִשּׁוּם דְּנָפִישׁ טִרְחַיְיהוּ חֲצִי קַב בִּשְׁתֵּי אַמּוֹת
כֵּיוָן דְּלָא נָפִישׁ טִרְחַיְיהוּ לָא מַפְקַר לְהוּ אוֹ
דִּלְמָא מִשּׁוּם דְּלָא חֲשִׁיבֵי *וַחֲצִי קַב בִּשְׁתֵּי
אַמּוֹת כֵּיוָן דְּלָא חֲשִׁיבֵי מַפְקַר לְהוּ קַבַּיִים
בִּשְׁמוֹנֶה אַמּוֹת מַהוּ קַב בְּאַרְבַּע אַמּוֹת
טַעְמָא מַאי מִשּׁוּם דְּנָפִישׁ טִרְחַיְיהוּ וְכ"ש
קַבַּיִים בִּשְׁמוֹנֶה אַמּוֹת כֵּיוָן דִּנְפִישָׁא טִרְחַיְיהוּ
טְפֵי מַפְקַר לְהוּ אוֹ דִּלְמָא מִשּׁוּם דְּלָא חֲשִׁיבֵי
וְקַבַּיִים בִּשְׁמוֹנֶה אַמּוֹת כֵּיוָן דַּחֲשִׁיבֵי לָא
מַפְקַר לְהוּ

 |

LABEL AND SUMMARIZE:

For each step, write what type of step it is and a brief explanation.

STEP 1
מֵימְרָא

If someone finds scattered produce, he may keep it.

STEP 2

STEP 3

STEP 4

STEP 5

STEP 6

STEP 7

STEP 8

In the last two שִׁיעוּרִים, we have learned that רַבִּי יִרְמְיָה asked two שְׁאֵלוֹת. These שְׁאֵלוֹת were about cases in which the amount and space of the scattered grain were different than the case of our מִשְׁנָה. In this שִׁיעוּר, we will learn the third שְׁאֵלָה of רַבִּי יִרְמְיָה. In this שְׁאֵלָה, the amount and space of the scattered produce will be the same as the case of our מִשְׁנָה (one קַב in four אַמּוֹת). However, the type of produce will be different. The גְּמָרָא will explain why that might make a difference in the הֲלָכָה.

A קַב of sesame seeds	קַב שׁוּמְשְׁמִין
in [an area of] four אַמּוֹת,	בְּאַרְבַּע אַמּוֹת
______________________?	מַהוּ

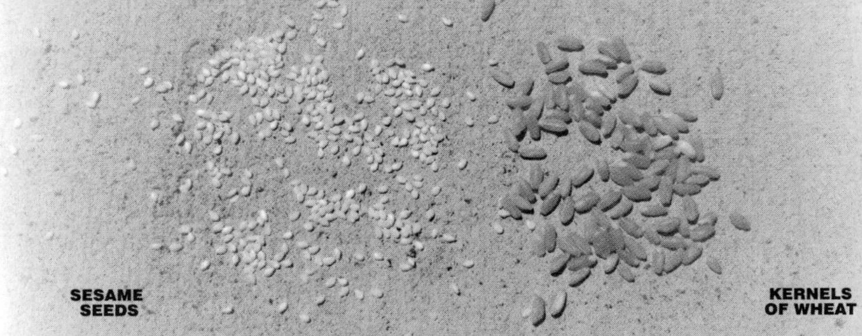

Sesame seeds are much smaller than kernels of grain. They also cost much more money for the same volume (a קַב of sesame seeds would cost much more money than a קַב of grain). Let's see how this might affect the הֲלָכָה:

[In the case of] a קַב [of kernels] in four אַמּוֹת,	קַב בְּאַרְבַּע אַמּוֹת
______ is the ________ [that the owner will make them הֶפְקֵר and the finder may keep them]?	טַעְמָא מַאי
[It is] __________ [a קַב of kernels] is not valuable [enough for the owner to go back];	מִשּׁוּם דְּלֹא חֲשִׁיבֵי
and [a קַב of] sesame seeds	וְשׁוּמְשְׁמִין
_________ they are valuable	כֵּיוָן דַּחֲשִׁיבֵי
he will not make them הֶפְקֵר [and the finder may not keep them].	לֹא מַפְקַר לְהוּ

Perhaps, the only reason that the owner does not come back for a קַב of grain in four אַמּוֹת is because one קַב is not valuable enough for it to be

worthwhile. However, a קַב of sesame seeds is much more valuable than a קַב of grain. Therefore, it is possible that the owner would come back, which means the finder may not keep it.

By now, you are becoming familiar with the wording of these שִׁיעוּרִים. By looking at the next two words "אוֹ דִלְמָא," you might already know what they mean. When discussing a שְׁאֵלָה, these words tell us that the גְמָרָא is finished presenting the סְבָרָא for one of the possible answers and is now going to present the סְבָרָא for the other possible answer.

Or ___________, [in the case of a קַב of kernels in four אַמּוֹת, the owner will make them הֶפְקֵר and the finder may keep them]	אוֹ דִלְמָא
_____________	מִשּׁוּם
there is __________ of bother [to collect them],	דְּנָפִישׁ טִרְחַיְיהוּ
and ___________________	וְכ"ש (וְכָל שֶׁכֵּן)
[in the case of a קַב of] sesame seeds,	שׁוּמְשְׁמִין
_________ there is ________ of bother [to collect them]	כֵּיוָן דְּנָפִישׁ טִרְחַיְיהוּ
[even] __________ [so],	טְפֵי
he will make them הֶפְקֵר [so the finder may keep them].	מַפְקַר לְהוּ

If the reason that the owner does not come back for a קַב of grain is because there is too much bother to collect it, he will certainly not come back for a קַב of sesame seeds. Because sesame seeds are smaller and there are many more of them, they are much more difficult to collect.

We now understand the third שְׁאֵלָה of רַבִּי יִרְמִיָה. In the next שִׁיעוּר we will learn the fourth (and final) שְׁאֵלָה.

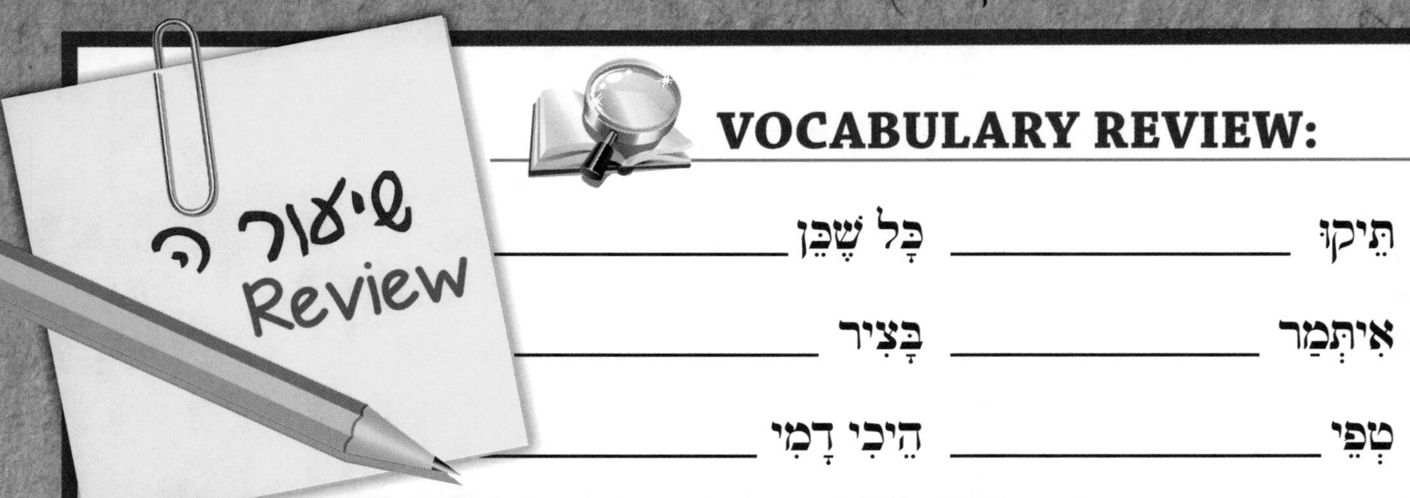

VOCABULARY REVIEW:

תֵּיקוּ ____________ כָּל שֶׁכֵּן ____________

אִיתְּמַר ____________ בָּצִיר ____________

טְפֵי ____________ הֵיכִי דָמֵי ____________

PUT IT ALL TOGETHER:

1. Read, translate and explain the following גְּמָרָא.

[א] קַב שׁוּמְשְׁמִין בְּאַרְבַּע אַמּוֹת
מַהוּ קַב בְּאַרְבַּע אַמּוֹת טַעֲמָא מַאי מִשּׁוּם דְּלָא חֲשִׁיבֵי וְשׁוּמְשְׁמִין כֵּיוָן דַּחֲשִׁיבֵי לָא מַפְקַר לְהוּ אוֹ דִּלְמָא מִשּׁוּם דִּנְפִישׁ טִרְחַיְיהוּ וְכ"ש שׁוּמְשְׁמִין כֵּיוָן דִּנְפִישׁ טִרְחַיְיהוּ טְפֵי מַפְקַר לְהוּ

2. Who is asking the שְׁאֵלָה in this שִׁיעוּר? ____________

3. What is the case of his שְׁאֵלָה in this שִׁיעוּר? ____________

4. What is the הֲלָכָה about a קַב of grain in four אַמּוֹת? ____________

5. Which of the following is a bigger bother to collect? (circle one)

a. קַב of grain in four אַמּוֹת　　b. קַב of sesame seeds in four אַמּוֹת

6. Which of the following is more valuable? (circle one)

a. קַב of grain in four אַמּוֹת　　b. קַב of sesame seeds in four אַמּוֹת

7. What is the סְבָרָא to say that the case of our שְׁאֵלָה should have the same הֲלָכָה as a קַב of grain in four אַמּוֹת? ____________

8. What is the סְבָרָא to say that the case of our שְׁאֵלָה should not have the same הֲלָכָה as a קַב of grain in four אַמּוֹת? ____________

____

IDENTIFY THE STEPS:
BE SURE TO INCLUDE EVERY WORD.

[א] קַב שׁוּמְשְׁמִין בְּאַרְבַּע אַמּוֹת
מהו קַב בְּאַרְבַּע אַמּוֹת טַעֲמָא מַאי מִשּׁוּם דְּלֹא חֲשִׁיבֵי וְשׁוּמְשְׁמִין כֵּיוָן דַּחֲשִׁיבֵי לֹא מַפְקַר לְהוּ אוֹ דִלְמָא מִשּׁוּם דְּנָפִישׁ טִרְחַיְיהוּ וְכ"ש שׁוּמְשְׁמִין כֵּיוָן דְּנָפִישׁ טִרְחַיְיהוּ טְפֵי מַפְקַר לְהוּ

What type of step is this? ______________________________

MATCHING:

_____	1. Step 8 of the סוּגְיָא is a _______	א. אוֹ דִלְמָא
_____	2. What happens to a קַב of grain בְּאַרְבַּע אַמּוֹת	ב. כֵּיוָן דְּנָפִישׁ טִרְחַיְיהוּ טְפֵי
_____	3. He asked a שְׁאֵלָה	ג. שׁוּמְשְׁמִין
_____	4. The (detailed) case of the שְׁאֵלָה	ד. כֵּיוָן דַּחֲשִׁיבֵי
_____	5. Why this case might have the same הֲלָכָה as קַב בְּאַרְבַּע אַמּוֹת	ה. מַפְקַר לְהוּ
_____	6. Why this case might NOT have the same הֲלָכָה as קַב בְּאַרְבַּע אַמּוֹת	ו. רַבִּי יִרְמְיָה
_____	7. Sesame seeds	ז. שְׁאֵלָה
_____	8. Words that tell us that the גְּמָרָא is about to present a סְבָרָא for the other side of the שְׁאֵלָה	ח. קַב שׁוּמְשְׁמִין בְּאַרְבַּע אַמּוֹת

STEP 9

In this שִׁיעוּר, we will learn the fourth and final שְׁאֵלָה of רַבִּי יִרְמְיָה. This שְׁאֵלָה will be the opposite of the שְׁאֵלָה that we learned in שִׁיעוּר ה׳. In שִׁיעוּר ה׳ we discussed a case where the produce (sesame seeds) was more valuable than grain, but more difficult to collect than grain. In this שִׁיעוּר, we will discuss produce that is much easier to collect than grain, but not more valuable (and maybe less valuable).

A קַב of dates	קַב תַּמְרֵי
in [an area of] four אַמּוֹת,	בְּאַרְבַּע אַמּוֹת
[or] a קַב of pomegranates	קַב רִמּוֹנֵי
in [an area of] four אַמּוֹת,	בְּאַרְבַּע אַמּוֹת
____________________?	מַהוּ

Dates and pomegranates are much larger than grain kernels. Therefore, a קַב of them far fewer pieces than a קַב of grain. This makes dates and pomegranates much easier to collect. However, a קַב of these fruits is not very valuable.

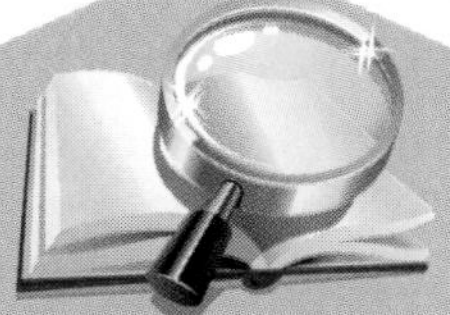

VOCABULARY WORDS

49. הֲוֵי
50. כּוּלֵי עָלְמָא
51. פָּלִיג

1 קַב OF DATES

1 קַב

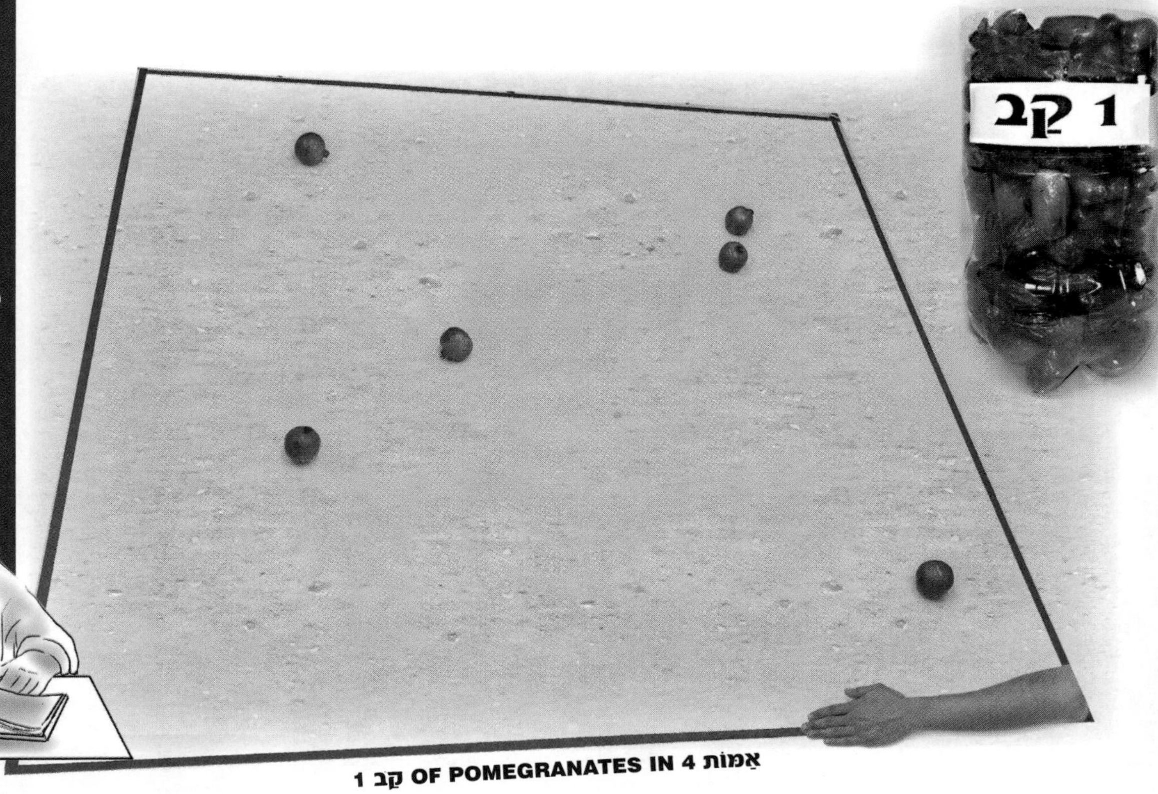

1 קַב OF POMEGRANATES IN 4 אַמּוֹת

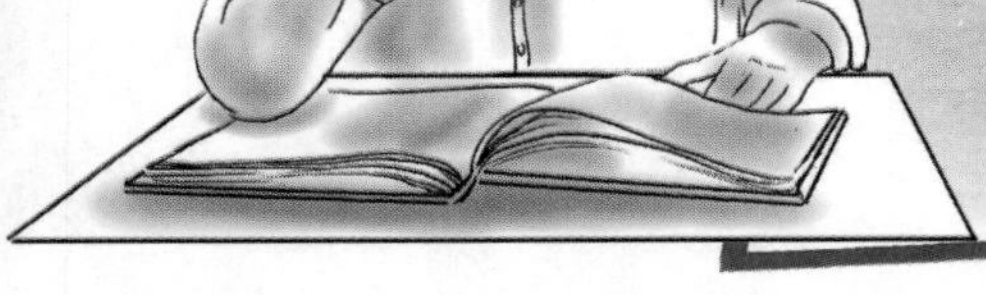

אלו מציאות
פרק שני
בבא מציעא

The גְּמָרָא will now discuss the two possible ways to understand the הֲלָכָה. First, we will learn the סְבָרָא for saying that the finder may keep the fruits:

[In the case of] a קַב [of kernels] in four אַמּוֹת,	קַב בְּאַרְבַּע אַמּוֹת
_______ is the _________ [that the owner will make them הֶפְקֵר and the finder may keep them]?	טַעֲמָא מַאי
[It is] ___________ [a קַב of kernels] is not valuable [enough for the owner to go back];	מִשּׁוּם דְּלָא חֲשִׁיבֵי
[and] a קַב of dates	קַב תַּמְרֵי
in [an area of] four אַמּוֹת,	בְּאַרְבַּע אַמּוֹת
[or] a קַב of pomegranates	קַב רִמּוֹנֵי
in [an area of] four אַמּוֹת,	בְּאַרְבַּע אַמּוֹת
________,	נַמִּי
_________ they are not valuable	כֵּיוָן דְּלָא חֲשִׁיבֵי
he will make them הֶפְקֵר [and the finder may keep them].	מַפְקַר לְהוּ

If the reason that the finder may keep a קַב of grain is because it is not valuable, the same will be true for a קַב of pomegranates or dates.

Now, the גְּמָרָא will present the סְבָרָא to say that the finder may not keep the fruits:

Or ________, [in the case of a קַב of kernels in four אַמּוֹת, the owner will make them הֶפְקֵר and the finder may keep them]	אוֹ דִּלְמָא
______________	מִשּׁוּם
there is ________ of bother [to collect them];	דִּנְפִישָׁא טִרְחַיְיהוּ
and a קַב of dates	וְקַב תַּמְרֵי
in [an area of] four אַמּוֹת,	בְּאַרְבַּע אַמּוֹת
or a קַב of pomegranates	וְקַב רִמּוֹנֵי
in [an area of] four אַמּוֹת,	בְּאַרְבַּע אַמּוֹת
________	כֵּיוָן
there is not ________ of bother [to collect them]	דְּלָא נְפִישׁ טִרְחַיְיהוּ
he will not make them הֶפְקֵר [so the finder may not keep them].	לָא מַפְקַר לְהוּ

If the reason that the finder may keep a קַב of grain is because it is too much bother to collect it (which means that owner will not want to come back), that would not apply to dates and pomegranates. These fruits are large and easy to collect. Therefore, the owner would want to come back and the finder may not keep them.

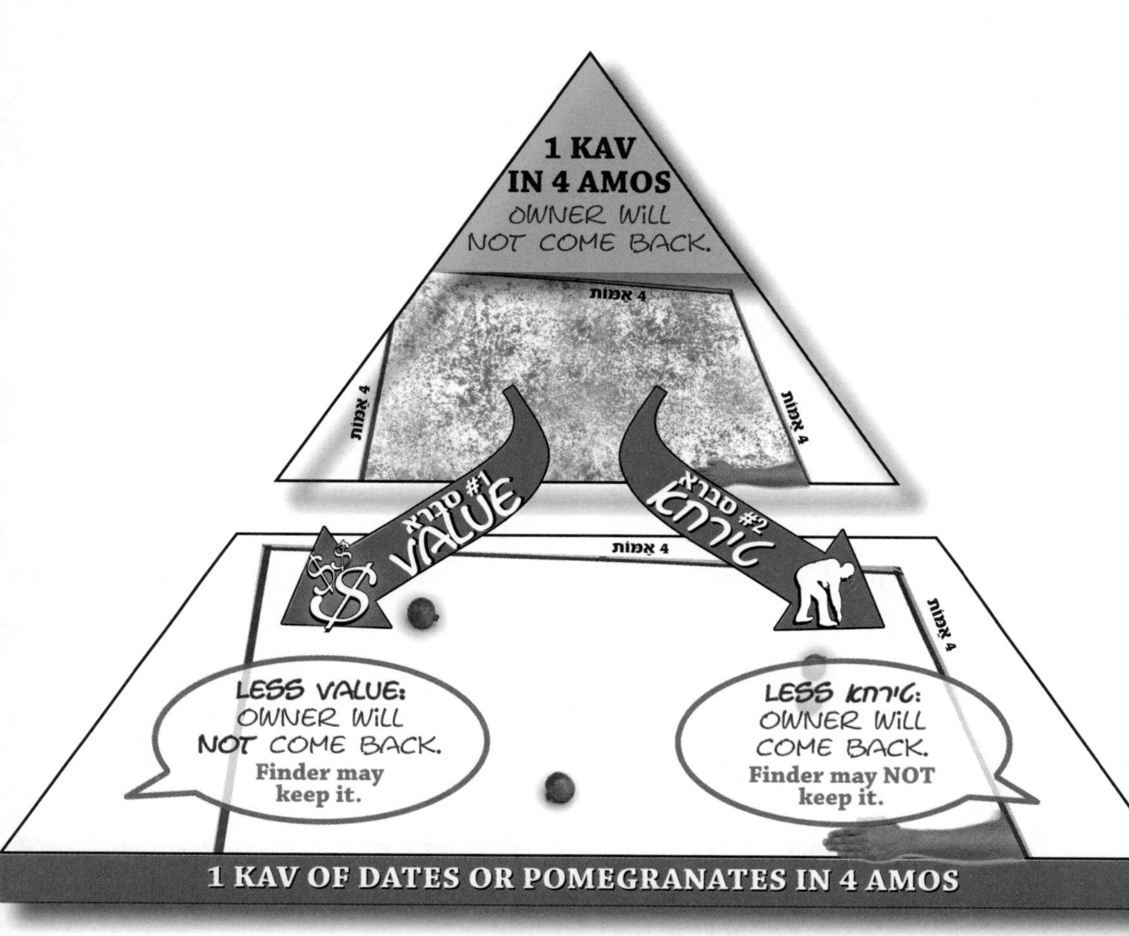

אלו מציאות
פרק שני
בבא מציעא

STEP 10

The גְּמָרָא now responds to the four שְׁאֵלוֹת of רַבִּי יִרְמְיָה:

_________ [is the דִּין in all four of these cases]?	מַאי
It stands as a שְׁאֵלָה.	תֵּיקוּ

The גְּמָרָא concludes that we do not have an answer for these שְׁאֵלוֹת. We cannot prove whether the main reason that the finder can keep a קַב of grain is because it is not valuable or due to the great bother that would be involved in collecting it. Therefore, we have no way to determine the הֲלָכָה in these four cases.

DID YOU KNOW?

תֵּיקוּ

Although the word "תֵּיקוּ" means that the שְׁאֵלָה stands (and remains unanswered), there are those who say that this word hints to something else as well. If we look at the letters of this word, we can see it as an abbreviation:

אֵלִיָּהוּ הַנָּבִיא (he is sometimes called אֵלִיָּהוּ הַתִּשְׁבִּי)	תִּשְׁבִּי
will answer	יְתָרֵץ
questions (about things that don't seem to make sense)	קוּשְׁיוֹת
and שְׁאֵלוֹת (questions asking for information).	וְאִבָּעְיוֹת

According to this understanding, the word "תֵּיקוּ" hints to the fact that the שְׁאֵלָה will remain unanswered until אֵלִיָּהוּ הַנָּבִיא comes to answer it.

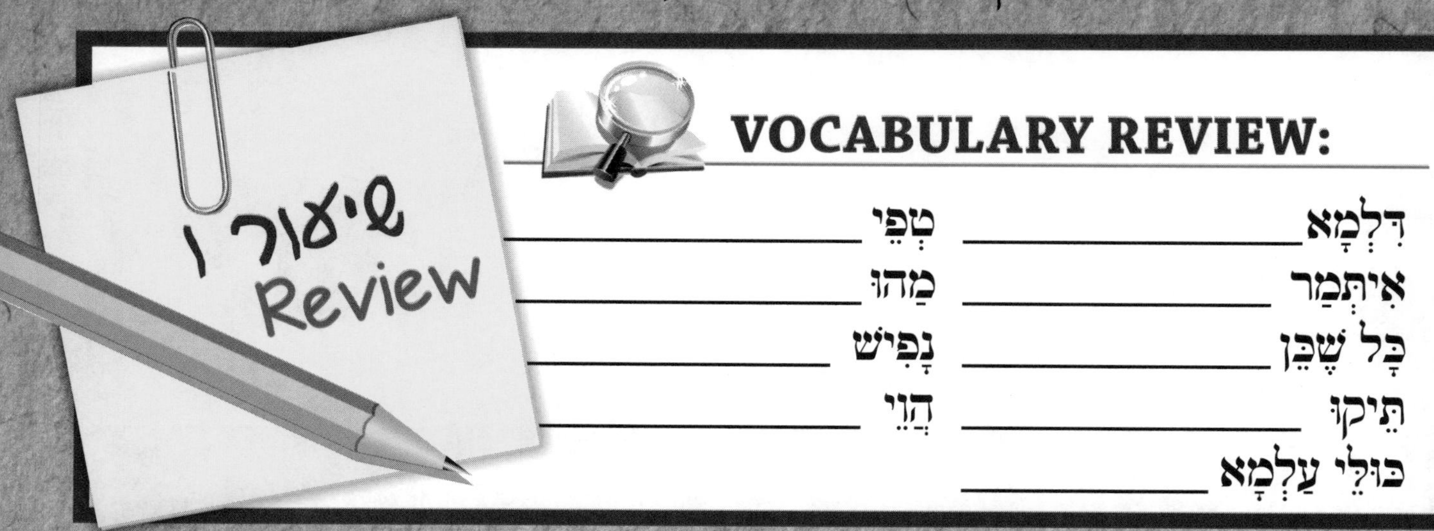

VOCABULARY REVIEW:

דִּלְמָא ______	טְפֵי ______
אִיתְּמַר ______	מַהוּ ______
כָּל שֶׁכֵּן ______	נָפִישׁ ______
תֵּיקוּ ______	הֲוֵי ______
כּוּלֵּי עָלְמָא ______	

PUT IT ALL TOGETHER:

1. Read, translate and explain the following גְּמָרָא.

קַב תַּמְרֵי בְּאַרְבַּע אַמּוֹת קַב רִמּוֹנֵי
בְּאַרְבַּע אַמּוֹת מַהוּ קַב בְּאַרְבַּע אַמּוֹת טַעְמָא מַאי מִשּׁוּם דְּלָא חֲשִׁיבֵי קַב
תַּמְרֵי בְּאַרְבַּע אַמּוֹת קַב רִמּוֹנֵי בְּאַרְבַּע אַמּוֹת נַמִּי כֵּיוָן דְּלָא חֲשִׁיבֵי מַפְקַר
לְהוּ אוֹ דִּלְמָא מִשּׁוּם דִּנְפִישָׁא טִרְחַיְיהוּ וְקַב תַּמְרֵי בְּאַרְבַּע אַמּוֹת וְקַב רִמּוֹנֵי
בְּאַרְבַּע אַמּוֹת כֵּיוָן דְּלָא נָפִישׁ טִרְחַיְיהוּ לָא מַפְקַר לְהוּ מַאי תֵּיקוּ:

2. Who is asking the שְׁאֵלָה in this שִׁיעוּר (Step 9)? ______

3. What is the case of his שְׁאֵלָה in this שִׁיעוּר? ______

4. What is the הֲלָכָה about a קַב of grain in four אַמּוֹת? ______

5. Which of the following is a bigger bother to collect? (circle one)

   a. קַב of grain in four אַמּוֹת   b. קַב of pomegranates/dates in four אַמּוֹת

6. Which of the following is more valuable? (circle one)

   c. קַב of grain in four אַמּוֹת   d. קַב of pomegranates/dates in four אַמּוֹת

7. What is the סְבָרָא to say that the case of our שְׁאֵלָה should have the same הֲלָכָה as a קַב of grain in four אַמּוֹת? ______

8. What is the סְבָרָא to say that the case of our שְׁאֵלָה should not have the same הֲלָכָה as a קַב of grain in four אַמּוֹת? ______

9. How does the גְּמָרָא respond to the four שְׁאֵלוֹת? ______

10. What is the meaning of the word תֵּיקוּ?

    א. The literal meaning ______

    ב. The hidden message in the word ______

IDENTIFY THE STEPS:

BE SURE TO INCLUDE EVERY WORD.

קַב תַּמְרֵי בְּאַרְבַּע אַמּוֹת קַב רִמּוֹנֵי
בְּאַרְבַּע אַמּוֹת מַהוּ קַב בְּאַרְבַּע אַמּוֹת טַעֲמָא מַאי מִשּׁוּם דְּלֹא חֲשִׁיבֵי קַב
תַּמְרֵי בְּאַרְבַּע אַמּוֹת קַב רִמּוֹנֵי בְּאַרְבַּע אַמּוֹת נַמִּי כֵּיוָן דְּלֹא חֲשִׁיבֵי מַפְקַר
לְהוּ אוֹ דִּלְמָא מִשּׁוּם דְּנְפִישָׁא טִרְחַיְיהוּ וְקַב תַּמְרֵי בְּאַרְבַּע אַמּוֹת וְקַב רִמּוֹנֵי
בְּאַרְבַּע אַמּוֹת כֵּיוָן דְּלֹא נְפִישׁ טִרְחַיְיהוּ לֹא מַפְקַר לְהוּ מַאי תֵּיקוּ:

Please (parenthesize) the שְׁאֵלָה

Please underline the מַסְקָנָא

MATCHING:

_____	1. Step 9 of the סוּגְיָא is a ________	א. מִשּׁוּם דְּלֹא חֲשִׁיבֵי
_____	2. Step 10 of the סוּגְיָא is a ___________	ב. תַּמְרֵי
_____	3. Another name for אֵלִיָּהוּ הַנָּבִיא	ג. תִּשְׁבִּי
_____	4. The case of the שְׁאֵלָה (Step 9)	ד. מִשּׁוּם דְּלֹא נְפִישׁ טִרְחַיְיהוּ
_____	5. Why this case might have the same הֲלָכָה as קַב בְּאַרְבַּע אַמּוֹת	ה. מַסְקָנָא
_____	6. Why this case might NOT have the same הֲלָכָה as קַב בְּאַרְבַּע אַמּוֹת	ו. קַב תַּמְרֵי\רִמּוֹנֵי בְּאַרְבַּע אַמּוֹת
_____	7. Dates	ז. שְׁאֵלָה
_____	8. Words that tell us that the גְּמָרָא is about to present a סְבָרָא for the other side of the שְׁאֵלָה	ח. אוֹ דִּלְמָא
_____	9. Pomegranates	ט. רִמּוֹנֵי
_____	10. The response to the שְׁאֵלוֹת	י. תֵּיקוּ

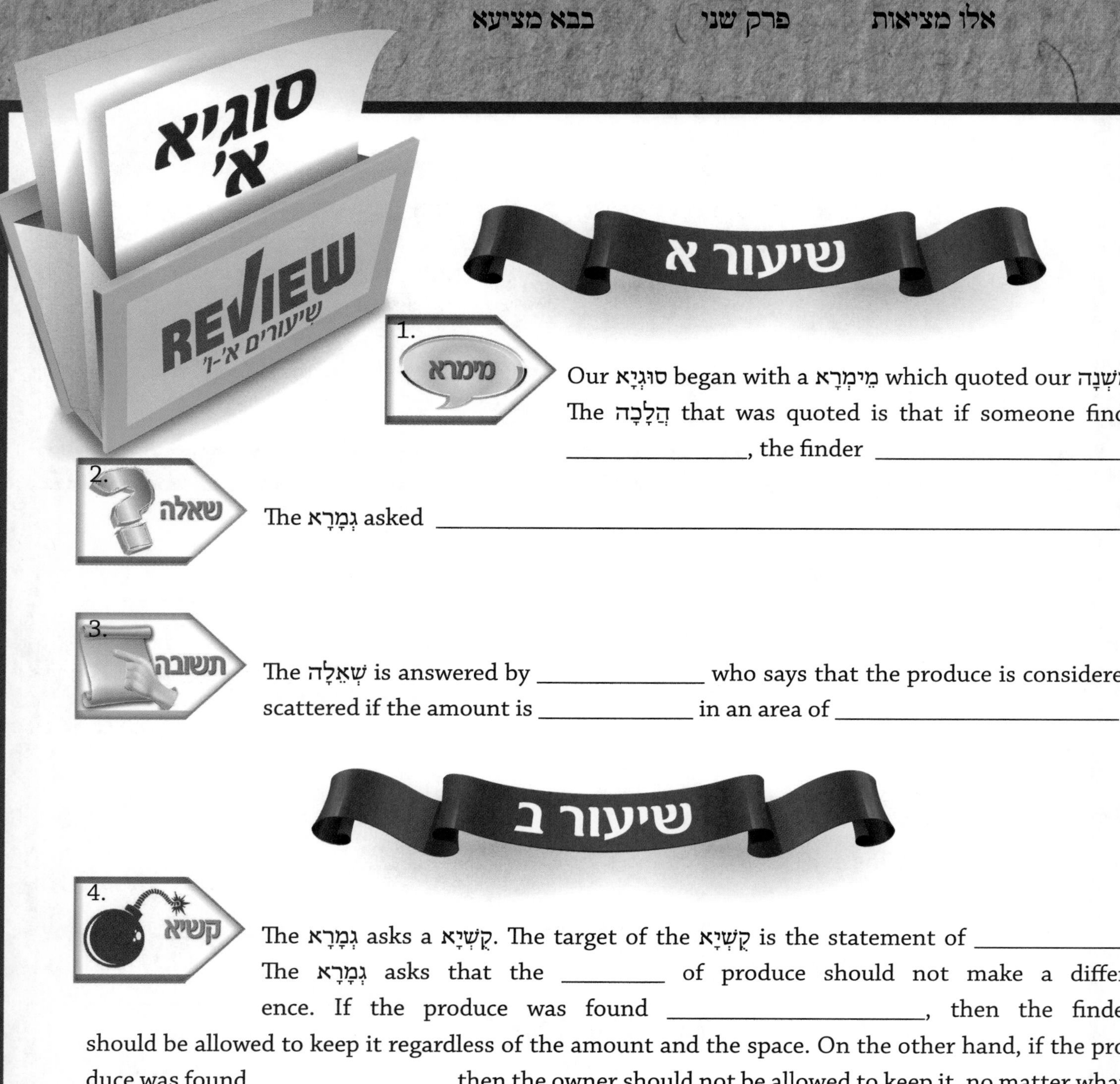

1. Our סוּגְיָא began with a מֵימְרָא which quoted our מִשְׁנָה. The הֲלָכָה that was quoted is that if someone finds ______________, the finder ____________________ .

2. The גְּמָרָא asked ____ .

3. The שְׁאֵלָה is answered by _____________ who says that the produce is considered scattered if the amount is ____________ in an area of ____________________ .

שיעור ב

4. The גְּמָרָא asks a קֻשְׁיָא. The target of the קֻשְׁיָא is the statement of ____________. The גְּמָרָא asks that the ________ of produce should not make a difference. If the produce was found ____________________, then the finder should be allowed to keep it regardless of the amount and the space. On the other hand, if the produce was found _______________, then the owner should not be allowed to keep it, no matter what.

5. The קֻשְׁיָא is answered by ________________ . He explains that our קֻשְׁיָא was based on the הֲוָה אַמִינָא that our מִשְׁנָה was talking about ________________________ . Really, the מִשְׁנָה was talking about ____________________________ . Therefore, the הֲלָכָה depends on the amount of produce and the space that it is in. If there is a _______ in a space of ______________, the finder may keep it because ________________________. However, if it is in a smaller space, the finder may not keep it because ______________________ .

6. שאלה

The גְּמָרָא tells us a שְׁאֵלָה that was asked by ______________. If there was ________________ of grain in an area __________________, what would be the הֲלָכָה? One way to look at it is that in the case of one קַב in four אַמּוֹת, there is a lot of ______________ to collect it, therefore the owner makes it ____________, so the finder is allowed to keep it. However, in the case of this שְׁאֵלָה, there is not a lot of _____________; therefore, the owner will go back to take it, so the finder ____________________________________.

On the other hand, perhaps the reason that the finder could keep one קַב in four אַמּוֹת is because it is not ________________, so the owner will not come back for it. In the case of our שְׁאֵלָה, it is even less ______________; therefore, the owner will definitely make it ____________, so the finder __________________________.

שיעור ד

7. שאלה

The גְּמָרָא tells us a second שְׁאֵלָה that was asked by _________________. If there were ______________________ of grain in space of ______________________, what would be the הֲלָכָה? One way to look at it is that in the case of one קַב in four אַמּוֹת, there is a lot of _________________ to collect it. Therefore, the owner makes it _______________, so the finder is allowed to keep it. Therefore, in the case of this שְׁאֵלָה, where there is even more __________________, the owner will certainly make it _________________, and the finder ____________ __________________________.

On the other hand, perhaps the reason that the finder could keep one קַב in four אַמּוֹת is because it is not _________________, so the owner will not come back for it. However, in the case of our שְׁאֵלָה, it is ____________________; therefore, the owner will return to take it and the finder ______________________________.

The גְמָרָא tells us the third שְׁאֵלָה that was asked by _______________. If there was one קַב of _______________ in space of _______________, what would be the הֲלָכָה? One way to look at it is that in the case of one קַב of grain in four אַמּוֹת, the finder was allowed to keep it because it is not _______________, so the owner will not come back for it. However, in the case of this שְׁאֵלָה, it is _____________; therefore, the owner will return to take it and the finder ____________________________.

On the other hand, perhaps the reason that the finder could keep one קַב of grain in four אַמּוֹת is because there is a lot of _____________ to collect it, therefore the owner makes it __________, so the finder is allowed to keep it. In the case of our שְׁאֵלָה, there is much more _________. Therefore the owner will not come back for it and the finder ___________________.

9. שאלה

The גְמָרָא tells us the fourth שְׁאֵלָה that was asked by ____________. If there was one קַב of _____________or________ in space of _________________, what would be the הֲלָכָה? One way to look at it is that in the case of one קַב of grain in four אַמּוֹת, the finder was allowed to keep it because it is not _____________ so the owner will not come back for it. In the case of this שְׁאֵלָה, it is also _________________; therefore, the owner will not come back for it and the finder _______________________________.

On the other hand, perhaps the reason that the finder could keep one קַב of grain in four אַמּוֹת is because there is a lot of _________ to collect it, so the owner will make it _____. In the case of our שְׁאֵלָה, there is not much _________. Therefore the owner will not make it _____ and the finder ______________.

The גְמָרָא responds to this שְׁאֵלָה with the word _______.

The literal meaning of this word is ____________________________. A hidden message in this word is ____.

PLACE A SMALL NUMBER AT THE BEGINNING OF EACH STEP (example: מָצָא פֵּירוֹת[1])

אֵלּוּ מְצִיאוֹת שֶׁלּוֹ וְאֵלּוּ חַיָּיב לְהַכְרִיז אֵלּוּ מְצִיאוֹת שֶׁלּוֹ מָצָא פֵּירוֹת מְפוּזָּרִין מָעוֹת מְפוּזָּרוֹת כְּרִיכוֹת בִּרְשׁוּת הָרַבִּים וְעִגּוּלֵי דְבֵילָה כִּכָּרוֹת שֶׁל נַחְתּוֹם *מַחְרוֹזוֹת שֶׁל דָּגִים וַחֲתִיכוֹת שֶׁל בָּשָׂר וְגִיזֵּי צֶמֶר הַלְּקוּחִין מִמְּדִינָתָן וַאֲנִיצֵי פִשְׁתָּן וּלְשׁוֹנוֹת שֶׁל אַרְגָּמָן הֲרֵי אֵלּוּ שֶׁלּוֹ *דִּבְרֵי רַבִּי מֵאִיר ר' יְהוּדָה אוֹמֵר *כָּל שֶׁיֵּשׁ בּוֹ שִׁינּוּי חַיָּיב לְהַכְרִיז כֵּיצַד מָצָא עִגּוּל וּבְתוֹכוֹ חֶרֶס כִּכָּר וּבְתוֹכוֹ מָעוֹת רַבִּי שִׁמְעוֹן בֶּן אֶלְעָזָר אוֹמֵר כָּל כְּלֵי אַנְפּוֹרְיָא אֵין חַיָּיב לְהַכְרִיז:

גמ' מָצָא פֵּירוֹת מְפוּזָּרִין וְכַמָּה א"ר יִצְחָק קַב בְּאַרְבַּע אַמּוֹת הֵיכִי דָּמֵי אִי דֶּרֶךְ נְפִילָה אֲפִילּוּ טוּבָא נַמִּי וְאִי דֶּרֶךְ הִינּוּחַ אֲפִילּוּ בָּצִיר מֵהָכֵי נַמִּי לָא א"ר עוּקְבָא בַּר חָמָא בְּמַכְנַשְׁתָּא דְּבֵי דָרֵי עָסְקִינָן קַב בְּאַרְבַּע אַמּוֹת דְּנָפִישׁ טִרְחַיְיהוּ לָא טָרַח אִינִישׁ וְלָא הָדַר אָתֵי וְשָׁקֵיל לְהוּ אַפְקוּרֵי מַפְקַר לְהוּ בָּצִיר מֵהָכֵי טָרַח וְהָדַר אָתֵי וְשָׁקֵיל לְהוּ וְלָא מַפְקַר לְהוּ בָּעֵי רַבִּי יִרְמְיָה חֲצִי קַב בִּשְׁתֵּי אַמּוֹת מַהוּ קַב בְּאַרְבַּע אַמּוֹת טַעְמָא מַאי מִשּׁוּם דְּנָפִישׁ טִרְחַיְיהוּ חֲצִי קַב בִּשְׁתֵּי אַמּוֹת כֵּיוָן דְּלָא נָפִישׁ טִרְחַיְיהוּ לָא מַפְקַר לְהוּ אוֹ דִלְמָא מִשּׁוּם דְּלָא חֲשִׁיבֵי *וַחֲצִי קַב בִּשְׁתֵּי אַמּוֹת כֵּיוָן דְּלָא חֲשִׁיבֵי מַפְקַר לְהוּ קַבַּיִים בִּשְׁמוֹנֶה אַמּוֹת מַהוּ קַב בְּאַרְבַּע אַמּוֹת טַעְמָא מַאי מִשּׁוּם דְּנָפִישׁ טִרְחַיְיהוּ וְכ"שׁ קַבַּיִים בִּשְׁמוֹנֶה אַמּוֹת כֵּיוָן דִּנְפִישָׁא טִרְחַיְיהוּ טְפֵי מַפְקַר לְהוּ אוֹ דִלְמָא מִשּׁוּם דְּלָא חֲשִׁיבֵי וְקַבַּיִים בִּשְׁמוֹנֶה אַמּוֹת כֵּיוָן דַּחֲשִׁיבֵי לָא מַפְקַר לְהוּ [א] קַב שׁוּמְשְׁמִין בְּאַרְבַּע אַמּוֹת מַהוּ קַב בְּאַרְבַּע אַמּוֹת טַעְמָא מַאי מִשּׁוּם דְּלָא חֲשִׁיבֵי וְשׁוּמְשְׁמִין כֵּיוָן דַּחֲשִׁיבֵי לָא מַפְקַר לְהוּ אוֹ דִלְמָא מִשּׁוּם דְּנָפִישׁ טִרְחַיְיהוּ וְכ"שׁ שׁוּמְשְׁמִין כֵּיוָן דְּנָפִישׁ טִרְחַיְיהוּ טְפֵי מַפְקַר לְהוּ קַב תְּמָרֵי בְּאַרְבַּע אַמּוֹת קַב רִמּוֹנֵי בְּאַרְבַּע אַמּוֹת מַהוּ קַב בְּאַרְבַּע אַמּוֹת טַעְמָא מַאי מִשּׁוּם דְּלָא חֲשִׁיבֵי קַב תְּמָרֵי בְּאַרְבַּע אַמּוֹת קַב רִמּוֹנֵי בְּאַרְבַּע אַמּוֹת נַמִּי כֵּיוָן דְּלָא חֲשִׁיבֵי מַפְקַר לְהוּ אוֹ דִלְמָא מִשּׁוּם דִּנְפִישָׁא טִרְחַיְיהוּ וְקַב תְּמָרֵי בְּאַרְבַּע אַמּוֹת וְקַב רִמּוֹנֵי בְּאַרְבַּע אַמּוֹת כֵּיוָן דְּלָא נָפִישׁ טִרְחַיְיהוּ לָא מַפְקַר לְהוּ מַאי תֵּיקוּ:

Our סוּגְיָא is made up of the following ten steps of שַׁקְלָא וְטַרְיָא. Briefly explain each one.

1. ______________________________

____

2. ______________________________

____

3. ______________________________

____

4. ______________________________

____

5. ____

____

6. ____

____

7. ____

____

8. ____

____

9. ____

____

10. ____

____

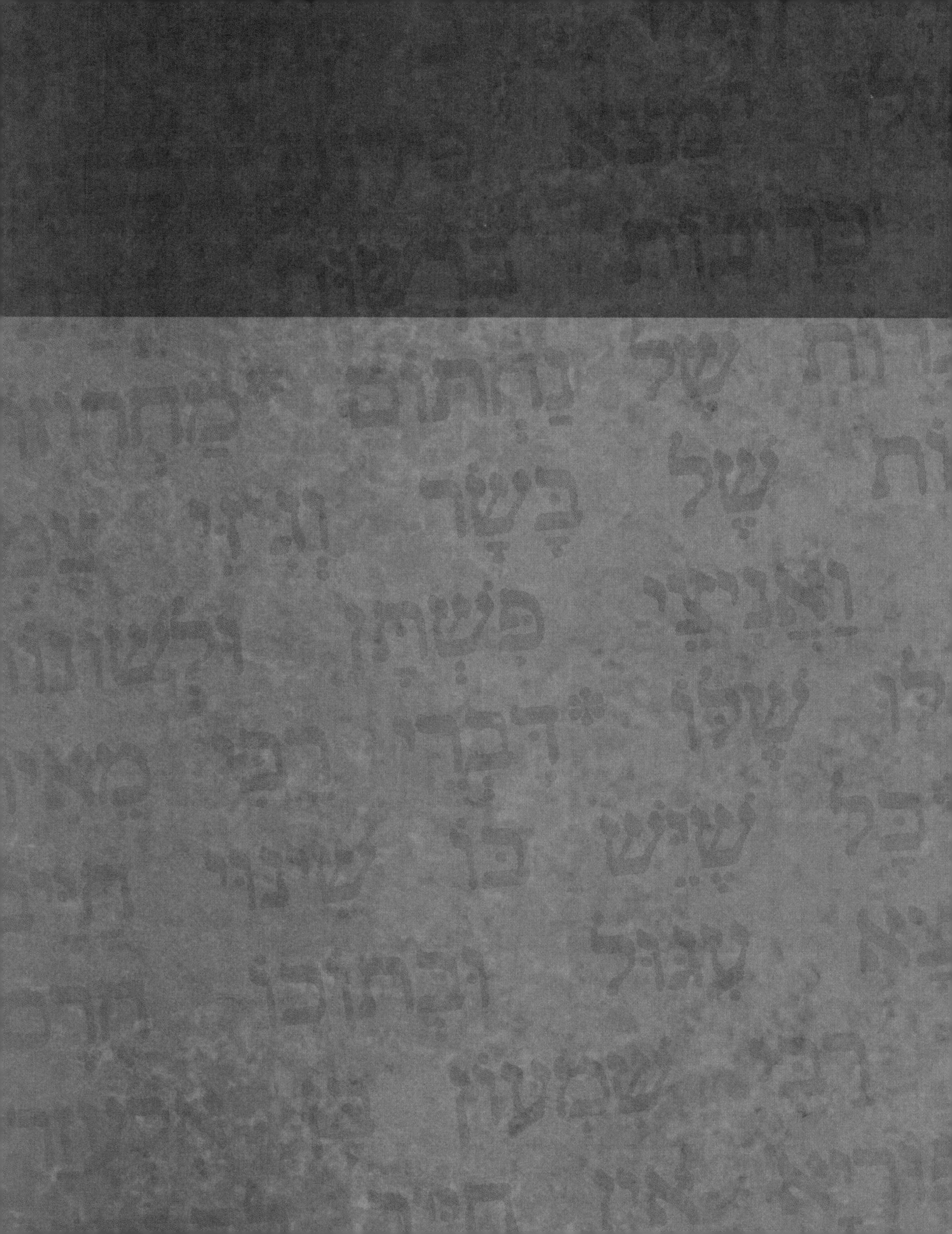

יאוש שלא מדעת

סוגיא ב'

שיעורים
ז' - כ"ג

The סוּגְיָא that we are now starting is very famous. Like many famous סוּגְיוֹת, it has a name; it is called "יֵאוּשׁ שֶׁלֹּא מִדַּעַת" (we will explain what that means shortly). It is known as a classic סוּגְיָא with a lot of שַׁקְלָא וְטַרְיָא. This סוּגְיָא will be a great opportunity to learn many new גְּמָרָא skills and become more comfortable with שַׁקְלָא וְטַרְיָא. It will also be your first experience with learning a long סוּגְיָא. In a long סוּגְיָא, it is important to make sure that you understand the basics of the סוּגְיָא really well. Otherwise, you might find it difficult to understand the rest of the סוּגְיָא, which you will be learning for quite some time. Therefore, we will spend some time right now to become familiar with the fundamental ideas needed for the סוּגְיָא of יֵאוּשׁ שֶׁלֹּא מִדַּעַת.

In *Introduction to גְּמָרָא*, Lesson 9, we learned about the concept of יֵאוּשׁ. In case you need to refresh your memory about what יֵאוּשׁ is, please review the following paragraph from that lesson:

> Introduction to גמרא LESSON 9
>
> *The thing that determines whether or not a person may keep the מְצִיאָה is if the owner has given up hope of getting it back. Giving up hope is known as יֵאוּשׁ. When a person has given up hope, we say that he was מְיָאֵשׁ. If the owner has been מְיָאֵשׁ on his אֲבֵידָה before the other person has even found it, the finder may keep it. If, however, when the finder finds the object, the owner still has hope of getting it back (he was not מְיָאֵשׁ), the finder must announce what he has found so that the owner can claim it.*

When it comes to יֵאוּשׁ, it seems that there are only two possibilities. Either the owner still hopes to get back his object (he was not מְיָאֵשׁ), or he has decided that there is no hope of getting it back (he was מְיָאֵשׁ). However, there is one more possibility. This will be the focus of our new סוּגְיָא. In order to understand that other possibility, consider the following example:

Imagine that you went on a trip and packed your knapsack with food. Whenever you were hungry, you reached into your knapsack and pulled out something to eat. Towards the end of your trip, you knew that you still had one snack left (a bag of your favorite corn chips). However, when you reached into your knapsack, you realized that it was empty. You looked at the knapsack and saw that you had left the zipper open and your corn chips had fallen out. In reality, the chips fell out of the knapsack three hours earlier when you were eating lunch in a crowded park. About two hours after that, someone was walking by and found your bag of chips.

It is unclear what the הֲלָכָה would be in this case. On one hand, at the moment that the finder found your bag of chips, you had not been מְיָאֵשׁ. You didn't even know that you had lost it; how could you possibly have been מְיָאֵשׁ?! On the other hand, if at the time that the finder found the bag of chips you would have known that it was lost, you would have been מְיָאֵשׁ. After all, it would be safe to assume that after an hour in a crowded park, someone would have found it. Since it was an ordinary bag of chips that did not have a סִימָן, even if the finder had announced what he had found, there would be no way for you to prove to the finder that it was yours. Therefore, he would not give it back. For this reason, you would certainly have been מְיָאֵשׁ.

Cases like this are called "יֵאוּשׁ שֶׁלֹּא מִדַּעַת". This literally means "Giving up hope without knowledge." What it really means is that the owner WOULD HAVE given up hope. However, he wasn't actually מְיָאֵשׁ because <u>he didn't know</u> that the object was lost. The גְּמָרָא will discuss what the הֲלָכָה is in this situation.

STEP 1

It was said:	אִיתְּמַר

The word "אִיתְּמַר" is often used to start a סוּגְיָא. It is usually followed by a מַחֲלוֹקֶת between אֲמוֹרָאִים. That is the case here as well.

Giving up hope without knowledge [that the object is missing]	**יֵאוּשׁ שֶׁלֹּא מִדַּעַת**
אַבַּיֵי said	**אַבַּיֵי אָמַר**
it is not [considered that the owner is] giving up hope [and the finder may not keep it]	**לֹא הָוֵי יֵאוּשׁ**
and רָבָא said	**וְרָבָא אָמַר**
it is [considered that the owner is] giving up hope [and the finder may keep it].	**הָוֵי יֵאוּשׁ**

The גְּמָרָא has told us the two שִׁיטוֹת (opinions). In the following שִׁיעוּרִים, the גְּמָרָא will begin to discuss and debate this interesting topic.

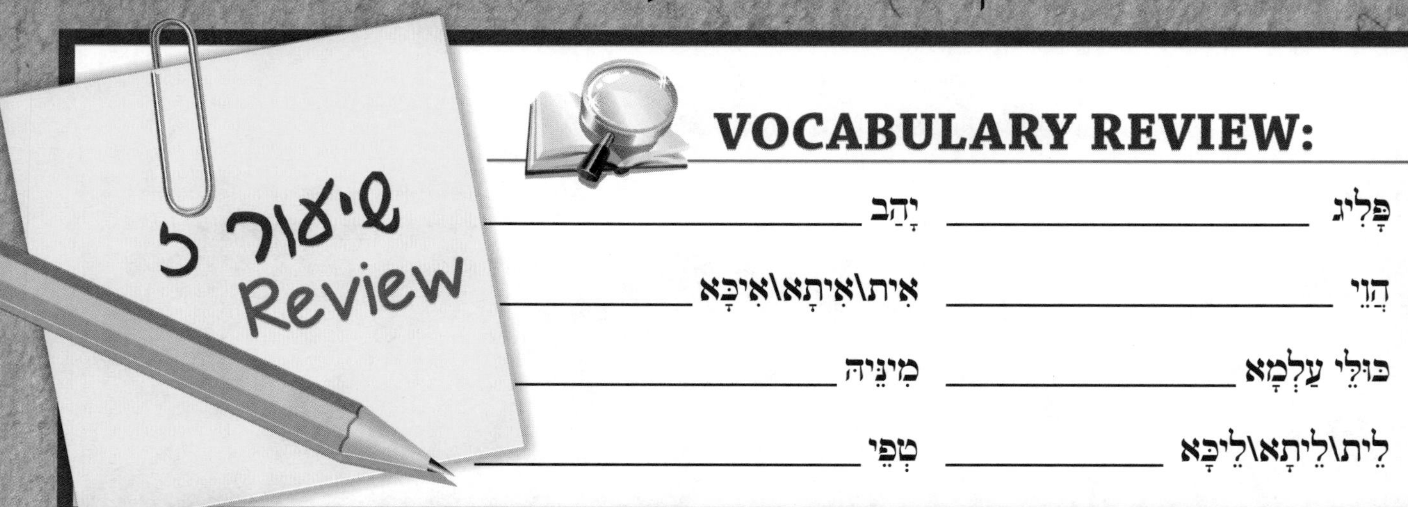

שיעור כ Review

VOCABULARY REVIEW:

פָּלִיג ______	יָהֵב ______
הֲוֵי ______	אִית\אִיתָא\אִיכָּא ______
כּוּלֵּי עַלְמָא ______	מִינֵּיהּ ______
לֵית\לֵיתָא\לֵיכָּא ______	טְפֵי ______

PUT IT ALL TOGETHER:

1. Read, translate and explain the following גְמָרָא.

אִיתְּמַר

יֵאוּשׁ שֶׁלֹּא מִדַּעַת אַבַּיֵי אָמַר לֹא הָוֵי יֵאוּשׁ
וְרָבָא אָמַר הָוֵי יֵאוּשׁ

2. What is the thing that determines whether the finder can keep the מְצִיאָה? ______

______

3. What is the case that we will be discussing in this סוּגְיָא? ______

______

______

4. What is the שִׁיטָה (opinion) of אַבַּיֵי? ______

______

5. What is the שִׁיטָה of רָבָא? ______

______

IDENTIFY THE STEPS:
BE SURE TO INCLUDE EVERY WORD.

אִיתְּמַר

יֵאוּשׁ שֶׁלֹּא מִדַּעַת אַבַּיֵי אָמַר לֹא הָוֵי יֵאוּשׁ
וְרָבָא אָמַר הָוֵי יֵאוּשׁ

What type of step is this?

____

MATCHING:

_____ 1. Step 1 of the סוּגְיָא is a ________ — א. לֹא הָוֵי יֵאוּשׁ

_____ 2. The שִׁיטָה of רָבָא — ב. יֵאוּשׁ שֶׁלֹּא מִדַּעַת

_____ 3. Often used to introduce a מַחֲלוֹקֶת between אֲמוֹרָאִים — ג. שַׁקְלָא וְטַרְיָא

_____ 4. What is needed for the finder to keep the מְצִיאָה — ד. הָוֵי יֵאוּשׁ

_____ 5. The שִׁיטָה of אַבַּיֵי — ה. מֵימְרָא

_____ 6. The name of our סוּגְיָא — ו. אִיתְּמַר

_____ 7. Our סוּגְיָא will have a lot of ________ — ז. יֵאוּשׁ

STEP 2

This step of the סוּגְיָא is a מֵימְרָא. Usually, a מֵימְרָא begins a new סוּגְיָא and is not a comment on something said before. However, this מֵימְרָא **does** discuss the previous מֵימְרָא. We call it a מֵימְרָא because it does not ask, answer, prove, or disprove anything. Instead, it is a statement which clarifies what we said in Step 1.

In שִׁיעוּר ז׳ we learned about the שִׁיטוֹת of אַבַּיֵי and רָבָא in a case of יֵאוּשׁ שֶׁלֹּא מִדַּעַת. After learning that שִׁיעוּר, it may seem as if אַבַּיֵי and רָבָא argue in all cases of יֵאוּשׁ שֶׁלֹּא מִדַּעַת. However, we will learn in this שִׁיעוּר that that is not so. There are some cases of יֵאוּשׁ שֶׁלֹּא מִדַּעַת in which both אַבַּיֵי and רָבָא agree that it is not considered to be יֵאוּשׁ and the finder may not keep it. There are also some cases in which they both agree that it is considered to be יֵאוּשׁ and the finder may keep it.

We can divide all the cases of יֵאוּשׁ שֶׁלֹּא מִדַּעַת into three categories:

אַבַּיֵי and רָבָא agree that it is not considered יֵאוּשׁ	אַבַּיֵי says that it is not considered יֵאוּשׁ and רָבָא says it is considered יֵאוּשׁ	אַבַּיֵי and רָבָא agree that it is considered יֵאוּשׁ

The גְּמָרָא will now explain which cases are in each of the three categories.

First, we will discuss the case in which אַבַּיֵי and רָבָא agree that יֵאוּשׁ שֶׁלֹּא מִדַּעַת is not considered to be יֵאוּשׁ and the finder may not keep it.

In [a case of] a thing (an אֲבֵידָה) that has a סִימָן,	**בְּדָבָר שֶׁיֵּשׁ בּוֹ סִימָן**
everyone doesn't argue (everyone agrees)	**כּוּלֵּי עָלְמָא לֹא פְּלִיגֵי**
that it is not [considered that the owner is] giving up hope. [Therefore, the finder may not keep it.]	**דְּלֹא הָוֵי יֵאוּשׁ**

If the מְצִיאָה has a סִימָן, the אֲמוֹרָאִים all agree that it is not considered that the owner has been מְיָאֵשׁ. Now, the גְּמָרָא will explain that this הֲלָכָה does not change even if the owner is מְיָאֵשׁ later on:

And even though	וְאַף עַל גַּב
that we heard him	דְשַׁמְעִינֵיהּ
that he was מְיָאֵשׁ at the end,	דִמְיָאֵשׁ לְסוֹף
it is [still] not [considered that the owner had] given up hope [by the time that the finder found it].	לֹא הָוֵי יֵאוּשׁ

The reason it is not considered יֵאוּשׁ is:

Because when it came to [the finder's] hand,	דְּכִי אָתָא לְיָדֵיהּ
[at a time that the finder was] forbidden [to keep it]	בְּאִיסוּרָא
it came to his hand.	הוּא דְאָתָא לְיָדֵיהּ

Why was the finder forbidden to keep it?

Because when [the owner] will know	דִּלְכִי יָדַע
that it fell from him,	דְנָפַל מִינֵּיהּ
he will not be מְיָאֵשׁ [at that moment],	לֹא מְיָאֵשׁ
[because] he will say,	מֵימַר אָמַר
"I have a סִימָן in it;	סִימָנָא אִית לִי בְּגַוֵּיהּ
I will give the סִימָן [to the finder]	יָהֲבְנָא סִימָנָא
and I will take it."	וְשָׁקִילְנָא לֵיהּ

When determining whether a finder may keep a מְצִיאָה, the only moment in time that matters is the moment that the finder found it. At that moment, even if the owner had already known that he had lost his object, he still would not yet have been מְיָאֵשׁ. After all, his object had a סִימָן. He would have been confident that he could provide the סִימָן and get back his object. It was only later (sometime after the finder had found it) that the owner gave up hope of finding it. When that happened, the finder had already become obligated to return the מְצִיאָה. Once the finder becomes חַיָּיב (obligated) to return the object, the fact that the owner is then מְיָאֵשׁ does not change the הֲלָכָה.

אַבַּיֵי and רָבָא agree that it is not considered יֵאוּשׁ	אַבַּיֵי says that it is not considered יֵאוּשׁ and רָבָא says it is considered יֵאוּשׁ	אַבַּיֵי and רָבָא agree that it is considered יֵאוּשׁ
בְּדָבָר שֶׁיֵּשׁ בּוֹ סִימָן		

Now the גְּמָרָא will tell us about the cases in which אַבַּיֵי and רָבָא agree that יֵאוּשׁ שֶׁלֹּא מִדַּעַת is considered to be יֵאוּשׁ and the finder may keep it:

[If the object was swept away] in the high tide of the sea	**בְּזוּטוֹ שֶׁל יָם**
or in the overflow of a river,	**וּבִשְׁלוּלִיתוֹ שֶׁל נָהָר**
even though	**אע״ג (אַף עַל גַּב)**
it has a סִימָן,	**דְּאִית בֵּיהּ סִימָן**
the תּוֹרָה has permitted [the finder to keep] it	**רַחְמָנָא שַׁרְיֵיהּ**
as we will need to say later on [in our סוּגְיָא].	**כִּדְבְעֵינַן לְמֵימַר לְקַמָּן**

Later on in this סוּגְיָא, we will learn that the regular הֲלָכוֹת of an אֲבֵידָה only apply to something that the owner has lost but is accessible to other people. However, if the אֲבֵידָה is lost not only to the owner, but is also unreachable by people in general (such as an object which was swept away by the sea or a river), then if someone manages to get it, he may keep it regardless of whether it has a סִימָן. It also does not matter whether the owner says that he has been מְיָאֵשׁ or not; in any case the תּוֹרָה permits the finder to keep it. This is because we assume that the owner was מְיָאֵשׁ, even if he doesn't admit it. Therefore, if the object has been washed away by a river (and it is a situation of יֵאוּשׁ שֶׁלֹּא מִדַּעַת), there is no מַחֲלוֹקֶת; both אַבַּיֵי and רָבָא agree that the finder may keep it.

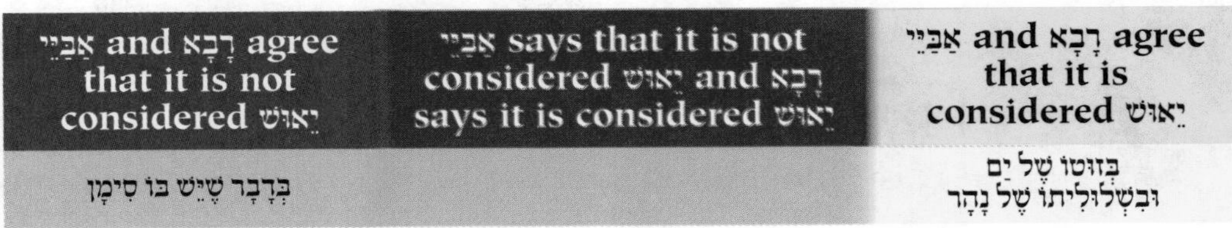

Now the גְמָרָא will tell us about the case in which אַבַּיֵי and רָבָא argue:

When do they argue?	כִּי פְּלִיגֵי
In [a case of] a thing (an אֲבֵידָה) that does not have a סִימָן	בְּדָבָר שֶׁאֵין בּוֹ סִימָן

If the object does not have a סִימָן and is lost in a way that people will be able to find it, there is a מַחֲלוֹקֶת in a case of יֵאוּשׁ שֶׁלֹּא מִדַּעַת.

Now the גְמָרָא will review the שִׁיטָה of אַבַּיֵי and teach us his סְבָרָא (reasoning):

אַבַּיֵי said	אַבַּיֵי אָמַר
it is not [considered that the owner is] giving up hope,	לֹא הָוֵי יֵאוּשׁ
because he does not know	דְּהָא לֹא יָדַע
that it fell from him.	דְּנָפַל מִינֵּיהּ

אַבַּיֵי says that since the owner does not know that the object has been lost, he could not have been מְיָאֵשׁ. It doesn't matter that he would have been מְיָאֵשׁ if he would have known that it was lost. The bottom line is that when the finder found the object, the owner had not yet been מְיָאֵשׁ. Therefore, the finder may not keep the מְצִיאָה.

Now the גְּמָרָא will review the שִׁיטָה of רָבָא and teach us his סְבָרָא:

רָבָא said	רָבָא אָמַר
it is [considered that the owner is] giving up hope	הָוֵי יֵאוּשׁ
because when he will know	דִּלְכִי יָדַע
that it fell from him,	דְּנָפַל מִינֵּיה
he will be מְיָאֵשׁ.	מְיָאֵשׁ

רָבָא continues his explanation by telling us why the owner will be מְיָאֵשׁ on his object as soon as he realizes that it is missing:

He will say,	מֵימַר אָמַר
"I have no סִימָן in it."	סִימָנָא לֵית לִי בְּגַוֵּיהּ
[Therefore,] from now (the time that it was lost)	מֵהַשְׁתָּא
it is [considered] that he has [actually] been מְיָאֵשׁ.	הוּא דִּמְיָאֵשׁ

רָבָא says that as soon as the owner realizes that the object is lost, he is מְיָאֵשׁ because he knows that he never had a chance to get it back. Therefore, the יֵאוּשׁ is considered to have happened as soon as he lost the object.* For this reason, the finder may keep the object just as if the יֵאוּשׁ had actually happened.

*For a more detailed explanation of why רָבָא considers the יֵאוּשׁ to take place at the time that the object was lost, please see Artscroll Schottenstein Gemara, Bava Metzia 22a note 16 (the second half of the note).

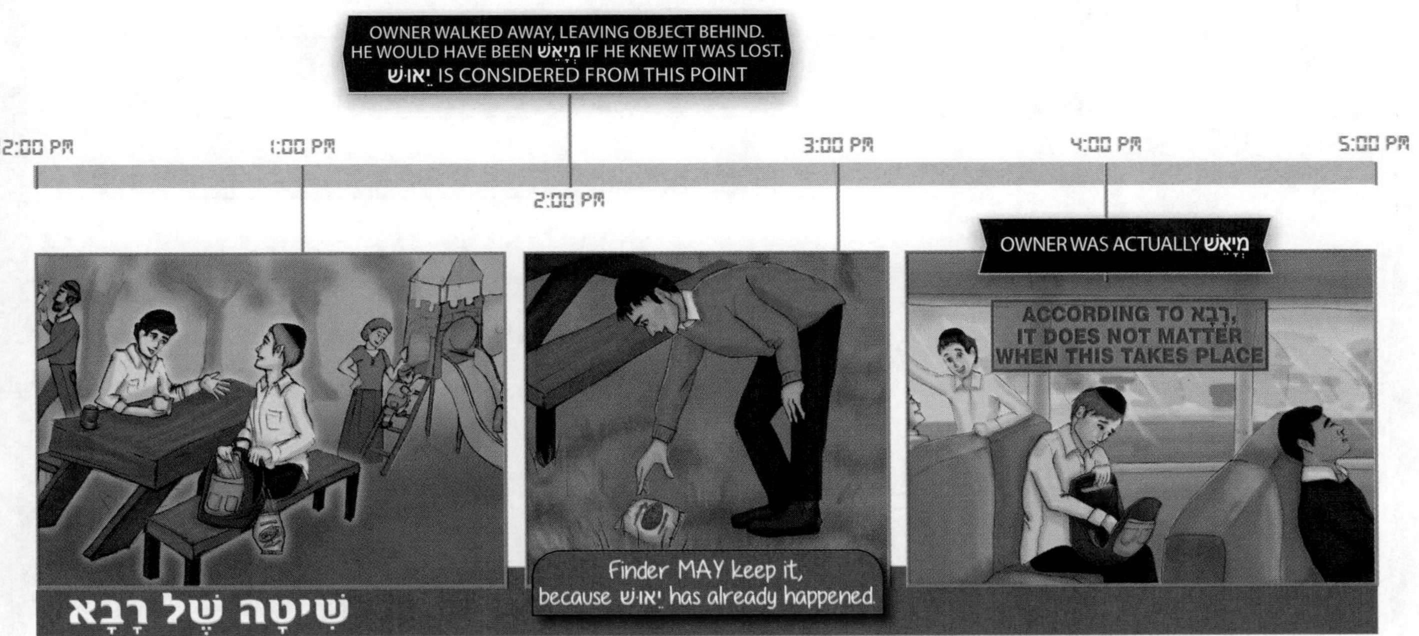

We now have a complete picture of the case in which רָבָא and אַבַּיֵי argue.

אַבַּיֵי and רָבָא agree that it is not considered יֵאוּשׁ	אַבַּיֵי says that it is not considered יֵאוּשׁ and רָבָא says it is considered יֵאוּשׁ	אַבַּיֵי and רָבָא agree that it is considered יֵאוּשׁ
בְּדָבָר שֶׁיֵּשׁ בּוֹ סִימָן	בְּדָבָר שֶׁאֵין בּוֹ סִימָן	בְּזוּטוֹ שֶׁל יָם וּבִשְׁלוּלִיתוֹ שֶׁל נָהָר

In the next group of שִׁיעוּרִים, we will learn a long debate with many רְאָיוֹת for each of the two שִׁיטוֹת. However, each time a רְאָיָה is attempted, it will be followed by a דְּחִיָּה which explains that it is not really a good proof. Finally, at the end of the סוּגְיָא we will present a final רְאָיָה that will not be disproven. At that point, we will have a מַסְקָנָא about which שִׁיטָה we follow as the הֲלָכָה.

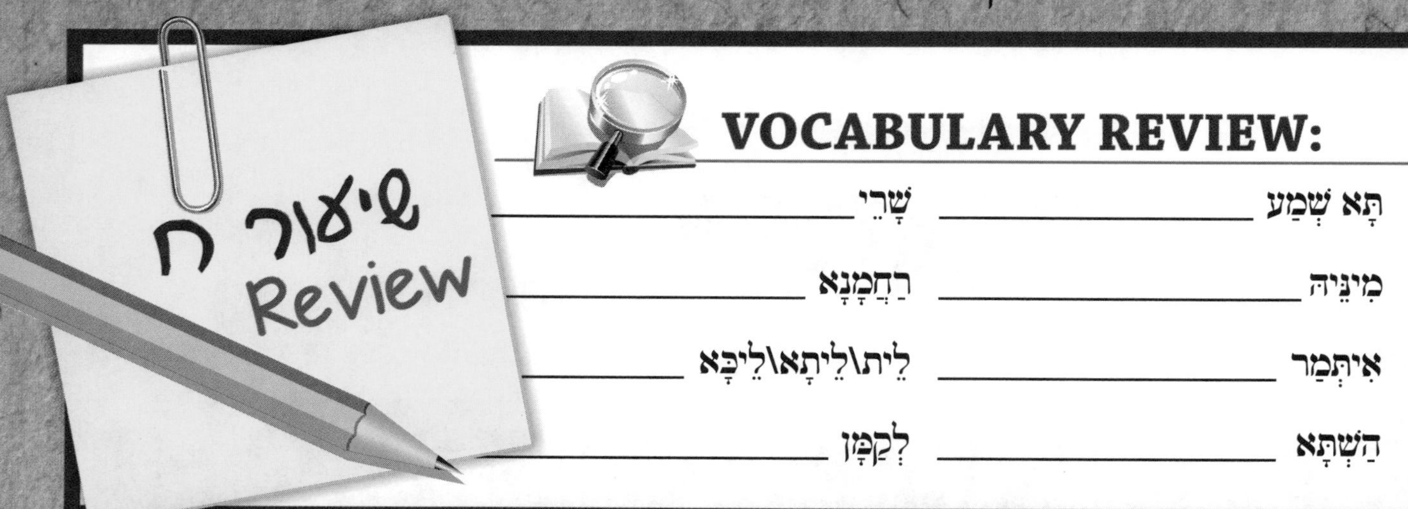

VOCABULARY REVIEW:

תָּא שְׁמַע ____________ שָׁרֵי ____________

מִינֵּיהּ ____________ רַחֲמָנָא ____________

אִיתְּמַר ____________ לֵית\לֵיתָא\לֵיכָּא ____________

הַשְׁתָּא ____________ לְקַמָּן ____________

PUT IT ALL TOGETHER:

בְּדָבָר שֶׁיֵּשׁ בּוֹ סִימָן
כּוּלֵּי עַלְמָא לֹא פְּלִיגֵי דְּלָא הָוֵי יֵאוּשׁ וְאַף
עַל גַּב דְּשַׁמְעִינֵיהּ דְּמְיָאֵשׁ (א) לְסוֹף לֹא הָוֵי
יֵאוּשׁ דְּכִי אָתָא לִידֵיהּ בְּאִיסּוּרָא הוּא דְּאָתָא
לִידֵיהּ דִּלְכִי יָדַע דְּנָפַל מִינֵּיהּ לֹא מְיָאֵשׁ
מֵימַר אָמַר סִימָנָא אִית לִי בְּגַוֵּיהּ יָהֲבְנָא
סִימָנָא וְשָׁקִילְנָא לֵיהּ בְּזוּטוֹ שֶׁל יָם וּבִשְׁלוּלִיתוֹ
שֶׁל נָהָר אע"ג דְּאִית בֵּיהּ סִימָן רַחֲמָנָא שַׁרְיֵיהּ
כִּדְבָעֵינַן לְמֵימַר לְקַמָּן כִּי פְּלִיגֵי בְּדָבָר שֶׁאֵין
בּוֹ סִימָן אַבַּיֵי אָמַר לֹא הָוֵי יֵאוּשׁ דְּהָא לֹא
יָדַע דְּנָפַל מִינֵּיהּ רָבָא אָמַר הָוֵי יֵאוּשׁ דִּלְכִי
יָדַע דְּנָפַל מִינֵּיהּ מְיָאֵשׁ מֵימַר אָמַר סִימָנָא
לֵית לִי בְּגַוֵּיהּ מֵהַשְׁתָּא הוּא דִּמְיָאֵשׁ

1. Read, translate and explain the following גְּמָרָא.
2. Briefly explain the meaning of יֵאוּשׁ שֶׁלֹּא מִדַּעַת. ____________
3. In which case do אַבַּיֵי and רָבָא agree that יֵאוּשׁ שֶׁלֹּא מִדַּעַת is not considered to be יֵאוּשׁ? ____________
4. Why does everyone agree in that case? ____________
5. In which case do אַבַּיֵי and רָבָא agree that יֵאוּשׁ שֶׁלֹּא מִדַּעַת is considered to be יֵאוּשׁ? ____________
6. Why does everyone agree in that case? ____________
7. In which case do אַבַּיֵי and רָבָא argue whether יֵאוּשׁ שֶׁלֹּא מִדַּעַת is considered to be יֵאוּשׁ? ____________
8. What is the שִׁיטָה (opinion) of אַבַּיֵי and what is his סְבָרָא (reasoning)? ____________
9. What is the שִׁיטָה of רָבָא and what is his סְבָרָא? ____________

 |

IDENTIFY THE STEPS:
BE SURE TO INCLUDE EVERY WORD.

בְּדָבָר שֶׁיֵּשׁ בּוֹ סִימָן
כּוּלֵּי עַלְמָא לָא פְּלִיגֵי דְּלָא הָוֵי יֵאוּשׁ וְאַף
עַל גַּב דְּשַׁמְעִינֵיהּ דְּמְיָאֵשׁ (א) לְסוֹף לָא הָוֵי
יֵאוּשׁ דְּכִי אָתָא לְיָדֵיהּ בְּאִיסּוּרָא הוּא דְּאָתָא
לְיָדֵיהּ דִּלְכִי יָדַע דְּנָפַל מִינֵּיהּ לָא מְיָאֵשׁ
מֵימַר אָמַר סִימָנָא אִית לִי בְּגַוֵּיהּ יָהֲבְנָא
סִימָנָא וְשָׁקִילְנָא לֵיהּ בְּזוּטוֹ שֶׁל יָם וּבִשְׁלוּלִיתוֹ
שֶׁל נָהָר אע"ג דְּאִית בֵּיהּ סִימָן רַחְמָנָא שַׁרְיֵיהּ
כִּדְבְעִינָן לְמֵימַר לְקַמָּן כִּי פְּלִיגֵי בְּדָבָר שֶׁאֵין
בּוֹ סִימָן אַבַּיֵי אָמַר לָא הָוֵי יֵאוּשׁ דְּהָא לָא
יָדַע דְּנָפַל מִינֵּיהּ רָבָא אָמַר הָוֵי יֵאוּשׁ דִּלְכִי
יָדַע דְּנָפַל מִינֵּיהּ מְיָאֵשׁ מֵימַר אָמַר סִימָנָא
לֵית לִי בְּגַוֵּיהּ מֵהַשְׁתָּא הוּא דְּמְיָאֵשׁ

What type of step is this?

____

In what way is this step different from most steps of this type?

____

____

____

MATCHING:

______ 1. Step 2 of the סוּגְיָא is a ________

______ 2. The שִׁיטָה of רָבָא

______ 3. The case that everyone agrees הָוֵי יֵאוּשׁ

______ 4. The reason that everyone agrees in the case discussed in #3

______ 5. The case that אַבַּיֵי and רָבָא disagree

______ 6. The שִׁיטָה of אַבַּיֵי

______ 7. The סְבָרָא of רָבָא

______ 8. The case that everyone agrees לָא הָוֵי יֵאוּשׁ

______ 9. The reason that everyone agrees in the case discussed in #8

______ 10. The סְבָרָא of אַבַּיֵי

א. לָא הָוֵי יֵאוּשׁ

ב. בְּדָבָר שֶׁאֵין בּוֹ סִימָן

ג. דְּהָא לָא יָדַע דְּנָפַל מִינֵּיהּ

ד. הָוֵי יֵאוּשׁ

ה. מֵימְרָא

ו. בְּזוּטוֹ שֶׁל יָם וּבִשְׁלוּלִיתוֹ שֶׁל נָהָר

ז. בְּדָבָר שֶׁיֵּשׁ בּוֹ סִימָן

ח. רַחְמָנָא שַׁרְיֵיהּ

ט. בְּאִיסּוּרָא הוּא דְּאָתָא לְיָדֵיהּ

י. דִּלְכִי יָדַע... מֵהַשְׁתָּא הוּא דְּמְיָאֵשׁ

VOCABULARY WORDS

61. אַמַּאי

62. אָזִיל

We are now ready to begin the debate. As we explained at the end of the last שִׁיעוּר, we will attempt many רַאֲיוֹת. Some of these proofs will prove that the שִׁיטָה of אַבַּיֵי is correct (that יֵאוּשׁ שֶׁלֹּא מִדַּעַת is not considered יֵאוּשׁ) and others will prove that the שִׁיטָה of רָבָא is correct (that יֵאוּשׁ שֶׁלֹּא מִדַּעַת is considered יֵאוּשׁ). However, as we explained, each of these רַאֲיוֹת (except for the last one) will be disproven by a דְּחִיָּה.

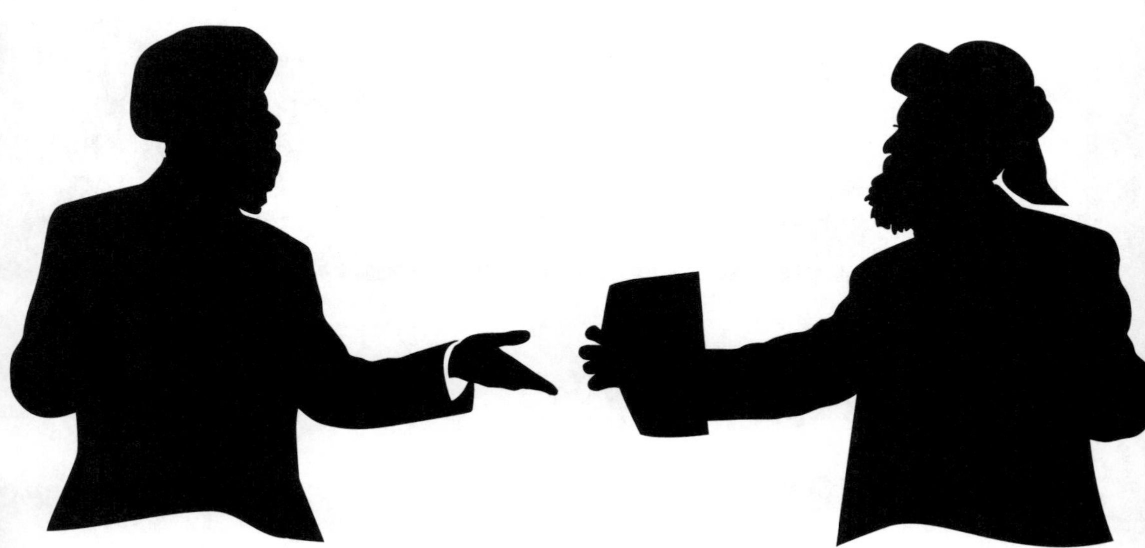

As we learned in *Introduction to* גְּמָרָא, there was a time when the גְּמָרָא was not written down. In order to know the סוּגְיָא, the חֲכָמִים had to memorize it. Certainly, this was always a difficult task. However, in a סוּגְיָא like this, where there are so many רַאֲיוֹת, it was even more difficult to remember all of the רַאֲיוֹת and their correct order. Therefore, the חֲכָמִים sometimes made mnemonic devices (memory tricks) called "סִימָנִים" to remember all of the parts of the סוּגְיָא. These סִימָנִים are included in our גְּמָרָא, but they are written in parentheses. The parentheses let us know that the סִימָן is not actually part of the discussion of the גְּמָרָא and does not belong to any step of the שַׁקְלָא וְטַרְיָא.

At this point, our סוּגְיָא has a סִימָן which is an abbreviation of the first word of each case that will be used as a רַאֲיָה in the סוּגְיָא. In this book we will not be explaining each letter of the סִימָן (or translating it). However, at the end of the סוּגְיָא, you can go back and see if you can figure out what each letter of the סִימָן stands for.

(סִימָן פמג"ש ממקגט"י ככסע"ז)

Before we begin to learn the רַאֲיוֹת and דְחִיוֹת, let's review what we learned in *Introduction to* גְמָרָא, Lesson 8, about the way these steps of גְמָרָא work:

Introduction to גמרא LESSON 8

ראיה *A PROOF – Sometimes,* ***the*** **גְמָרָא** ***will seek to prove that something which was said is correct****. This is called a* רַאֲיָה*. To understand a* רַאֲיָה*, we need to know two things. First of all, what is it that we are trying to prove? We need to know which statement we are trying to claim must be correct. We will call this* **"the object."** *Secondly, we need to know how it is that we are proving it. What is our reasoning for being sure that the statement is right? We will call this* **"the support."**

There are two main types of רַאֲיוֹת*:*

a. Using logic to show that the statement must be true

b. Quoting the words of a תַּנָא *(in a* מִשְׁנָה *or* בְּרַיְיתָא*) who says the same thing as an* אֲמוֹרָא*. If a* תַּנָא *had said the same thing, no other* אֲמוֹרָא *can argue against it.*

דחיה *A REJECTION OF A* רַאֲיָה *– Not every* רַאֲיָה *is as solid as we thought it was when it was first presented. There are times when the* גְמָרָא *is able to show that what was thought to be a good support does not actually prove the object to be correct. This is called a* דְחִיָה*. A* דְחִיָה *is very similar to a* תֵּירוּץ*. It is also made up of a* הֲוָה אַמִינָא *and* מַסְקָנָא*. The* גְמָרָא *will explain that the proof was based on an incorrect assumption. The* גְמָרָא *then gives us the correct conclusion which leaves us without a proof at all.*

With this introduction, we are now ready to begin learning this amazing debate.

STEP 3

Come and hear [a proof]: **תָּא שְׁמַע**

The גְמָרָא introduces this step (and all of the רַאֲיוֹת in this סוּגְיָא) with the words תָּא שְׁמַע. These words tell us that we are about to prove something (or at least try to prove it). Therefore, these words are usually the start of a רַאֲיָה (however, they can also be the start of a תְּשׁוּבָה).

Now let us learn the actual proof. Let's remember that the מַחֲלוֹקֶת between רָבָא and אַבַּיֵי is only in cases where the the מְצִיאָה does not have a סִימָן and the owner does not know that he lost it. This means that each proof will have to involve an object that has no סִימָן and the owner does not know that he has lost it. If we can find a מִשְׁנָה (or בְּרַיְיתָא) which teaches such a case and its הֲלָכָה (that the finder may or may not keep it), that would be a good proof to all cases of יֵאוּשׁ שֶׁלֹא מִדַעַת. We will begin by examining our מִשְׁנָה for such a case.

[The מִשְׁנָה taught that if someone finds] scattered produce [he may keep it].	פֵּירוֹת מְפוּזָּרִין
But [the owner] doesn't know	הָא לֹא יָדַע
that it fell from him?	דְּנָפַל מִינֵּיהּ

The first case of the מִשְׁנָה was about scattered produce. This produce has no סִימָן. There is a very good chance that when the finder found the produce, the owner still did not know that he had lost it. This case seems to be a case of יֵאוּשׁ שֶׁלֹּא מִדַּעַת in which אַבַּיֵי and רָבָא would argue. The מִשְׁנָה taught us that the finder of the produce may keep it. This seems to be a proof for the שִׁיטָה of רָבָא that יֵאוּשׁ שֶׁלֹּא מִדַּעַת is considered יֵאוּשׁ. After all, if אַבַּיֵי was correct that יֵאוּשׁ שֶׁלֹּא מִדַּעַת is not considered יֵאוּשׁ, the finder would not be allowed to keep the produce.

STEP SUMMARY

ראיה

The Object THE THING WHICH WE ARE PROVING	The שִׁיטָה of רָבָא - "יֵאוּשׁ שֶׁלֹּא מִדַּעַת הָוֵי יֵאוּשׁ"
The Support THE STATEMENT OR LOGIC WHICH PROVES THE OBJECT	The מִשְׁנָה taught - "פֵּירוֹת מְפוּזָּרִין הֲרֵי אֵלּוּ שֶׁלּוֹ" even though the owner might not know that he lost it.

STEP 4

In order to disprove this רַאֲיָה, we will need to find a way to explain that the case of scattered produce is not actually a case of יֵאוּשׁ שֶׁלֹּא מִדַּעַת. We will have to find the thing that we had been assuming incorrectly (the הֲוָה אַמִינָא) and correct it (with a מַסְקָנָא). Fortunately, the גְּמָרָא has already done this for us in the last סוּגְיָא (in שִׁיעוּר ב׳, Step 5). The גְּמָרָא will now remind us of what we have already learned:

But רַב עוּקְבָא בַּר חָמָא said	**הָא אָמַר רַב עוּקְבָא בַּר חָמָא**
"Here (in the case of scattered produce)	**הָכָא**
with the gathering of the threshing floor	**בְּמַכְנַשְׁתָּא דְּבִיזְרֵי***
we are dealing,"	**עָסְקִינַן**
which is an object that was lost intentionally.	**דַּאֲבֵידָה מִדַּעַת הִיא**

The גְּמָרָא explains that our הֲוָה אַמִינָא was that the מִשְׁנָה was talking about a case in which the owner had unknowingly lost his produce. Therefore, we thought that this was a case of יֵאוּשׁ שֶׁלֹּא מִדַּעַת. However, our מַסְקָנָא is that the מִשְׁנָה was discussing a case in which the owner intentionally left some of the produce behind because it was not worth it for him to go back and get it. That is the reason why the finder may keep it. Therefore, this is not a case of יֵאוּשׁ שֶׁלֹּא מִדַּעַת and the הֲלָכָה that the מִשְׁנָה teaches in this case cannot be used as a רַאֲיָה.

STEP SUMMARY

The הֲוָה אַמִינָא WHAT WE WERE ASSUMING THAT ALLOWED US TO HAVE A רַאֲיָה	The מִשְׁנָה was discussing grain which was lost.
The מַסְקָנָא THE CONCLUSION, WHERE OUR MISTAKEN ASSUMPTION IS CORRECTED, LEAVING US WITH NO MORE רַאֲיָה	The מִשְׁנָה was discussing grain which was intentionally left behind at the threshing floor.

In this שִׁיעוּר the גְּמָרָא tried to prove that the שִׁיטָה of רָבָא is correct. However, at the end of the שִׁיעוּר, we do not have a successful proof.

*The הַגָּהוֹת הַבַּ"ח changes the text of this גְּמָרָא to read "בְּמַכְנַשְׁתָּא דְּבֵי דָרֵי". For a detailed explanation of why we have הַגָּהוֹת הַבַּ"ח and how to use it, please see the box on the next page.

BY THE WAY

TEXT CORRECTIONS

It is important for us to understand something about the nature of the way גְּמָרָא was passed down through the ages.

After רַבִינָא and רַב אַשִׁי wrote the גְּמָרָא, copies were made and distributed to the יְשִׁיבוֹת of the world. What made those copies interesting is the fact that they were copied by hand!! Every set of שַׁ״ס had to be painstakingly handwritten by a skilled scribe. You can imagine how precious and expensive each גְּמָרָא was. גְּמָרוֹת were made this way for nearly one thousand years, until the printing press was invented.

Aside from the cost and effort involved, the drawback to these copies was that because all humans make mistakes, these גְּמָרוֹת would always have some errors. If a גְּמָרָא had a mistake in it and that גְּמָרָא was used to make additional copies, many more גְּמָרוֹת would have that mistake, besides for any new mistakes made during the copying. Unfortunately, over the centuries, our sacred גְּמָרָא has become full of mistakes.

Because of this, we have to spend much time making sure that we have the correct **גִירְסָא – text**. Many מְפָרְשִׁים make corrections to the גִירְסָא of the גְּמָרָא. This helps us learn the גְּמָרָא the way that רַבִינָא and רַב אַשִׁי wrote it for us.

Some of these מְפָרְשִׁים made such crucial corrections that they were printed in the margins of the גְּמָרָא. These corrections are called **הַגָּהוֹת – edits**. The two מְפָרְשִׁים who wrote the most well-known הַגָּהוֹת were the בַּ״ח[1] and the גְרָ״א[2].

In this שִׁיעוּר the הַגָּהוֹת הַבַּ״ח makes a change in the גִירְסָא. On the fourth line of the שִׁיעוּר you will see a רַשִׁ״י print ב in parentheses: (ב). If you then look at the inside margin of the page, you will see the הַגָּהוֹת הַבַּ״ח and the same (ב). What this tells us is that at this point in the גְּמָרָא, the בַּ״ח is correcting our גִירְסָא. In our case, he is telling us to change the word דְבִיזְרֵי and instead read it as דְבֵי דָרֵי (the way we originally learned רַב עוּקְבָא בַּר חָמָא's statement on דַף כא עָמוּד א).

[1]The בַּ״ח was Harav Yoel Sirkis. He was called the בַּ״ח because he wrote a פֵּירוּשׁ on the טוּר called ״בַּיִת חָדָשׁ״

[2]The גְרָ״א was הַגָּאוֹן רַבֵּינוּ אֵלִיָּהוּ Kramer. He was most famously known as the Vilna Gaon.

 |

גירסא - TEXT

מפוזרין הא לא ידע דנפל מיניה הא אמר רב עוקבא בר חמא הכא במכנשתא (ג) דבי דרי

הגהות הב"ח

(א) גמ' דמיאש לנסוף לא: (ג) שם במכנשתא דבי דרי עסקינן: (ג) תום' ד"ה ת"ש וכו' שהרבים מצוין שם. נ"ב ע"ל דף כד ע"א:

EDITS - הגהות

שיעור C Review

PUT IT ALL TOGETHER:

1. Read, translate and explain the following גְּמָרָא.

(סִימָן)
פמג"ש ממקגט"י ככסע"ז) תָּא שְׁמַע פֵּירוֹת מְפוּזָּרִין הָא לֹא יָדַע דְּנָפַל מִינֵּיהּ הָא אָמַר רַב עוּקְבָא בַּר חָמָא הָכָא בְּמַכְנַשְׁתָּא (ג) דְּבִיזְרֵי עָסְקִינַן דַּאֲבֵידָה מִדַּעַת הִיא

2. Briefly explain the elements of a רַאֲיָה and a דְּחִיָּה. (Explain what these terms mean in general, not how they apply in this שִׁיעוּר.)

ראיה
- The Object
- The Support

דחיה
- The הֲוָה אַמִינָא
- The מַסְקָנָא

3. A step that is introduced with the words תָּא שְׁמַע is usually a ______________________ , but sometimes the גְּמָרָא uses these words to introduce a ______________________ .

4. In order to prove one of the שִׁיטוֹת correct, we must find a case in which the מְצִיאָה does not ______________________ and the owner does not ______________________ .

5. Please explain the רַאֲיָה and דְּחִיָּה that we learned in this שִׁיעוּר.

ראיה
- The Object
- The Support

דחיה
- The הֲוָה אַמִינָא
- The מַסְקָנָא

6. AT THE END OF THE שִׁיעוּר - what have we successfully proven? (circle one)

a. the שִׁיטָה of אַבַּיֵי b. the שִׁיטָה of רָבָא c. nothing

VOCABULARY REVIEW:

שָׁרֵי ____________　　לְקַמָּן ____________

אָזִיל ____________　　רַחֲמָנָא ____________

הַשְׁתָּא ____________　　תָּא שְׁמַע ____________

אַמַּאי ____________　　פָּלִיג ____________

IDENTIFY THE STEPS:

BE SURE TO INCLUDE EVERY WORD.

Please underline the רַאֲיָה

Please [bracket] the דְחִיָּה

(סִימָן)
פמג"ש ממקגט"י ככסע"ז) תָּא שְׁמַע פֵּירוֹת מְפוּזָּרִין הָא לֹא יָדַע דְּנָפַל מִינֵּיהּ הָא אָמַר רַב עוּקְבָא בַּר חָמָא הָכָא בְּמַכְנַשְׁתָּא (ג) דְּבִיזְרֵי עָסְקִינָן דַּאֲבֵידָה מִדַּעַת הִיא

MATCHING:

____ 1. Step 3 of the סוּגְיָא is a ________

____ 2. Step 4 of the סוּגְיָא is a ________

____ 3. Words that the גְמָרָא uses to introduce a רַאֲיָה

____ 4. The object of the רַאֲיָה

____ 5. The support of the רַאֲיָה

____ 6. The הֲוָה אַמִינָא

____ 7. The מַסְקָנָא

א. אֲבֵידָה מִדַּעַת הִיא

ב. יֵאוּשׁ שֶׁלֹּא מִדַּעַת הֲוֵי יֵאוּשׁ

ג. פֵּירוֹת מְפוּזָּרִין הֲרֵי אֵלוּ שֶׁלּוֹ

ד. רַאֲיָה

ה. לֹא יָדַע דְּנָפַל מִינֵּיהּ

ו. תָּא שְׁמַע

ז. דְחִיָּה

The סוגיא to this point

שיעורים ד-ט

NUMBER THE STEPS:

PLACE A SMALL NUMBER BY THE BEGINNING OF EACH STEP

(example: אִיתְּמַר[1])

אִיתְּמַר

יֵאוּשׁ שֶׁלֹּא מִדַּעַת אַבַּיֵּי אָמַר לֹא הָוֵי יֵאוּשׁ
וְרָבָא אָמַר הָוֵי יֵאוּשׁ בְּדָבָר שֶׁיֵּשׁ בּוֹ סִימָן
כּוּלֵּי עָלְמָא לֹא פְּלִיגֵי דְּלֹא הָוֵי יֵאוּשׁ וְאַף
עַל גַּב דְּשַׁמְעִינֵיהּ דְּמְיָאֵשׁ (א) לְסוֹף לֹא הָוֵי
יֵאוּשׁ דְּכִי אָתָא לְיָדֵיהּ בְּאִיסּוּרָא הוּא דְּאָתָא
לְיָדֵיהּ דְּלְכִי יָדַע דְּנָפַל מִינֵּיהּ לֹא מְיָאֵשׁ
מֵימַר אָמַר סִימָנָא אִית לִי בְּגַוֵּיהּ יָהֲבְנָא
סִימָנָא וְשָׁקִילְנָא לֵיהּ בְּזוּטוֹ שֶׁל יָם וּבִשְׁלוּלִיתוֹ
שֶׁל נָהָר אע"ג דְּאִית בֵּיהּ סִימָן רַחֲמָנָא שַׁרְיֵיהּ
כִּדְבְעִינָן לְמֵימַר לְקַמָּן כִּי פְּלִיגֵי בְּדָבָר שֶׁאֵין
בּוֹ סִימָן אַבַּיֵּי אָמַר ״לֹא הָוֵי יֵאוּשׁ דְּהָא לֹא
יָדַע דְּנָפַל מִינֵּיהּ רָבָא אָמַר הָוֵי יֵאוּשׁ דְּלְכִי
יָדַע דְּנָפַל מִינֵּיהּ מְיָאֵשׁ מֵימַר אָמַר סִימָנָא
לֵית לִי בְּגַוֵּיהּ מֵהַשְׁתָּא הוּא דִּמְיָאֵשׁ (סִימָן
פמג"ש ממקגט"י ככסע"ז) תָּא שְׁמַע פֵּירוֹת
מְפוּזָּרִין הָא לֹא יָדַע דְּנָפַל מִינֵּיהּ הָא אָמַר
רַב עוּקְבָא בַּר חָמָא הָכָא בְּמַכְנַשְׁתָּא (ב) דְּבִיזְרֵי
עָסְקִינָן דַּאֲבֵידָה מִדַּעַת הִיא

VOCABULARY REVIEW:

הָוֵי ______________	לָן ______________
כּוּלֵּי עַלְמָא ______________	אָתֵי ______________
מִינֵּיהּ ______________	עַסְקִינָן ______________
דִּלְמָא ______________	לֵיהּ ______________
טַעְמָא ______________	דְּ ______________

 |

LABEL AND SUMMARIZE:

For each step, write what type of step it is and a brief explanation.

שיעור ז

STEP 1 מֵימְרָא

In the case of יֵאוּשׁ שֶׁלֹּא מִדַּעַת,

אַבַּיֵי says it is not considered יֵאוּשׁ and רָבָא says it is.

שיעור ח

STEP 2

If the object has a סִימָן, everyone agrees that _______________ .

In a case of _______________ the תּוֹרָה permits it.

They only argue in a case where _______________ .

שיעור ט

STEP 3

STEP 4

VOCABULARY WORDS

63. בָּתַר

64. נְהִי

STEP 5

In שִׁיעוּר ט׳, we had our first attempted רַאֲיָה and the דְחִיָה which disproved it. In שִׁיעוּר י׳ we will try again to prove that the שִׁיטָה of רָבָא is correct.

Just as we did in שִׁיעוּר ט׳, we will use a case from our מִשְׁנָה. Remember, in order for the case to be a proof, the מְצִיאָה cannot have a סִימָן and the owner has to be unaware that he lost it.

Once more, the רַאֲיָה will be introduced with the words תָּא שְׁמַע. In middle of the רַאֲיָה, the גְמָרָא will use the word אַמַּאי – why. Although the word "why" means that we are asking a question, it is still part of the רַאֲיָה. The גְמָרָא will be using a question to prove its point.

Come and hear [a proof]:	**ת״ש**
[The מִשְׁנָה taught that if someone finds] scattered money,	**מָעוֹת מְפוּזָּרוֹת**
these are his [to keep].	**הֲרֵי אֵלּוּ שֶׁלּוֹ**
Why [can he keep it]?	**אַמַּאי**
But [the owner] doesn't know	**הָא לֹא יָדַע**
that it fell from him?	**דְּנָפַל מִינֵּיהּ**

Scattered money has no סִימָן. Furthermore, it seems very likely that the owner of the money does not know that he has lost it. Therefore, the case of מָעוֹת מְפוּזָּרוֹת seems to be a case of יֵאוּשׁ שֶׁלֹּא מִדַּעַת in which אַבַּיֵי and רָבָא argue. The מִשְׁנָה taught that in this case the finder may keep the scattered money. This seems to be a proof that רָבָא was correct when he said that יֵאוּשׁ שֶׁלֹּא מִדַּעַת is considered to be יֵאוּשׁ!

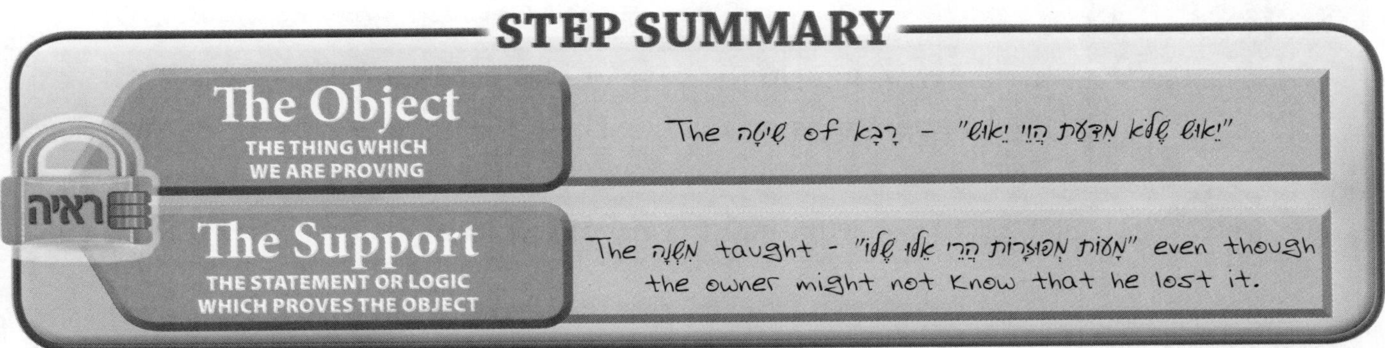

STEP 6

As always, the דְחִיָּה will find something that we had been assuming (the הֲוָה אַמִינָא) and inform us what is really correct (the מַסְקָנָא). For the second time in a row, the דְחִיָּה will show us that we were assuming that the owner did not know that he lost something, when, in fact, he did know about it. Our הֲוָה אַמִינָא was that the owner did not know that he lost his money. The גְמָרָא will explain that before the finder found the money, the owner already knew that his money was lost.

In order to explain how the owner knew that his money was lost, we will quote something that will be taught by רַבִּי יִצְחָק (one of the אֲמוֹרָאִים) later on in our סוּגְיָא:

There [in the case of scattered money]	**הָתָם**
also [the owner knew that the object was lost],	**נַמִּי**
like רַבִּי יִצְחָק [taught].	**כִּדְרַבִּי יִצְחָק**
That he said [about a different case],	**דְּאָמַר**
"A person is accustomed	**אָדָם עָשׂוּי**
to feel his [money] pouch	**לְמַשְׁמֵשׁ בְּכִיסוֹ**
at every moment (very often)."	**בְּכָל שָׁעָה וְשָׁעָה**

Later in the סוּגְיָא we will learn that רַבִּי יִצְחָק says that people regularly check their money pouches (the bag in which they used to keep their coins). When a person is carrying something that is valuable, he is constantly nervous about it getting lost. This causes him to keep checking to make sure that it is still there. If it does go missing, the owner will know about it right away. The next time he checks, he will not find it. Therefore, we can assume that if someone loses money (or anything that is valuable), he will know about it before the finder finds it. We will now use this principle of רַבִּי יִצְחָק to disprove the רְאָיָה that we learned in the beginning of this שִׁיעוּר.

שיעור
ו

כא: lines 18-23
Continued

Here, too [in the case of scattered money],	הָכָא נַמִּי
a person is accustomed	אָדָם עָשׂוּי
to feel his [money] pouch	לְמַשְׁמֵשׁ בְּכִיסוֹ
at every moment (very often).	בְּכָל שָׁעָה וְשָׁעָה

We had been assuming that the case of מָעוֹת מְפוּזָּרוֹת is a case of יֵאוּשׁ שֶׁלֹּא מִדַּעַת. The rule of רַבִּי יִצְחָק helps us understand that this is not so. By the time the finder saw the money, the owner had already checked his pouch and noticed that the coins were missing. Because the coins have no סִימָן, the owner was מְיָאֵשׁ immediately. It is for this reason that the מִשְׁנָה taught us that the finder of the coins may keep them.

STEP SUMMARY

דחיה

The הֲוָה אַמִינָא WHAT WE WERE ASSUMING THAT ALLOWED US TO HAVE A רַאֲיָה	The owner did not know that he lost his money.
The מַסְקָנָא THE CONCLUSION, WHERE OUR MISTAKEN ASSUMPTION IS CORRECTED, LEAVING US WITH NO MORE רַאֲיָה	The owner knew that the money was lost because he frequently checks his pouch.

Once again, we end the שִׁיעוּר without proving either of the שִׁיטוֹת correct.

DID YOU KNOW?

In this שִׁיעוּר, we learned a teaching from the אֲמוֹרָא who was referred to as **רַבִּי יִצְחָק**. You may have noticed that some תַּלְמִידֵי חֲכָמִים have the title רַבִּי, while others have the title רַב. It may seem like the titles of the חֲכָמִים are random. However, we can actually learn a lot about a חָכָם just from his title:

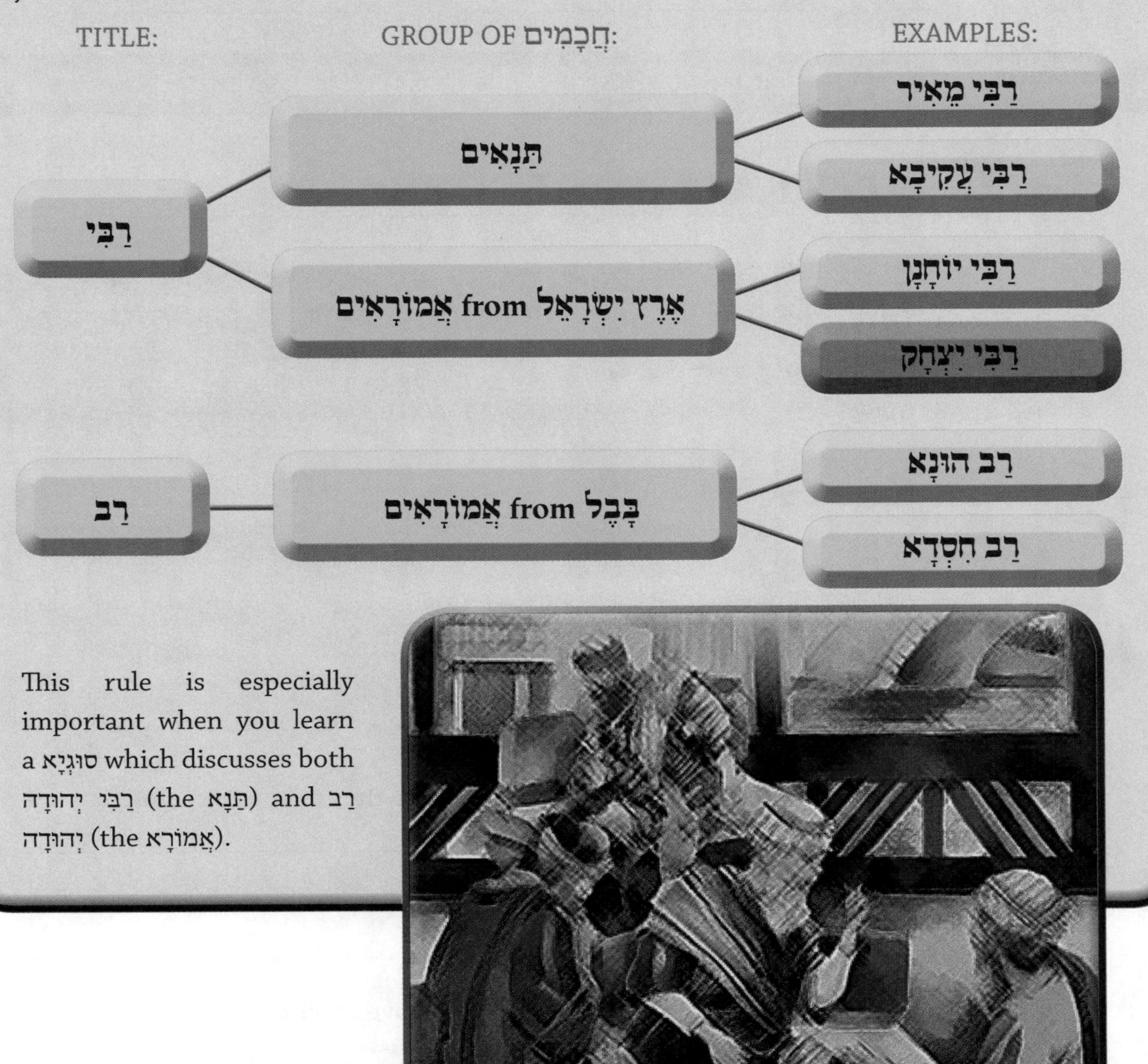

This rule is especially important when you learn a סוּגְיָא which discusses both רַבִּי יְהוּדָה (the תַּנָּא) and רַב יְהוּדָה (the אֲמוֹרָא).

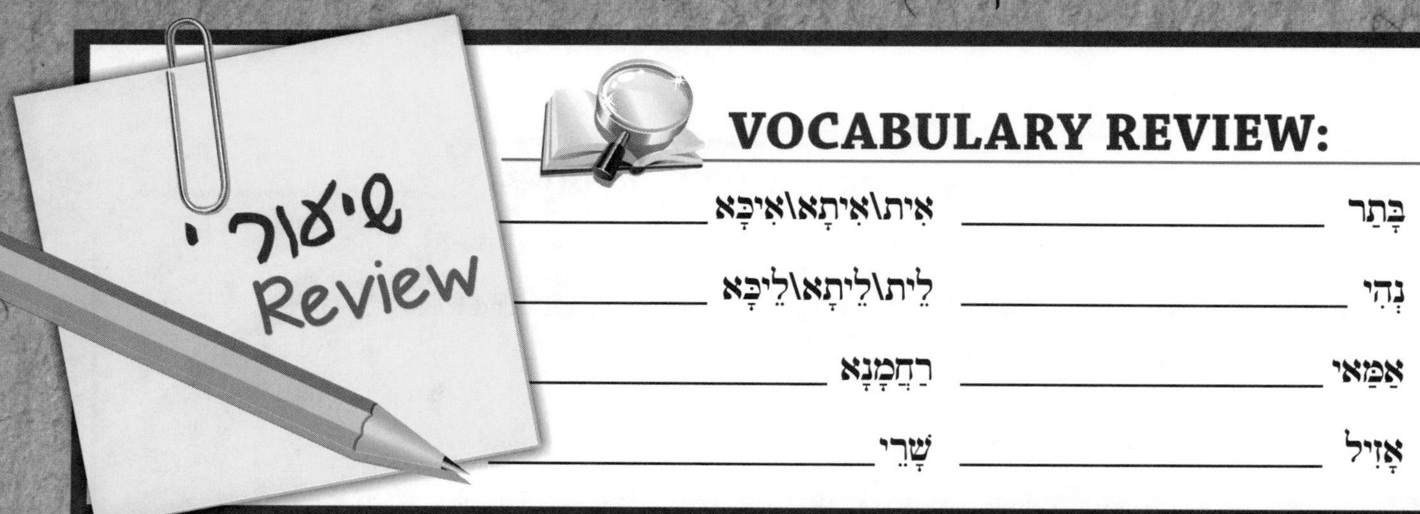

VOCABULARY REVIEW:

בָּתַר	________	אִית\אִיתָא\אִיכָּא	________
נְהִי	________	לֵית\לֵיתָא\לֵיכָּא	________
אַמַּאי	________	רַחֲמָנָא	________
אָזִיל	________	שָׁרֵי	________

PUT IT ALL TOGETHER:

1. Read, translate and explain the following גְּמָרָא.

2. Please explain the רַאֲיָה and דְּחִיָּה that we learned in this שִׁיעוּר.

ת״ש מָעוֹת
מְפוּזָּרוֹת הֲרֵי אֵלּוּ שֶׁלּוֹ אַמַּאי הָא לֹא יָדַע דְּנָפַל מִינֵּיהּ הָתָם נַמִּי כִּדְרַבִּי *יִצְחָק דְּאָמַר אָדָם עָשׂוּי לְמַשְׁמֵשׁ בְּכִיסוֹ בְּכָל שָׁעָה וְשָׁעָה הָכָא נַמִּי אָדָם עָשׂוּי לְמַשְׁמֵשׁ בְּכִיסוֹ בְּכָל שָׁעָה וְשָׁעָה

The Object	
The Support	
The הֲוָה אַמִינָא	
The מַסְקָנָא	

3. What did רַבִּי יִצְחָק teach us about the way people act when they have something valuable?
____

4. How did the teaching of רַבִּי יִצְחָק change the way we understood the case of מָעוֹת מְפוּזָּרוֹת?
____

5. At the end of the שִׁיעוּר - what have we successfully proven? (circle one)
   a. the שִׁיטָה of אַבַּיֵי   b. the שִׁיטָה of רָבָא   c. nothing

6. Which group(s) of חֲכָמִים got each of the following titles?
   רַב - ________________________
   רַבִּי - a) ________________________ b) ________________________

IDENTIFY THE STEPS:

BE SURE TO INCLUDE EVERY WORD.

ת"ש מָעוֹת
מְפוּזָּרוֹת הֲרֵי אֵלּוּ שֶׁלּוֹ אַמַּאי הָא לֹא יָדַע
דְּנָפַל מִינֵּיהּ הָתָם נַמִּי כִּדְרַבִּי *יִצְחָק דְּאָמַר
בּאָדָם עָשׂוּי לְמַשְׁמֵשׁ בְּכִיסוֹ בְּכָל שָׁעָה
וְשָׁעָה גהָכָא נַמִּי אָדָם עָשׂוּי לְמַשְׁמֵשׁ בְּכִיסוֹ
בְּכָל שָׁעָה וְשָׁעָה

Please **underline** the רַאֲיָה

Please [**bracket**] the דְחִיָה

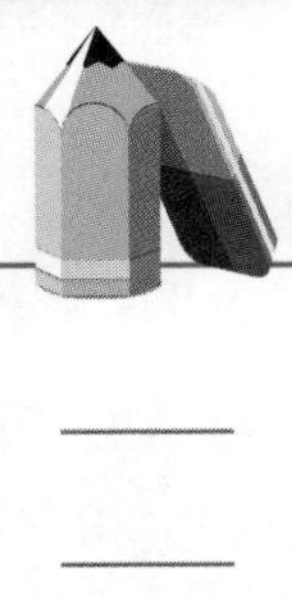

MATCHING:

____ 1. Step 5 of the סוּגְיָא is a ________

____ 2. Step 6 of the סוּגְיָא is a ________

____ 3. Words that the גְּמָרָא uses to introduce a רַאֲיָה

____ 4. The object of the רַאֲיָה

____ 5. The support of the רַאֲיָה

____ 6. The הֲוָה אַמִינָא

____ 7. The מַסְקָנָא

____ 8. How often a person checks his money pouch

____ 9. He taught us about the way a person checks his money pouch

____ 10. Word that asks a question but is part of the רַאֲיָה

____ 11. Title for תַּנָּאִים and אֲמוֹרָאִים from אֶרֶץ יִשְׂרָאֵל

____ 12. Title for אֲמוֹרָאִים from בָּבֶל

א. The owner knew that the object was lost

ב. בְּכָל שָׁעָה וְשָׁעָה

ג. מָעוֹת מְפוּזָּרוֹת הֲרֵי אֵלּוּ שֶׁלּוֹ

ד. יֵאוּשׁ שֶׁלֹּא מִדַּעַת הָוֵי יֵאוּשׁ

ה. רַב

ו. אַמַּאי

ז. דְחִיָה

ח. רַבִּי

ט. הָא לֹא יָדַע דְּנָפַל מִינֵּיהּ

י. רַאֲיָה

יא. תָּא שְׁמַע

יב. רַבִּי יִצְחָק

By now you are probably getting used to the way this סוּגְיָא works. We find a הֲלָכָה that seems to be discussing a case of יֵאוּשׁ שֶׁלֹּא מִדַּעַת and use that הֲלָכָה as a רַאֲיָה to one of the שִׁיטוֹת (so far, all of the רַאֲיוֹת have been for רָבָא). We then find a way to explain that the case is not actually a case of יֵאוּשׁ שֶׁלֹּא מִדַּעַת. That explanation is the דְחִיָה to the רַאֲיָה.

Because you are now more comfortable with these רַאֲיוֹת and דְחִיוֹת, in this שִׁיעוּר we will learn two רַאֲיוֹת and the דְחִיָה for each one (for a total of four steps).

STEP 7

The גְמָרָא will now attempt its third רַאֲיָה to prove that יֵאוּשׁ שֶׁלֹּא מִדַּעַת is considered יֵאוּשׁ (like the שִׁיטָה of רָבָא). Again, the proof begins by quoting our מִשְׁנָה:

Come and hear [a proof]:	**ת״ש**
[The מִשְׁנָה taught that if someone finds] circles of pressed figs	**עִיגּוּלֵי דְבֵילָה**
and loaves [of bread] of a baker	**וְכִכָּרוֹת שֶׁל נַחְתּוֹם**
these are his [to keep].	**הֲרֵי אֵלּוּ שֶׁלּוֹ**
Why [can he keep them]?	**אַמַּאי**
But [the owner] doesn't know	**וְהָא לֹא יָדַע**
that it fell from him?	**דְּנָפַל מִינֵּיהּ**

Circles of pressed figs and loaves of bread from a baker do not have a סִימָן (all fig circles look the same and all loaves of a particular baker look the same.) Since it seems logical that the finder might find them before the owner is aware that he lost them, this seems to be a case of יֵאוּשׁ שֶׁלֹּא מִדַּעַת. Even so, the מִשְׁנָה teaches that the finder may keep them. This seems to prove that יֵאוּשׁ שֶׁלֹּא מִדַּעַת is considered יֵאוּשׁ.

By now you should be able to identify the object and support of this רַאֲיָה:

STEP 8

The גְּמָרָא will disprove the רַאֲיָה by explaining that this is not actually a case of יֵאוּשׁ שֶׁלֹּא מִדַּעַת:

There [in the cases of כִּכָּרוֹת שֶׁל נַחְתּוֹם and עִיגּוּלֵי דְבֵילָה]	**הָתָם**
also [they are not cases of יֵאוּשׁ שֶׁלֹּא מִדַּעַת];	**נַמִּי**
because they are heavy	**אַגַּב דְּיַקִּירֵי**
he will know about them [that they are lost].	**מֵידַע יָדַע בְּהוּ**

These items are heavy. Very soon after the owner loses them, he will realize that his load is considerably lighter. He will check and see that he has lost his fig circles or loaves of bread. Therefore, we can assume that by the time the finder has found them, the owner already knew that they were lost and he was מְיָאֵשׁ. This is not a case of יֵאוּשׁ שֶׁלֹּא מִדַּעַת and cannot be used as a רַאֲיָה.

By now you should be able to identify the הֲוָה אַמִינָא and the מַסְקָנָא:

STEP 9

Once again, we will try to use a case from our מִשְׁנָה as a רַאֲיָה for the שִׁיטָה of רָבָא:

Come and hear [a proof]:	**ת״ש**
[The מִשְׁנָה taught that if someone finds] tongues of purple wool	**וּלְשׁוֹנוֹת שֶׁל אַרְגָּמָן**
these are his [to keep].	**הֲרֵי אֵלּוּ שֶׁלּוֹ**
Why [can he keep them]?	**וְאַמַּאי**
But [the owner] doesn't know	**הָא לֹא יָדַע**
that it fell from him?	**דְּנָפַל מִינֵּיהּ**

Tongues of purple wool have no סִימָן (they all look the same). As of now, we don't see any reason to assume that the owner knew they were lost before the finder found it. Therefore, the הֲלָכָה that the finder may keep it seems like a רַאֲיָה that יֵאוּשׁ שֶׁלֹּא מִדַּעַת is considered יֵאוּשׁ.

Again, please identify the object and support of this רַאֲיָה:

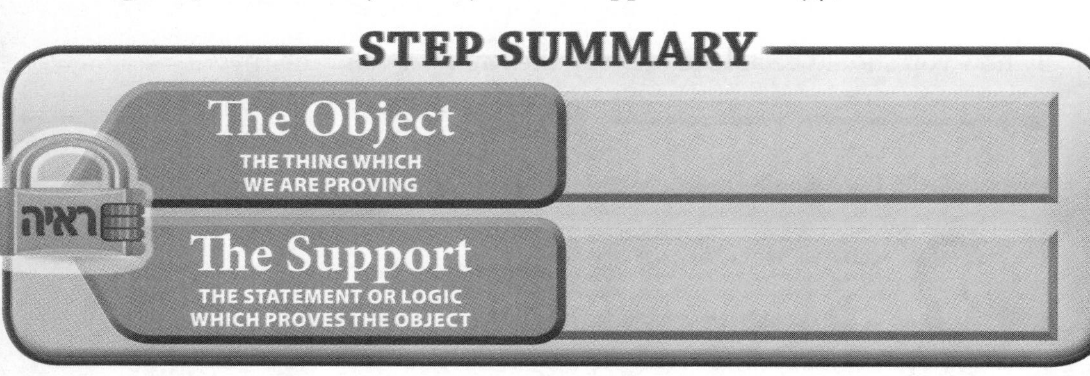

STEP 10

Once again, the גְּמָרָא will explain that when someone finds tongues of purple wool, it is not a case of יֵאוּשׁ שֶׁלֹּא מִדַּעַת:

There [in the case of לְשׁוֹנוֹת שֶׁל אַרְגָּמָן]	הָתָם
also [it is not a case of יֵאוּשׁ שֶׁלֹּא מִדַּעַת];	נַמִּי
because they are valuable	אַגַּב דַּחֲשִׁיבֵי
[the owner constantly] feels for them [and will know that he lost them]	מַשְׁמוּשֵׁי מְמַשְׁמֵשׁ בְּהוּ
and [this case is] like [the case of] רַבִּי יִצְחָק.	וּכְדְרַבִּי יִצְחָק

Later in the סוּגְיָא, רַבִּי יִצְחָק will teach us that a person frequently feels his money pouch to make sure that his money is still there. In this step, the גְּמָרָא teaches us that רַבִּי יִצְחָק's rule does not only apply to money. People tend to check for anything valuable that they are carrying. Tongues of purple wool were very valuable. (In the days of the תַּנָּאִים and אֲמוֹרָאִים, only wealthy people could afford to have colored clothing.) Therefore, if someone was carrying לְשׁוֹנוֹת שֶׁל אַרְגָּמָן, he would check for them frequently. If he lost them, he would know about it right away, even before the finder would find them. This case is not a case of יֵאוּשׁ שֶׁלֹּא מִדַּעַת and cannot be used as a רַאֲיָה.

Again, please identify the הֲוָה אַמִינָא and the מַסְקָנָא:

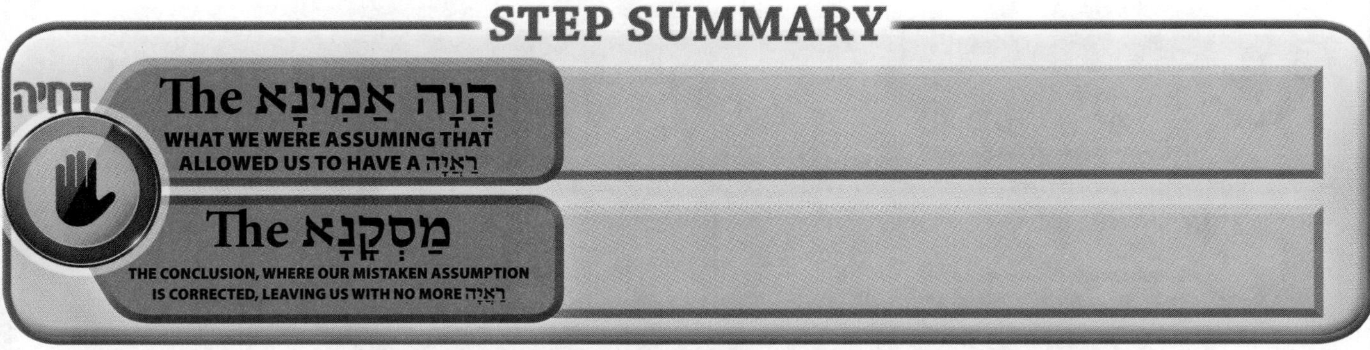

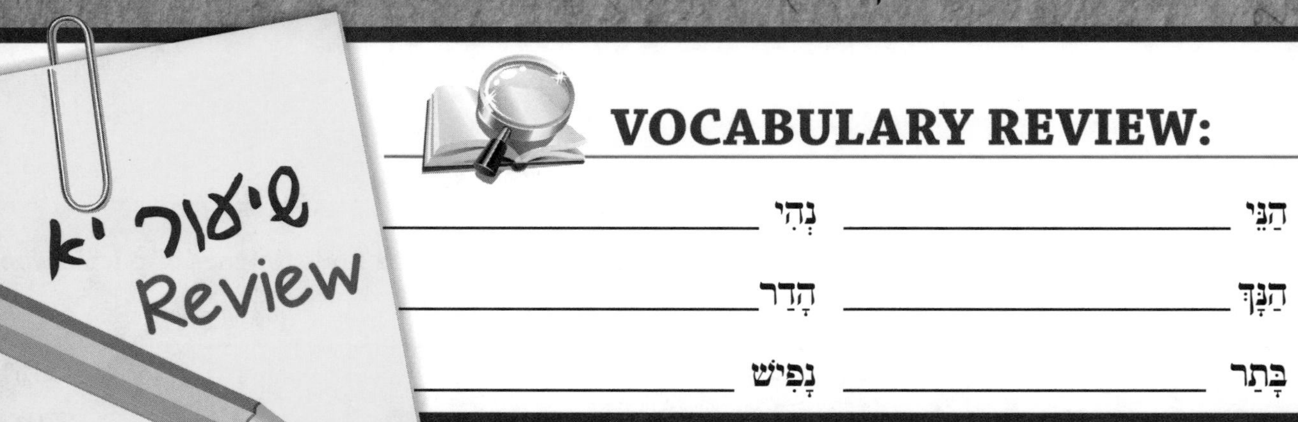

VOCABULARY REVIEW:

הַנֵּי ________________ נְהִי ________________

הַנָּךְ ________________ הָדַר ________________

בָּתַר ________________ נָפִישׁ ________________

PUT IT ALL TOGETHER:

ת״ש עִיגּוּלֵי דְּבֵילָה וְכִכָּרוֹת
שֶׁל נַחְתּוֹם הֲרֵי אֵלּוּ שֶׁלּוֹ אַמַּאי וְהָא לֹא יָדַע
דְּנָפַל מִינֵּיהּ הָתָם נַמִּי [א] ד אַגַּב דְּיַקִּירֵי מֵידַע
יָדַע בְּהוּ ת״ש וּלְשׁוֹנוֹת שֶׁל אַרְגָּמָן הֲרֵי אֵלּוּ
שֶׁלּוֹ וְאַמַּאי הָא לֹא יָדַע דְּנָפַל מִינֵּיהּ הָתָם
נַמִּי ה אַגַּב דַּחֲשִׁיבֵי מַשְׁמוּשֵׁי מְמַשְׁמֵשׁ בְּהוּ
וּכְדְרַבִּי יִצְחָק

1. Read, translate and explain the following גְּמָרָא.

2. Please fill in the chart based on the first רַאֲיָה and דְּחִיָּה of this שִׁיעוּר.

The Object	
The Support	
The הֲוָה אַמִינָא	
The מַסְקָנָא	

3. Please fill in the chart based on the second רַאֲיָה and דְּחִיָּה of this שִׁיעוּר.

The Object	
The Support	
The הֲוָה אַמִינָא	
The מַסְקָנָא	

4. At the end of the שִׁיעוּר - what have we successfully proven? (circle one)
   a. the שִׁיטָה of אַבַּיֵי b. the שִׁיטָה of רָבָא c. nothing

5. רַבִּי יִצְחָק taught that a person will feel his pouch to check for his __________. In this שִׁיעוּר, the גְּמָרָא explains that a person will also check for anything that is ______________.

 |

IDENTIFY THE STEPS:
BE SURE TO INCLUDE EVERY WORD.

ת"ש עִיגּוּלֵי דְּבֵילָה וְכִכָּרוֹת
שֶׁל נַחְתּוֹם הֲרֵי אֵלּוּ שֶׁלּוֹ אַמַּאי וְהָא לֹא יָדַע
דְּנָפַל מִינֵּיהּ הָתָם נַמִּי [א] [ד]אַגַּב דְּיַקִּירֵי מֵידַע
יָדַע בְּהוּ ת"ש וּלְשׁוֹנוֹת שֶׁל אַרְגָּמָן הֲרֵי אֵלּוּ
שֶׁלּוֹ וְאַמַּאי הָא לֹא יָדַע דְּנָפַל מִינֵּיהּ הָתָם
נַמִּי [ה]אַגַּב דַּחֲשִׁיבֵי מַשְׁמוּשֵׁי מְמַשְׁמֵשׁ בְּהוּ
וּכְדְרַבִּי יִצְחָק

Please [bracket] the first רַאֲיָה

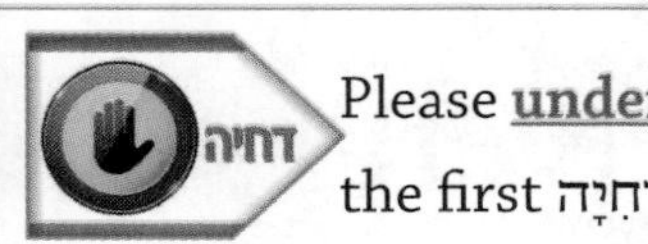

Please underline the first דְּחִיָּה

Please (parenthesize) the second רַאֲיָה

Please (circle) the second דְּחִיָּה

MATCHING:

_____ 1. Steps 7 & 9 of the סוּגְיָא are _______

_____ 2. Steps 8 & 10 of the סוּגְיָא are _______

_____ 3. The object of both רַאֲיוֹת

_____ 4. The הֲלָכָה that was used as a support in the first רַאֲיָה

_____ 5. The הֲוָה אַמִינָא (that led to both רַאֲיוֹת)

_____ 6. The מַסְקָנָא in the first דְּחִיָּה

_____ 7. The הֲלָכָה that was used as a support in the second רַאֲיָה

_____ 8. The מַסְקָנָא in the second דְּחִיָּה

_____ 9. One word that refers to the cases of עִיגּוּלֵי דְּבֵילָה and כִּכָּרוֹת שֶׁל נַחְתּוֹם

_____ 10. "because"

א. אַגַּב דַּחֲשִׁיבֵי מַשְׁמוּשֵׁי מְמַשְׁמֵשׁ בְּהוּ

ב. אַגַּב

ג. לְשׁוֹנוֹת שֶׁל אַרְגָּמָן הֲרֵי אֵלּוּ שֶׁלּוֹ

ד. יֵאוּשׁ שֶׁלֹּא מִדַּעַת הֲוֵי יֵאוּשׁ

ה. דְּחִיּוֹת

ו. עִיגּוּלֵי דְּבֵילָה וְכִכָּרוֹת שֶׁל נַחְתּוֹם הֲרֵי אֵלּוּ שֶׁלּוֹ

ז. אַגַּב דְּיַקִּירֵי מֵידַע יָדַע בְּהוּ

ח. הָתָם

ט. לֹא יָדַע דְּנָפַל מִינֵּיהּ

י. רַאֲיוֹת

The סוגיא to this point

שיעורים ז-יא

NUMBER THE STEPS:

PLACE A SMALL NUMBER BY THE BEGINNING OF EACH STEP

(example: אִיתְּמַר[1])

אִיתְּמַר

יֵאוּשׁ שֶׁלֹּא מִדַּעַת אַבַּיֵּי אָמַר לֹא הָוֵי יֵאוּשׁ
וְרָבָא אָמַר הָוֵי יֵאוּשׁ בְּדָבָר שֶׁיֵּשׁ בּוֹ סִימָן
כּוּלֵּי עָלְמָא לָא פְּלִיגִי דְּלָא הָוֵי יֵאוּשׁ וְאַף
עַל גַּב דְּשַׁמְעִינֵיהּ דִּמְיָאֵשׁ (א) לְסוֹף לָא הָוֵי
יֵאוּשׁ דְּכִי אָתָא לִידֵיהּ בְּאִיסּוּרָא הוּא דְּאָתָא
לִידֵיהּ דִּלְכִי יָדַע דְּנָפַל מִינֵּיהּ לָא מְיָאֵשׁ
מֵימַר אָמַר סִימָנָא אִית לִי בְּגַוֵּיהּ יָהֵבְנָא
סִימָנָא וְשָׁקֵילְנָא לֵיהּ בְּזוּטוֹ שֶׁל יָם וּבִשְׁלוּלִיתוֹ
שֶׁל נָהָר אע"ג דְּאִית בֵּיהּ סִימָן רַחֲמָנָא שַׁרְיֵיהּ
כִּדְבָעִינַן לְמֵימַר לְקַמָּן כִּי פְּלִיגִי בְּדָבָר שֶׁאֵין
בּוֹ סִימָן אַבַּיֵּי אָמַר [א]לָא הָוֵי יֵאוּשׁ דְּהָא לָא
יָדַע דְּנָפַל מִינֵּיהּ רָבָא אָמַר הָוֵי יֵאוּשׁ דִּלְכִי
יָדַע דְּנָפַל מִינֵּיהּ מְיָאֵשׁ מֵימַר אָמַר סִימָנָא
לֵית לִי בְּגַוֵּיהּ מֵהַשְׁתָּא הוּא דִּמְיָאֵשׁ (סִימָן
פמג"ש ממקגט"י ככסע"ז) תָּא שְׁמַע פֵּירוֹת
מְפוּזָּרִין הָא לָא יָדַע דְּנָפַל מִינֵּיהּ הָא אָמַר
רַב עוּקְבָא בַּר חָמָא הָכָא בְּמַכְנַשְׁתָּא (ג) דְּבִיזְרֵי
עָסְקִינַן דַּאֲבֵידָה מִדַּעַת הִיא ת"ש מָעוֹת
מְפוּזָּרוֹת הֲרֵי אֵלוּ שֶׁלּוֹ אַמַּאי הָא לָא יָדַע
דְּנָפַל מִינֵּיהּ הָתָם נַמִּי כִּדְרַבִּי *יִצְחָק דְּאָמַר
[ב]אָדָם עָשׂוּי לְמַשְׁמֵשׁ בְּכִיסוֹ בְּכָל שָׁעָה
וְשָׁעָה [ג]הָכָא נַמִּי אָדָם עָשׂוּי לְמַשְׁמֵשׁ בְּכִיסוֹ
בְּכָל שָׁעָה וְשָׁעָה ת"ש עִיגּוּלֵי דְבֵילָה וְכִכָּרוֹת
שֶׁל נַחְתּוֹם הֲרֵי אֵלוּ שֶׁלּוֹ אַמַּאי וְהָא לָא יָדַע
דְּנָפַל מִינֵּיהּ הָתָם נַמִּי [א] [ד]אַגַּב דְּיַקִּירֵי מֵידַע
יָדַע בְּהוּ ת"ש וּלְשׁוֹנוֹת שֶׁל אַרְגָּמָן הֲרֵי אֵלוּ
שֶׁלּוֹ וְאַמַּאי הָא לָא יָדַע דְּנָפַל מִינֵּיהּ הָתָם
נַמִּי [ה]אַגַּב דַּחֲשִׁיבֵי מַשְׁמוּשֵׁי מְמַשְׁמֵשׁ בְּהוּ
וּכְדְרַבִּי יִצְחָק

VOCABULARY REVIEW:

בְּעֵי ______________________ דִּלְמָא ______________________

מִשּׁוּם ______________________ כָּל שֶׁכֵּן ______________________

LABEL AND SUMMARIZE:

For each step, write what type of step it is and a brief explanation.

שיעור ז
STEP 1 מֵימְרָא
In the case of יֵאוּשׁ שֶׁלֹּא מִדַּעַת, אַבַּיֵי says it is not considered יֵאוּשׁ and רָבָא says it is.

שיעור ח
STEP 2
They only argue in a case where ______.

שיעור ט
STEP 3

STEP 4

שיעור י
STEP 5

STEP 6

שיעור יא
STEP 7

STEP 8

STEP 9

STEP 10

שיעור יב
כא: lines 29-34

VOCABULARY WORDS

67. דוּכְתָּא
68. מֵעִיקָּרָא

STEP 11

יאוש שלא מדעת ראיה #5 FIFTH PROOF FOR THE שיטה OF רָבָא

Come and hear [a proof from a בְּרַיְיתָא]: ת"ש

The גְּמָרָא will now try again to prove that the שִׁיטָה of רָבָא is correct. However, this time the proof will not come from the מִשְׁנָה at the beginning of the פֶּרֶק. Instead, the proof will come from a בְּרַיְיתָא. In case you need a quick reminder of what a בְּרַיְיתָא is, let's review what we learned in *Introduction to גְּמָרָא*, Lesson 6:

When רֶבִּי was putting together the מִשְׁנָיוֹת, it was not possible for him to collect each and every teaching of each and every תַּנָא. Some things had to be left out. Any teaching of a תַּנָא that was not included in a מִשְׁנָה is called a בְּרַיְיתָא. It is very common for the גְּמָרָא to teach and quote בְּרַיְיתוֹת.

When the גְּמָרָא quotes a בְּרַיְיתָא for the purpose of proving something (or asking something), **it is important to first learn the בְּרַיְיתָא on its own without trying to understand the proof at the same time**. After you know the בְּרַיְיתָא well, then you can see how it fits into the סוּגְיָא that we are learning. In other words, when the גְּמָרָא quotes a בְּרַיְיתָא, learn it the same way you learn a מִשְׁנָה – as something to be learned independently.

Here is the בְּרַיְיתָא:

One who finds money	**הַמּוֹצֵא מָעוֹת**
in shuls or בָּתֵּי מִדְרָשׁוֹת*	**בְּבָתֵּי כְּנֵסִיּוֹת וּבְבָתֵּי מִדְרָשׁוֹת**
or in any place	**וּבְכָל מָקוֹם**
that the public is found there,	**שֶׁהָרַבִּים מְצוּיִין שָׁם**
these [coins] are his [to keep],	**הֲרֵי אֵלּוּ שֶׁלּוֹ**
because	**מִפְּנֵי**
the owner has given up hope from [getting] them.	**שֶׁהַבְּעָלִים מִתְיָאֲשִׁין מֵהֶן**

*בָּתֵּי מִדְרָשׁוֹת is plural for בֵּית הַמִּדְרָשׁ. A בֵּית הַמִּדְרָשׁ is a room where people gather to learn תּוֹרָה. To this very day, תַּלְמִידִים of post-high school יְשִׁיבוֹת spend most of their day learning and davening in the בֵּית הַמִּדְרָשׁ.

The בְּרַיְיתָא has taught us that if someone finds money in a shul or any public place, the finder may keep the money. Since the money was lost in a public place, there is a good chance that it was found by someone who would not return it. Therefore, the owner will give up any hope of getting the money back.

Now that we understand the בְּרַיְיתָא, we are ready to learn how the גְמָרָא will use it as a רַאֲיָה for the שִׁיטָה of רָבָא:

But [the owner] doesn't know	**וְהָא לֹא יָדַע**
that it fell from him?	**דְּנָפַל מִינֵּיהּ**

The גְמָרָא points out that the owner may not know that he dropped the money. Therefore, this is a case of יֵאוּשׁ שֶׁלֹּא מִדַּעַת. Since the בְּרַיְיתָא has taught us that the finder can assume that the owner was מְיָאֵשׁ, the בְּרַיְיתָא must mean that יֵאוּשׁ שֶׁלֹּא מִדַּעַת is considered to be יֵאוּשׁ (otherwise, the finder would not be allowed to keep the money). This seems to be a good proof for the שִׁיטָה of רָבָא.

STEP 12

The גְּמָרָא will reject the רַאֲיָה by explaining that the case of the בְּרַיְיתָא is not a case of יֵאוּשׁ שֶׁלֹּא מִדַּעַת.

For some of the דְּחִיּוֹת that we have had so far in this סוּגְיָא, we have quoted the teaching of רַבִּי יִצְחָק. Each time, we said that we were quoting the words that רַבִּי יִצְחָק will teach "later in the סוּגְיָא." This is the point in the סוּגְיָא when רַבִּי יִצְחָק actually taught this:

רַבִּי יִצְחָק said,	**אָמַר רַבִּי יִצְחָק**
"A person is accustomed	**אָדָם עָשׂוּי**
to feel his [money] pouch	**לְמַשְׁמֵשׁ בְּכִיסוֹ**
at every moment (very often)."	**בְּכָל שָׁעָה**

As we have already learned, רַבִּי יִצְחָק teaches that people generally check their money pouches (nowadays it would be their wallets) very often. Therefore, when someone loses money, they usually know about it right away. That is why the בְּרַיְיתָא teaches that someone who finds money in a public place may keep it. We can assume that the owner has felt for his missing money pouch and knows that he has lost it. The finder can also assume that the owner has been מְיָאֵשׁ because the money was lost in a public place.

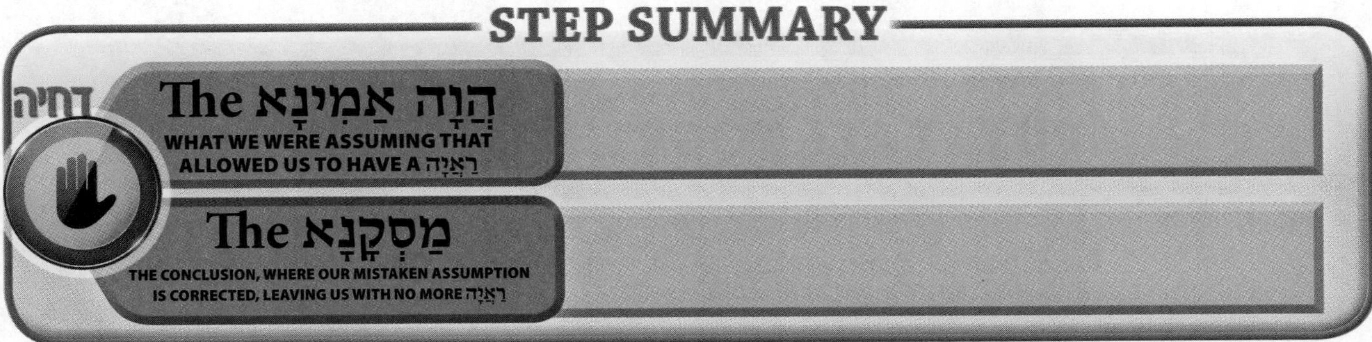

Once again, we end the שִׁיעוּר without proving either of the שִׁיטוֹת correct.

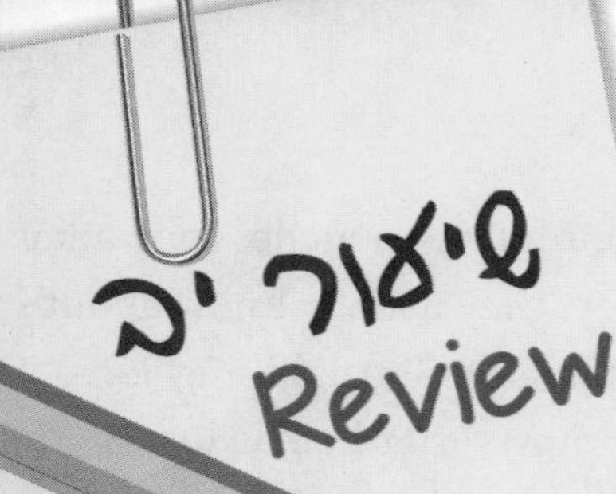

VOCABULARY REVIEW:

דוּכְתָּא ______ הַנָּךְ ______

מֵעִיקָּרָא ______ הֵיכִי ______

הַנֵּי ______ הָכִי ______

PUT IT ALL TOGETHER:

ת"ש ׳הַמּוֹצֵא מָעוֹת בְּבָתֵּי כְּנֵסִיּוֹת וּבְבָתֵּי מִדְרָשׁוֹת וּבְכָל מָקוֹם שֶׁהָרַבִּים מְצוּיִין שָׁם הֲרֵי אֵלּוּ שֶׁלּוֹ מִפְּנֵי שֶׁהַבְּעָלִים מִתְיָאֲשִׁין מֵהֶן וְהָא לֹא יָדַע דְּנָפַל מִינֵּיהּ אָמַר רַבִּי יִצְחָק אָדָם עָשׂוּי לְמַשְׁמֵשׁ בְּכִיסוֹ בְּכָל שָׁעָה

1. Read, translate and explain the following גְּמָרָא.
2. What is a בְּרַיְיתָא? ______
3. When the גְּמָרָא quotes a בְּרַיְיתָא in order to prove something, what do we have to do before trying to understand the רַאֲיָה? ______
4. In this שִׁיעוּר we quoted a בְּרַיְיתָא.
   What הֲלָכָה did the בְּרַיְיתָא teach? ______
   What reason did the בְּרַיְיתָא give for that הֲלָכָה? ______
5. Please explain the רַאֲיָה and דְּחִיָּה that we learned in this שִׁיעוּר.

The Object

The Support

The הֲוָה אַמִינָא

The מַסְקָנָא

6. We have already learned the teaching of רַבִּי יִצְחָק in several שִׁיעוּרִים. What is different about the way it is learned in this שִׁיעוּר than the way it was learned in previous שִׁיעוּרִים? ______
7. At the end of the שִׁיעוּר - what have we successfully proven? (circle one)
   a. the שִׁיטָה of אַבַּיֵי b. the שִׁיטָה of רָבָא c. nothing

 |

IDENTIFY THE STEPS:
BE SURE TO INCLUDE EVERY WORD.

ת"ש "הַמּוֹצֵא מָעוֹת בְּבָתֵּי
כְּנֵסִיּוֹת וּבְבָתֵּי מִדְרָשׁוֹת וּבְכָל מָקוֹם שֶׁהָרַבִּים
מְצוּיִין שָׁם הֲרֵי אֵלּוּ שֶׁלּוֹ מִפְּנֵי שֶׁהַבְּעָלִים
מִתְיָאֲשִׁין מֵהֶן וְהָא לֹא יָדַע דְּנָפַל מִינֵּיהּ אָמַר
רַבִּי יִצְחָק אָדָם עָשׂוּי לְמַשְׁמֵשׁ בְּכִיסוֹ בְּכָל
שָׁעָה

Please [**bracket**] the רַאֲיָה

Please **underline** the דְחִיָּה

MATCHING:

_____	1. Step 11 of the סוּגְיָא is a _______	א. בְּרַיְיתָא
_____	2. Step 12 of the סוּגְיָא is a _______	ב. יֵאוּשׁ שֶׁלֹּא מִדַּעַת הֲוֵי יֵאוּשׁ
_____	3. The object of the רַאֲיָה	ג. The owner knew that the money was lost
_____	4. The support of the רַאֲיָה	
_____	5. The הֲוָה אַמִינָא	ד. רַבִּי יִצְחָק
_____	6. The מַסְקָנָא	ה. לֹא יָדַע דְּנָפַל מִינֵּיהּ
_____	7. A type of place where the found money may be kept by the finder	ו. רַאֲיָה
_____	8. A teaching of a תַּנָּא that is not in the מִשְׁנָה	ז. מִפְּנֵי שֶׁהַבְּעָלִים מִתְיָאֲשִׁין מֵהֶן
_____	9. The reason that the finder may keep the money	ח. הַמּוֹצֵא מָעוֹת בְּבָתֵּי כְּנֵסִיּוֹת... הֲרֵי אֵלּוּ שֶׁלּוֹ
_____	10. His teaching was quoted earlier, but he actually taught it in this שִׁיעוּר	ט. שֶׁהָרַבִּים מְצוּיִין שָׁם
		י. דְחִיָּה

STEP 13

Yet again, the גְּמָרָא will try to prove that the שִׁיטָה of רָבָא is correct. This is another רַאֲיָה that יֵאוּשׁ שֶׁלֹּא מִדַּעַת is considered to be יֵאוּשׁ. (How many רַאֲיוֹת have we had so far? Have you been counting?)

יאוש שלא מדעת
ראיה #6
SIXTH PROOF FOR THE שִׁיטָה OF רָבָא

VOCABULARY WORDS

69. רֵישָׁא

70. סֵיפָא

Come and hear [a proof]: **ת״ש**

The support of this רַאֲיָה is a מִשְׁנָה, but not a מִשְׁנָה in this פֶּרֶק (or even in this מַסֶּכְתָּא). The מִשְׁנָה is found in מַסֶּכֶת פֵּאָה פֶּרֶק ח׳ מִשְׁנָה א׳.

In שִׁיעוּר י״ב, we discussed the fact that when the גְּמָרָא proves something from a בְּרַיְיתָא, it is important to learn and understand the בְּרַיְיתָא on its own before trying to understand the רַאֲיָה. The same rule applies when the גְּמָרָא quotes a מִשְׁנָה that we have not learned yet. Therefore, we will first learn the מִשְׁנָה before we discuss the proof.

This מִשְׁנָה is discussing the מִצְוָה of לֶקֶט. The מִצְוָה of לֶקֶט applies to farmers when they are reaping (cutting) their fields of grain. The way that a farmer would reap the grain (before tractors were invented) was as follows: With one hand, he would grab a handful of stalks (which were still attached to the ground). With his other hand, he would swing a special knife called a sickle. The blade of the sickle would cut the stalks off of the ground.

During this process, the farmer would occasionally drop some stalks. If he dropped one or two stalks on one swing of the sickle, he may not pick it/them up. Instead, the מִצְוָה of לֶקֶט is to leave the fallen stalks on the ground, and allow the poor people to come and collect them. (If three or more stalks fall in one sickle swing, the farmer is allowed to pick them up.)

It is important to understand that when one or two stalks fall, they are owned collectively by all of the (Jewish) poor people of the world. Then, when one poor person picks it/them up, he takes complete ownership for himself.

However, the poor people will not necessarily pick up every stalk of לֶקֶט. It is certainly possible that some of the לֶקֶט will be left behind after the poor people have finished collecting. The הֲלָכָה that applies to those stalks that the poor people have left behind is taught in the following מִשְׁנָה, which is found in מַסֶּכֶת פֵּאָה, פֶּרֶק ח׳ מִשְׁנָה א׳:

From when (at what point)	**מֵאֵימָתַי**
[is] any person (even those who are not poor)	**כָּל אָדָם**
permitted [to take] לֶקֶט?	**מוּתָּרִים בְּלֶקֶט**
From when the נְמוּשׁוֹת have gone through [the field].	**מִשֶּׁיֵּלְכוּ בָּהּ הַנְּמוּשׁוֹת**

The מִשְׁנָה has taught us that there comes a time when anyone (even people who are not poor) may take the לֶקֶט that has been left behind. Once the נְמוּשׁוֹת have gone through the field, the remaining לֶקֶט stalks may be taken by anyone. Of course, in order to understand this הֲלָכָה properly, we need to know what נְמוּשׁוֹת are. (I bet you were wondering the same thing.) The גְּמָרָא will now tell us a מַחֲלוֹקֶת between two אֲמוֹרָאִים about the meaning of the word נְמוּשׁוֹת:

And we said:	**וְאַמְרִינַן**
What are נְמוּשׁוֹת?	**מַאי נְמוּשׁוֹת**
And רַבִּי יוֹחָנָן said	**וְא״ר יוֹחָנָן**
[they are] old men	**סָבֵי**
that walk with a cane.	**דְּאַזְלֵי אַתִּיגְרָא**
רֵישׁ לָקִישׁ said	**רֵישׁ לָקִישׁ אָמַר**
[they are the] pickers [who came] after [the first group of] pickers.	**לְקוּטֵי בָּתַר לְקוּטֵי**

רַבִּי יוֹחָנָן and רֵישׁ לָקִישׁ have different opinions about the meaning of the word נְמוּשׁוֹת. However, they both understand the הֲלָכָה of the מִשְׁנָה in the same way.

According to רַבִּי יוֹחָנָן, the נְמוּשׁוֹת are the old men who walk on canes. Because these people walk so slowly, they usually don't miss any stalks, unlike the younger people who move quickly through the field and don't see everything. Therefore, when other poor people see the נְמוּשׁוֹת going through the field, they are מְיָאֵשׁ from finding any more לֶקֶט and will no longer search that field.

שיעור יג

כא: lines 34-41 *Continued*

רֵישׁ לָקִישׁ explains that the נְמוּשׁוֹת are the second group of pickers to pass through their field (regardless of their age or speed). When the first wave of poor people comes through the field, they take most of the לֶקֶט but leave some over. The second group is more thorough and usually takes whatever is left. Therefore, after the second group has passed through the field, the other poor people are מְיָאֵשׁ on finding any more לֶקֶט in the field. At that point, no additional poor people will be coming to look for לֶקֶט.

Once the final group of poor people (the נְמוּשׁוֹת) leave the לֶקֶט behind, it is as if all of the poor people have left behind something that they owned. Therefore, it is considered an אֲבֵידָה – an object which was lost by the poor people of the world. When someone who is not poor finds it, it is considered a מְצִיאָה – a found object.

We know that whether the finder can keep a מְצִיאָה depends on whether the owner has been מְיָאֵשׁ. In the case of the לֶקֶט stalks which have been left behind, the same rule applies. The מִשְׁנָה teaches us that when the נְמוּשׁוֹת pass through the field, the other poor people are מְיָאֵשׁ on finding any more לֶקֶט. For that reason, the מִשְׁנָה teaches that any person may take the לֶקֶט that remains after the נְמוּשׁוֹת have passed.

Now that we understand the מִשְׁנָה and the explanations of רַבִּי יוֹחָנָן and רֵישׁ לָקִישׁ, we are ready to learn the רַאֲיָה that the גְּמָרָא will present based on this מִשְׁנָה:

And why [can any person take it]?	וְאַמַּאי
It is true	נְהִי
that the poor people here (near this field)	דַּעֲנִיִּים דְּהָכָא
have given up hope,	מִיָּאֲשֵׁי
[but] there are poor people	אִיכָּא עֲנִיִּים
in another place (not near this field)	בְּדוּכְתָּא אַחֲרִיתָּא
who have not given up hope!	דְּלֹא מִיָּאֲשֵׁי

Remember that לֶקֶט is owned by all of the poor people, not just the ones that are close to the field where it dropped. The לֶקֶט belongs to the עֲנִיִּים no matter where they live, even if they are hundreds of miles away. Before the inventions of modern technology, it seems impossible for all of them to have been מְיָאֵשׁ. After all, they had no way of knowing that the נָמוּשׁוֹת had passed through the field. (There was no website to check or hotline to call.) Only the local עֲנִיִּים knew it. For the עֲנִיִּים who were further away, this was a case of יֵאוּשׁ שֶׁלֹּא מִדַּעַת. Yet, the מִשְׁנָה teaches us that any person may take the לֶקֶט. This proves that יֵאוּשׁ שֶׁלֹּא מִדַּעַת is considered to be יֵאוּשׁ.

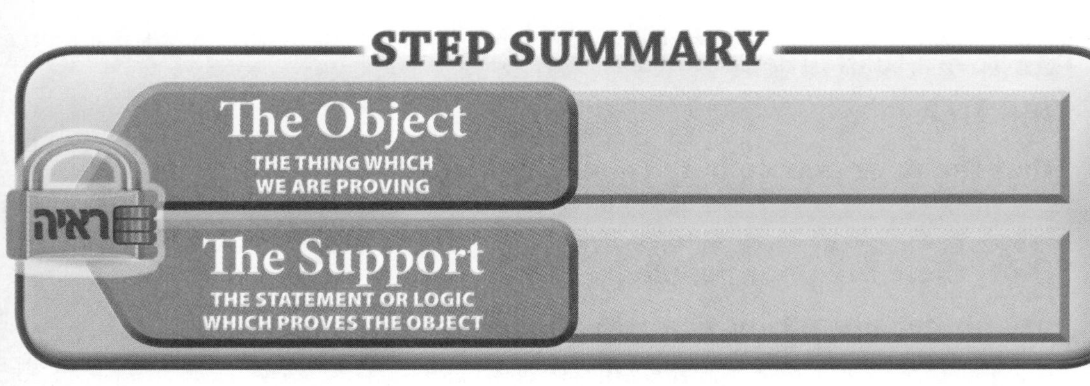

STEP 14

The גְּמָרָא rejects the רַאֲיָה by explaining that all of the עֲנִיִּים were מְיָאֵשׁ (not only the ones who were close to the field).

They said (the חֲכָמִים explained)	**אַמְרֵי**
since	**כֵּיוָן**
there are poor people here,	**דְּאִיכָּא עֲנִיִּים הָכָא**
those [poor people]	**הַנָּךְ**
originally	**מֵעִיקָּרָא**
had given up hope	**אַיְאוּשֵׁי מְיָאֵשׁ**
and they said:	**וְאַמְרֵי**
The poor people over there	**עֲנִיִּים דְּהָתָם**
have gathered it.	**מְלַקְּטֵי לֵיהּ**

The גְּמָרָא explains that all of the עֲנִיִּים were מְיָאֵשׁ. The עֲנִיִּים who live far away (and wouldn't know when the נְמוּשׁוֹת passed through the field) were actually the first ones to be מְיָאֵשׁ. They would give up hope on getting that לֶקֶט from the start. After all, what hope did they ever have of getting it when there were עֲנִיִּים who were so much closer? Then, when the נְמוּשׁוֹת pass through the field, the local עֲנִיִּים would be מְיָאֵשׁ. At that point, all of the עֲנִיִּים were מְיָאֵשׁ. For that reason, any person may take the לֶקֶט. However, this is not a case of יֵאוּשׁ שֶׁלֹּא מִדַּעַת since the עֲנִיִּים were actually מְיָאֵשׁ. This case cannot be used a רַאֲיָה for either of the שִׁיטוֹת.

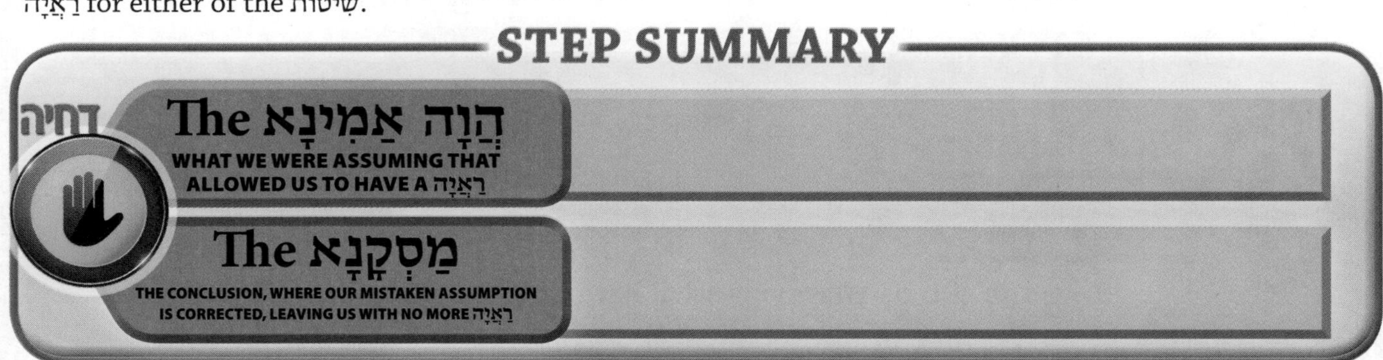

VOCABULARY REVIEW:

רֵישָׁא	______	מֵעִיקָּרָא	______
סֵיפָא	______	הַשְׁתָּא	______
דוּכְתָּא	______	מִינֵּיהּ	______

PUT IT ALL TOGETHER:

ת"ש *)מֵאֵימָתַי כָּל אָדָם מוּתָּרִים בְּלֶקֶט מִשֶּׁיֵּלְכוּ בָּהּ הַנְּמוּשׁוֹת וְאַמְרִינָן מַאי נְמוּשׁוֹת וְא"ר יוֹחָנָן סָבֵי דְּאַזְלֵי **)אַתִּיגְרָא רֵישׁ לָקִישׁ אָמַר לְקוּטֵי בָּתַר לְקוּטֵי וְאַמַּאי נְהִי דַּעֲנִיִּים דְּהָכָא מְיָאֲשֵׁי אִיכָּא עֲנִיִּים בְּדוּכְתָּא אַחֲרִיתָא דְּלָא מְיָאֲשֵׁי אַמְרֵי כֵּיוָן דְּאִיכָּא עֲנִיִּים הָכָא הַנָּךְ מֵעִיקָּרָא אַיְאוּשֵׁי מְיָאֵשׁ וְאַמְרֵי עֲנִיִּים דְּהָתָם מְלַקְּטֵי לֵיהּ

1. Read, translate and explain the following גְּמָרָא.
2. Our proof comes from a ______ in ______ מַסֶּכֶת.
3. What is לֶקֶט? ______
4. The מִשְׁנָה teaches us the point in time when any person may ______.
5. This point in time is when the ______ go through the field.
6. What are נְמוּשׁוֹת?
   a. According to רַבִּי יוֹחָנָן: ______
   b. According to רֵישׁ לָקִישׁ: ______
7. Why is anyone allowed to take the לֶקֶט after the נְמוּשׁוֹת have passed through the field? ______
8. Please explain the רְאָיָה and דְּחִיָּה that we learned in this שִׁיעוּר.

The Object ______

The Support ______

דחיה

The הֲוָה אַמִינָא ______

The מַסְקָנָא ______

9. AT THE END OF THE שִׁיעוּר - what have we successfully proven? (circle one)
   a. the שִׁיטָה of אַבַּיֵּי b. the שִׁיטָה of רָבָא c. nothing

IDENTIFY THE STEPS:
BE SURE TO INCLUDE EVERY WORD.

ת"ש *)מֵאֵימָתַי כָּל אָדָם מוּתָּרִים
בְּלֶקֶט מִשֶּׁיֵּלְכוּ בָּהּ הַנְּמוּשׁוֹת וְאַמְרִינָן מַאי
נְמוּשׁוֹת וְא"ר יוֹחָנָן סָבֵי דְּאָזְלֵי **)אַתִּיגְרָא
רֵישׁ לָקִישׁ אָמַר לְקוּטֵי בָּתַר לְקוּטֵי וְאַמַּאי
נְהִי דַּעֲנִיִּים דְּהָכָא מְיָאֲשֵׁי אִיכָּא עֲנִיִּים
בְּדוּכְתָּא אַחֲרִיתָּא דְּלָא מְיָאֲשֵׁי אַמְרֵי כֵּיוָן
דְּאִיכָּא עֲנִיִּים הָכָא הַנָּךְ מֵעִיקָּרָא אַיְאוּשֵׁי
מְיָאַשׁ וְאַמְרֵי עֲנִיִּים דְּהָתָם מְלַקְּטֵי לֵיהּ

Please [**bracket**]
the רַאֲיָה

Please **underline**
the דְחִיָה

MATCHING:

_____	1. Step 13 of the סוּגְיָא is a ______	א.	לֶקֶט
_____	2. Step 14 of the סוּגְיָא is a ______	ב.	רַאֲיָה
_____	3. The object of the רַאֲיָה	ג.	All of the poor people had given up hope
_____	4. The support of the רַאֲיָה	ד.	אִיכָּא עֲנִיִּים... דְּלָא מְיָאֲשֵׁי
_____	5. The הֲוָה אַמִינָא	ה.	יֵאוּשׁ שֶׁלֹּא מִדַּעַת הֲוֵי יֵאוּשׁ
_____	6. The מַסְקָנָא	ו.	דְחִיָה
_____	7. נְמוּשׁוֹת according to רַבִּי יוֹחָנָן	ז.	לְקוּטֵי בָּתַר לְקוּטֵי
_____	8. נְמוּשׁוֹת according to רֵישׁ לָקִישׁ	ח.	אִיכָּא עֲנִיִּים הָכָא
_____	9. The poor people who live far away are מְיָאֵשׁ because _______	ט.	מֵאֵימָתַי... מִשֶּׁיֵּלְכוּ בָּהּ הַנְּמוּשׁוֹת
_____	10. Fallen stalks that must be left for the poor	י.	סָבֵי דְּאַזְלֵי אַתִּיגְרָא

VOCABULARY WORDS

71. בִּשְׁלָמָא

72. הוֹאִיל

STEP 15

The next רַאֲיָה in the סוּגְיָא is based on a בְּרַיְיתָא. As we have mentioned before, it is important to learn and understand the בְּרַיְיתָא very well before we try to understand the proof. Therefore, in this שִׁיעוּר we will only learn the בְּרַיְיתָא. Then, after we know it well and have reviewed it, we will learn the actual proof in the next שִׁיעוּר.

Come and hear [a proof]:	ת"ש

The גְּמָרָא will now teach the בְּרַיְיתָא that is the support of the רַאֲיָה.

This בְּרַיְיתָא discusses the הֲלָכָה in a case when a person finds fruits near a tree. In this situation, we can assume that the fruits grew from that tree and fell off. The בְּרַיְיתָא will teach us if the finder may keep the fruits or if he must leave them for the owner of the tree:

Figs which were cut and dried*	קְצִיעוֹת
[which are found] on the road	בַּדֶּרֶךְ
even if they are next to a field of cut and dried figs,	וַאֲפִילוּ בְּצַד שְׂדֵה קְצִיעוֹת
and so too,	וְכֵן
a fig tree which is leaning toward the road	תְּאֵנָה הַנּוֹטָה לַדֶּרֶךְ
and he finds figs	וּמָצָא תְּאֵנִים
beneath it,	תַּחְתֶּיהָ
they are permitted [to be taken and are not considered] as stolen	מוּתָּרוֹת מִשּׁוּם גָּזֵל

The בְּרַיְיתָא has taught us that if someone finds figs, he may keep them. This is true even if they were found next to a tree or field and the finder can easily find out who the owner is. Even in such a case, the figs are considered הֶפְקֵר (abandoned and ownerless), so the finder may keep them.

Next, the בְּרַיְיתָא will tell us an additional הֲלָכָה about these figs. This additional הֲלָכָה has to do with a person's obligation to give מַעֲשֵׂר from his fruits (which grew in אֶרֶץ יִשְׂרָאֵל). If a person grows fruit, he must give 10%

*רַשִׁ"י explains that קְצִיעוֹת are figs which have been cut with a knife, allowing the juice to flow out of them. Then, they are spread out in a field to dry in the sun.

of them to a לֵוִי. Similarly, if a person buys fruit from a farmer and the farmer has not yet given מַעֲשֵׂר himself, the buyer must give the מַעֲשֵׂר to the לֵוִי.*

However, if a person takes fruit that were הֶפְקֵר, he does not have to give מַעֲשֵׂר from them. The בְּרַיְיתָא will now tell us whether or not the finder of the figs must give מַעֲשֵׂר from his find:

and [the finder is] **פָּטוּר from [giving] מַעֲשֵׂר [from them].	**וּפְטוּרוֹת מִן הַמַּעֲשֵׂר**

The בְּרַיְיתָא teaches us that because the figs were הֶפְקֵר, the finder does not need to give מַעֲשֵׂר. (He would only have to give מַעֲשֵׂר if he grew the fruit himself or bought it from the grower, not if it was הֶפְקֵר.)

Now, the בְּרַיְיתָא will tell us about certain fruits that have a different הֲלָכָה than the figs mentioned earlier:

[However,] by olives and carobs [that are found under the tree]	**בְּזֵיתִים וּבַחֲרוּבִים**
it is forbidden [to take them].	**אָסוּר**

The בְּרַיְיתָא has taught that if someone finds carobs or olives, they are not considered הֶפְקֵר and the finder may not keep them.

In the next שִׁיעוּר we will learn why the הֲלָכָה is different by carobs and olives than it is by figs. Remember, in this שִׁיעוּר we have simply learned the בְּרַיְיתָא. The actual proof will come in the next שִׁיעוּר. We will also learn how this בְּרַיְיתָא can be a proof to one of the sides of our מַחְלוֹקֶת about יֵאוּשׁ שֶׁלֹּא מִדַּעַת.

*This is a basic description of the מִצְוָה of מַעֲשֵׂר. In reality, the הֲלָכוֹת of מַעֲשֵׂר are much more complex. This includes which fruits must have מַעֲשֵׂר taken, how it is taken, to whom it may be given, what we do with מַעֲשֵׂר nowadays, and the other מִצְוֹת that apply, such as תְּרוּמָה. It is not necessary to know all of these הֲלָכוֹת in order to learn this שִׁיעוּר. However, if you would like to learn more about this topic, you can learn many of the מַסֶּכְתּוֹת in סֵדֶר זְרָעִים, including דְּמַאי, תְּרוּמוֹת, מַעַשְׂרוֹת, and מַעֲשֵׂר שֵׁנִי.

**The word פָּטוּר is the opposite of the word חַיָּיב. The word חַיָּיב means "obligated" and the word פָּטוּר means "not obligated" or "exempt."

VOCABULARY REVIEW:

בִּשְׁלָמָא	______	סֵיפָא	______
הוֹאִיל	______	הָכָא	______
רֵישָׁא	______	הָתָם	______

PUT IT ALL TOGETHER:

1. Read, translate and explain the following גְּמָרָא.

ת"ש
*[ח]קְצִיעוֹת בַּדֶּרֶךְ וַאֲפִילּוּ בְּצַד שְׂדֵה קְצִיעוֹת
[ט]וְכֵן תְּאֵנָה הַנּוֹטָה לַדֶּרֶךְ וּמָצָא תְּאֵנִים
תַּחְתֶּיהָ מוּתָּרוֹת מִשּׁוּם גָּזֵל וּפְטוּרוֹת מִן
הַמַּעֲשֵׂר בְּזֵיתִים וּבַחֲרוּבִים אָסוּר

2. The גְּמָרָא will be bringing a proof from a ______________________________.

3. In this שִׁיעוּר, why did we not learn the actual proof? ______________________

4. What are קְצִיעוֹת? ______________________________

5. What is מַעֲשֵׂר? ______________________________

6. If a person finds figs near a field or under a tree:

a. May he keep them? ______________________

b. Why/why not? ______________________

c. Does he have to give מַעֲשֵׂר? ______________________

d. Why/why not? ______________________

7. If a person finds carobs or olives near a tree, may he keep them? ______

 |

IDENTIFY THE STEPS:
BE SURE TO INCLUDE EVERY WORD.

ת"ש
*[ח]קְצִיעוֹת בַּדֶּרֶךְ וַאֲפִילּוּ בְּצַד שְׂדֵה קְצִיעוֹת
[ט]וְכֵן תְּאֵנָה הַנּוֹטָה לַדֶּרֶךְ וּמָצָא תְּאֵנִים
תַּחְתֶּיהָ מוּתָּרוֹת מִשּׁוּם גָּזֵל וּפְטוּרוֹת מִן
הַמַּעֲשֵׂר בְּזֵיתִים וּבַחֲרוּבִים אָסוּר

This שִׁיעוּר is part of what type of step? ______________

MATCHING:

_____	1. Step 15 of the סוּגְיָא is a ______	א. מַעֲשֵׂר
_____	2. In this שִׁיעוּר we are only trying to understand the __________	ב. קְצִיעוֹת
_____	3. 10% of the fruit is given to a לֵוִי as _____	ג. זֵיתִים
_____	4. Cut and dried figs	ד. רַאֲיָה
_____	5. Where the קְצִיעוֹת were found	ה. תְּאֵנָה הַנּוֹטָה לַדֶּרֶךְ ... תַּחְתֶּיהָ
_____	6. Where the (regular) figs were found	ו. אָסוּר
_____	7. The הֲלָכָה when one finds figs	ז. בְּרַיְיתָא
_____	8. Olives	ח. חֲרוּבִים
_____	9. Carobs	ט. בְּצַד שְׂדֵה קְצִיעוֹת
_____	10. The הֲלָכָה when one finds olives or carobs	י. מוּתָּרוֹת מִשּׁוּם גָּזֵל וּפְטוּרוֹת מִן הַמַּעֲשֵׂר

STEP 15 continued

Now that we have learned the בְּרַיְיתָא in שִׁיעוּר י״ד, we are ready to learn the actual proof for which the בְּרַיְיתָא was quoted in the first place.

If we examine the הֲלָכוֹת that the בְּרַיְיתָא taught, we notice something that seems confusing. It seems safe to assume that the owner of the fruits, who was discussed in the בְּרַיְיתָא, does not know that his fruits were lost. After all, it is unlikely that he knew that some fruit fell from his tree or that he dropped some קְצִיעוֹת near his field. Therefore, these fruits are a case of יֵאוּשׁ שֶׁלֹּא מִדַּעַת.

The רֵישָׁא (the beginning) of the בְּרַיְיתָא teaches us that the finder may keep the figs. This seems to prove that יֵאוּשׁ שֶׁלֹּא מִדַּעַת is considered to be יֵאוּשׁ. This would be a proof for רָבָא and a problem for אַבַּיֵי (because it is a קָשְׁיָא on his שִׁיטָה). However, the סֵיפָא (the end) of the בְּרַיְיתָא taught that when someone finds olives or carobs under a tree, he may not keep them. This seems to prove that יֵאוּשׁ שֶׁלֹּא מִדַּעַת is not considered to be יֵאוּשׁ. This would be a proof for אַבַּיֵי and a problem for רָבָא (because it is a קָשְׁיָא on his שִׁיטָה).

סֵיפָא OLIVES & CAROBS: Finder may not take them	רֵישָׁא FIGS: Finder may take them	
יֵאוּשׁ שֶׁלֹּא מִדַּעַת לֹא הָוֵי יֵאוּשׁ	?	How אַבַּיֵי explains the בְּרַיְיתָא
?	יֵאוּשׁ שֶׁלֹּא מִדַּעַת הָוֵי יֵאוּשׁ	How רָבָא explains the בְּרַיְיתָא

Needless to say, this is a problem for us. We cannot simply say that the two parts of the בְּרַיְיתָא prove two opposite things.

In order to deal with this problem, the גְּמָרָא will explain that the רֵישָׁא does not actually prove that יֵאוּשׁ שֶׁלֹּא מִדַּעַת is considered to be יֵאוּשׁ. Once that has been explained, we will only be left with the רַאֲיָה from the סֵיפָא that יֵאוּשׁ שֶׁלֹּא מִדַּעַת is not considered to be יֵאוּשׁ. At that point, we will have a רַאֲיָה for the שִׁיטָה of אַבַּיֵי.

First, the גְּמָרָא will explain why the רֵישָׁא is not a problem for אַבַּיֵי:

It is understandable	**בִּשְׁלָמָא**
[that] the beginning [of the בְּרַיְיתָא]	**רֵישָׁא**
is not a קֻשְׁיָא on [the שִׁיטָה of] אַבַּיֵי;	**לְאַבַּיֵי לֹא קַשְׁיָא**
since [the קְצִיעוֹת] are valuable,	**אַגַּב דַּחֲשִׁיבֵי**
he will feel them.*	**מְמַשְׁמֵשׁ בְּהוּ**

We have learned the teaching of רַבִּי יִצְחָק that a person frequently checks his money pouch. The גְּמָרָא also taught us that this applies to anything that a person carries which is valuable. Here, the גְּמָרָא is telling us that a person checks through valuable things, even if he is not carrying them. If a person has a field of קְצִיעוֹת (which are valuable), he will frequently check through them to make sure that they are all there. Therefore, by the time the finder has found them, the owner already knows that they have been lost. We now see that this is not a case of יֵאוּשׁ שֶׁלֹּא מִדַּעַת and is not a קֻשְׁיָא on the שִׁיטָה of אַבַּיֵי.

Now the גְּמָרָא will explain why the case of regular figs which fell from a tree is also not a case of יֵאוּשׁ שֶׁלֹּא מִדַּעַת:

[By] a fig tree [it is] also [not a case of יֵאוּשׁ שֶׁלֹּא מִדַּעַת]	**תְּאֵנָה נַמִּי**
[because the owner] knows that they drop.	**מֵידַע יָדִיעַ דְּנַתְרָא**

The גְּמָרָא explains that the owner of the fig tree knows that figs will fall from the tree and he is מְיָאֵשׁ on the figs that fall. Therefore, even though the owner did not see these figs, it is not a case of יֵאוּשׁ שֶׁלֹּא מִדַּעַת. This case is also not a קֻשְׁיָא on the שִׁיטָה of אַבַּיֵי.

סֵיפָא OLIVES & CAROBS: Finder may not take them	רֵישָׁא FIGS: Finder may take them	
יֵאוּשׁ שֶׁלֹּא מִדַּעַת לֹא הָוֵי יֵאוּשׁ	The owner already knows that the figs are lost קְצִיעוֹת – מְמַשְׁמֵשׁ בְּהוּ תְּאֵנִים – מֵידַע יָדִיעַ דְּנַתְרָא	How אַבַּיֵי explains the בְּרַיְיתָא
?	יֵאוּשׁ שֶׁלֹּא מִדַּעַת הָוֵי יֵאוּשׁ	How רָבָא explains the בְּרַיְיתָא

*The גְּמָרָא says that he will feel them, but this is just the גְּמָרָא's way of saying that he will check on them.

Now that the גְּמָרָא has explained why the רֵישָׁא of the בְּרַיְיתָא cannot be used as a רַאֲיָה, it will explain how the סֵיפָא of the בְּרַיְיתָא is a רַאֲיָה:

Rather,	**אֶלָּא**
the end [of the בְּרַיְיתָא]	**סֵיפָא**
is a קֻשְׁיָא on the שִׁיטָה of רָבָא (and a רַאֲיָה to the שִׁיטָה of אַבַּיֵי)	**לְרָבָא קַשְׁיָא**
because the בְּרַיְיתָא taught	**דְּקָתָנֵי**
by olives and carobs it is forbidden [for the finder to take them].	**בְּזֵיתִים וּבַחֲרוּבִים אָסוּר**

Olives and carobs are not like figs. First of all, they are not expensive like קְצִיעוֹת. Therefore, the owner will not check on them. When the finder finds them, the owner probably doesn't know that they were lost. Second of all, we assume that olives and carobs don't fall off the tree like figs do. Since the owner doesn't expect them to fall, he is not aware that they have fallen until he actually sees that they have. Therefore, this is a case of יֵאוּשׁ שֶׁלֹּא מִדַּעַת. If רָבָא is correct that יֵאוּשׁ שֶׁלֹּא מִדַּעַת is considered to be יֵאוּשׁ, the finder would be allowed to keep the olives and carobs. The fact that the בְּרַיְיתָא says that the finder may not keep them is a קֻשְׁיָא on the שִׁיטָה of רָבָא and a רַאֲיָה to the שִׁיטָה of אַבַּיֵי.

Remember, because אַבַּיֵי and רָבָא are arguing, any רַאֲיָה for אַבַּיֵי is also a קֻשְׁיָא on the שִׁיטָה of רָבָא. In order to keep things consistent, we are calling this step a רַאֲיָה (even though the גְּמָרָא uses the word קֻשְׁיָא). However, it would not be incorrect to call this step a קֻשְׁיָא. Similarly, we will call the next step a דְּחִיָּה. For those who refer to this step as a קֻשְׁיָא, the next step would be a תֵּירוּץ.

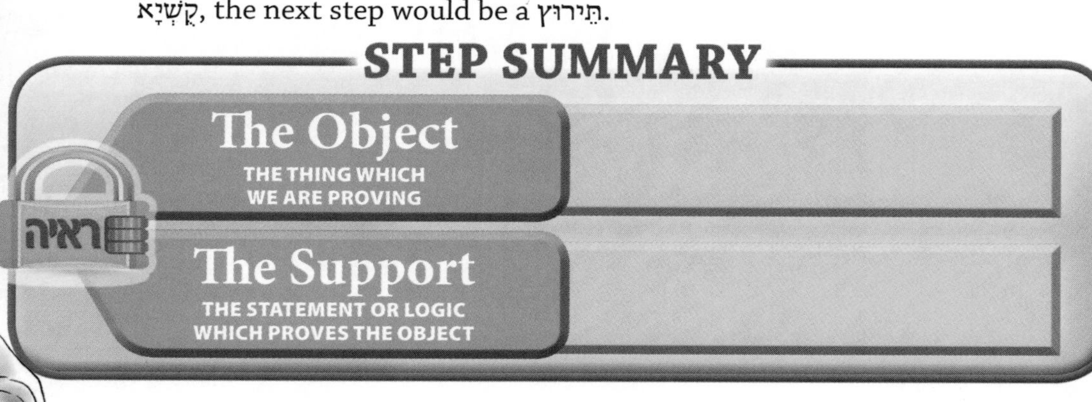

STEP 16

The גְּמָרָא explains why the finder may not keep the olives even if they do fall off the tree:

רַבִּי אֲבָהוּ said,	אָמַר רַבִּי אֲבָהוּ
An olive is different	שַׁאנִי זַיִת
since	הוֹאִיל
its appearance	וְחָזוּתוֹ
proves [who the owner is].	מוֹכִיחַ עָלָיו
And even though the olives drop [from the tree],	וְאע"ג (וְאַף עַל גַּב) דְּנָתְרִין זֵיתֵי
it is known	מֵידַע יְדִיעַ
[that in] the place of a person	דּוּכְתָּא דְּאִינִישׁ
[the olives belong to that] person.	אִינִישׁ הוּא

Even though we originally assumed that olives don't fall off of the tree, the גְּמָרָא now says that sometimes they do. However, the owner still will not be מְיָאֵשׁ. The reason for this is because the olives of each field have a unique look (because of the color and shade of the olives) which is a good סִימָן. When someone finds olives near the field, he will be able to compare them to the olives growing on the trees. The finder will know that the olives grew in that field. Therefore, even though the owner knows that olives will fall, he still won't be מְיָאֵשׁ. He will expect the finder to leave the olives by the field where they grew. When the בְּרַיְיתָא is explained this way, it is not a case of יֵאוּשׁ שֶׁלֹּא מִדַּעַת; rather, it is a case of the owner not being מְיָאֵשׁ at all. For this reason, the בְּרַיְיתָא taught that the finder may not keep the olives. This same reason applies to carobs, which also have a unique appearance in each field.

סֵיפָא OLIVES & CAROBS: Finder may not take them	רֵישָׁא FIGS: Finder may take them	
יֵאוּשׁ שֶׁלֹּא מִדַּעַת לֹא הָוֵי יֵאוּשׁ	The owner already knows that the figs are lost קְצִיעוֹת – מְמַשְׁמֵשׁ בְּהוּ תְּאֵנִים – מֵידַע יְדִיעַ דְּנָתְרָא	How אַבַּיֵי explains the בְּרַיְיתָא
The owner knows that the olives have fallen, but he is not מְיָאֵשׁ because they are recognizable as his. מֵידַע יְדִיעַ דּוּכְתָּא דְּאִינִישׁ אִינִישׁ הוּא	יֵאוּשׁ שֶׁלֹּא מִדַּעַת הָוֵי יֵאוּשׁ	How רָבָא explains the בְּרַיְיתָא

כא: lines 45-53
Continued

With this understanding, we no longer have a רַאֲיָה to the שִׁיטָה of אַבַּיֵי (or a קֻשְׁיָא on the שִׁיטָה of רָבָא).

STEP SUMMARY

דחיה

The הֲוָה אַמִינָא WHAT WE WERE ASSUMING THAT ALLOWED US TO HAVE A רַאֲיָה	The reason that the finder may not keep olives and carobs is because the owner doesn't expect them to fall and is therefore not מְיָאֵשׁ.
The מַסְקָנָא THE CONCLUSION, WHERE OUR MISTAKEN ASSUMPTION IS CORRECTED, LEAVING US WITH NO MORE רַאֲיָה	The reason that the finder may not keep them is because they have a סִימָן (their appearance).

STEP 17

The גְּמָרָא has successfully defended the שִׁיטָה of רָבָא. However, the גְּמָרָא's explanation of the סֵיפָא of the בְּרַיְיתָא (the הֲלָכָה of olives and carobs) causes us to have a קֻשְׁיָא on the רֵישָׁא (the הֲלָכָה of figs):

If so,	**אִי הָכֵי**

If it is true that people can tell that the fruit near the field belongs to the owner of the field:

Even [in the case of] the רֵישָׁא [this should] also [be true]!?	**אֲפִילוּ רֵישָׁא נַמִּי**

People should also be able to recognize that the figs belong to the owner of the field. Therefore, the owner should not be מְיָאֵשׁ on the fallen figs (just as he is not מְיָאֵשׁ on the fallen olives or carobs). Why, then, did the רֵישָׁא of בְּרַיְיתָא teach that the finder of the figs may keep them?

סֵיפָא OLIVES & CAROBS: Finder may not take them	רֵישָׁא FIGS: Finder may take them	
יֵאוּשׁ שֶׁלֹּא מִדַּעַת לֹא הֲוֵי יֵאוּשׁ	The owner already knows that the figs are lost קְצִיעוֹת – מִמַּשְׁמֵשׁ בְּהוּ תְּאֵנִים – מִידַע יָדִיעַ דְּנָתְרָא	How אַבַּיֵי explains the בְּרַיְיתָא
The owner knows that the olives have fallen, but he is not מְיָאֵשׁ because they are recognizable as his. מִידַע יָדִיעַ דְּזֵיתָא דְּאִינִישׁ אִינִישׁ הוּא	יֵאוּשׁ שֶׁלֹּא מִדַּעַת ... יֵאוּשׁ	

The owner of the field is not מְיָאֵשׁ on fallen fruit because it can be recognized as coming from his field

In this קֻשְׁיָא, the target is the statement which said that people recognize who owns the olives (the דְחִיָה - Step 16). Our attack is the רֵישָׁא of our בְּרַיְיתָא, which seems to show that this statement is not true.

STEP 18

To answer this קֻשְׁיָא, the גְמָרָא will explain that we were making an incorrect assumption about the רֵישָׁא of the בְּרַיְיתָא. The בְּרַיְיתָא taught that the finder may keep the figs that he finds. This is because the owner was מְיָאֵשׁ. We were assuming that the reason that the owner is מְיָאֵשׁ is because the finder will not know whose figs they are. They may have fallen from the trees in the field, but they also may have fallen from someone who was walking by. However, now that we have said that the appearance of the fruit proves that it came from that field, we must find a different reason why the owner was מְיָאֵשׁ on the figs. An אֲמוֹרָא named רַב פָּפָּא will teach us that reason:

רַב פָּפָּא said,	**אָמַר רַב פָּפָּא**
A fig	**תְּאֵנָה**
when it falls	**עִם נְפִילָתָהּ**
it becomes disgusting.	**נִמְאֶסֶת**

Our הֲוָה אַמִינָא was that the owner was מְיָאֵשׁ on fallen figs because no one would know whose they were. Our מַסְקָנָא (as explained by רַב פָּפָּא) is that everyone can tell whose figs they are. The reason that the owner is מְיָאֵשׁ is because he knows that once the figs fall from the tree, they will become disgusting.* That is the reason why the רֵישָׁא taught that the finder may keep them. On the other hand, olives and carobs (which are more firm and dry when they fall off the tree) do not become disgusting. For that reason, the סֵיפָא of the בְּרַיְיתָא taught that the finder may not keep them.

We have successfully explained that this בְּרַיְיתָא is not a case of יֵאוּשׁ שֶׁלֹּא מִדַּעַת. Therefore, at this point, the גְמָרָא has no proof for either שִׁיטָה in our מַחֲלוֹקֶת.

סֵיפָא OLIVES & CAROBS: Finder may not take them	רֵישָׁא FIGS: Finder may take them	
יֵאוּשׁ שֶׁלֹּא מִדַּעַת לֹא הָוֵי יֵאוּשׁ	The owner already knows that the figs are lost קציעות – ממשמש בהו תאנים – מידע ידעי דנתרא	How אַבַּיֵי explains the בְּרַיְיתָא
The owner knows that the olives have fallen, but he is not מְיָאֵשׁ because they are recognizable as his. מידע ידיע דוכתא דאיניש איניש הוא	The owner of fallen figs is מְיָאֵשׁ because they become disgusting. תְּאֵנָה עִם נְפִילָתָהּ נִמְאֶסֶת	How רָבָא explains the בְּרַיְיתָא

*Perhaps, this is because when ripe figs are detached from the tree, juice comes out of them which makes them sticky. When the sticky figs lay on the ground, they get dirty and become disgusting.

PUT IT ALL TOGETHER:

1. Read, translate and explain the following גְּמָרָא.

בִּשְׁלָמָא
רֵישָׁא לְאַבַּיֵי לָא קַשְׁיָא אַגַּב דַּחֲשִׁיבֵי
מְמַשְׁמֵשׁ בְּהוּ תְּאֵנָה נַמִּי מֵידַע יָדִיעַ דְּנַתְרָא
אֶלָּא סֵיפָא לְרָבָא קַשְׁיָא דְּקָתָנֵי בְּזֵיתִים
וּבַחֲרוּבִים אָסוּר אָמַר רַבִּי אֲבָהוּ שֶׁאנִי זַיִת
הוֹאִיל וְחָזוּתוֹ מוֹכִיחַ עָלָיו וְאע"ג דְּנָתְרִין
זֵיתֵי מֵידַע יָדִיעַ *דּוּכְתָּא דְּאִינִישׁ אִינִישׁ
הוּא אִי הָכִי אֲפִילּוּ רֵישָׁא נַמִּי אָמַר רַב
פָּפָּא תְּאֵנָה עִם נְפִילָתָהּ נִמְאֶסֶת

2. What הֲלָכָה was said in the רֵישָׁא of the בְּרַיְיתָא? ______________________________

3. The רֵישָׁא seemed like it could be a קַשְׁיָא on the שִׁיטָה of ______. The גְּמָרָא says that it is not a קַשְׁיָא because ______________________________

4. The סֵיפָא is a קַשְׁיָא on the שִׁיטָה of ____________ or a רַאֲיָה to the שִׁיטָה of ____________.

5. Please explain the רַאֲיָה and דְּחִיָּה that we learned in this שִׁיעוּר:

ראיה

The Object	
The Support	

דחיה

The הֲוָה אַמִינָא	
The מַסְקָנָא	

6. Please explain the קַשְׁיָא and תֵּירוּץ that we learned in this שִׁיעוּר:

The Target	
The Attack	
The הֲוָה אַמִינָא	
The מַסְקָנָא	

7. At the end of the שִׁיעוּר - what have we successfully proven? (circle one)
a. the שִׁיטָה of אַבַּיֵי b. the שִׁיטָה of רָבָא c. nothing

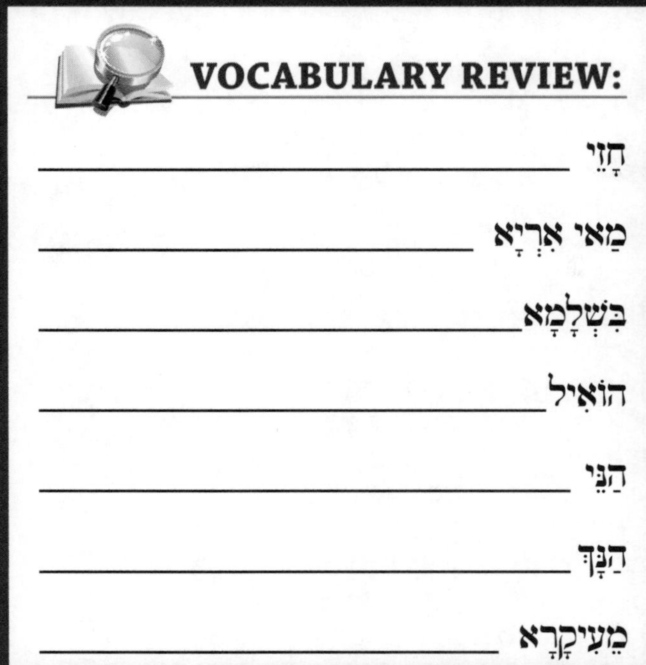

VOCABULARY REVIEW:

חָזֵי ______________________

מַאי אִרְיָא ______________________

בִּשְׁלָמָא ______________________

הוֹאִיל ______________________

הַנֵּי ______________________

הַנָּךְ ______________________

מֵעִיקָּרָא ______________________

IDENTIFY THE STEPS:

BE SURE TO INCLUDE EVERY WORD.

בִּשְׁלָמָא
רֵישָׁא לְאַבַּיֵי לֹא קַשְׁיָא אַגַּב דַּחֲשִׁיבֵי
מְמַשְׁמֵשׁ בְּהוּ תְּאֵנָה נַמִּי מֵידַע יָדִיעַ דְּנַתְרָא
אֶלָּא סֵיפָא לְרָבָא קַשְׁיָא דְּקָתָנֵי בְּזֵיתִים
וּבַחֲרוּבִים אָסוּר אָמַר רַבִּי אֲבָהוּ שַׁאנִי זַיִת
הוֹאִיל וְחָזוּתוֹ מוֹכִיחַ עָלָיו וְאע"ג דְּנָתְרִין
זֵיתֵי מֵידַע יָדִיעַ *דּוּכְתָּא דְּאִינִישׁ אִינִישׁ
הוּא אִי הָכִי אֲפִילּוּ רֵישָׁא נַמִּי אָמַר רַב
פַּפָּא תְּאֵנָה עִם נְפִילָתָהּ נִמְאֶסֶת

Please [bracket] the	Please underline the	Please (parenthesize) the	Please box the
ראיה	דחיה	קשיא	תירוץ

MATCHING:

(HINT: ONE OF THE CHOICES IS USED TWICE.)

_____ 1. Step 15 of the סוּגְיָא is a _______

_____ 2. Step 16 of the סוּגְיָא is a _______

_____ 3. Step 17 of the סוּגְיָא is a _______

_____ 4. Step 18 of the סוּגְיָא is a _______

_____ 5. The object of the רַאֲיָה

_____ 6. The support of the רַאֲיָה

_____ 7. The הֲוָה אַמִינָא (part of the דְחִיָּה)

_____ 8. The מַסְקָנָא (part of the דְחִיָּה)

_____ 9. The target of the קֻשְׁיָא

_____ 10. The attack of the קֻשְׁיָא

_____ 11. The הֲוָה אַמִינָא (part of the תֵּירוּץ)

_____ 12. The מַסְקָנָא (part of the תֵּירוּץ)

א. תֵּירוּץ

ב. The finder can't keep the olives because the owner doesn't know that they fell

ג. רַאֲיָה

ד. The owner was מְיָאֵשׁ on the figs because the finder can't recognize who owns them

ה. יֵאוּשׁ שֶׁלֹּא מִדַּעַת לֹא הֲוֵי יֵאוּשׁ

ו. קֻשְׁיָא

ז. שַׁאנִי זַיִת הוֹאִיל וְחָזוּתוֹ מוֹכִיחַ עָלָיו

ח. תְּאֵנָה הַנּוֹטָה לַדֶּרֶךְ וּמָצָא תְּאֵנִים תַּחְתֶּיהָ מוּתָּרוֹת מִשּׁוּם גָּזֵל

ט. דְחִיָּה

י. בְּזֵיתִים וּבַחֲרוּבִים אָסוּר

יא. תְּאֵנָה עִם נְפִילָתָהּ נִמְאֶסֶת

PLACE A SMALL NUMBER BY THE BEGINNING OF EACH STEP

(example: אִיתְּמַר[1])

שיעורים ד-טר

12345 NUMBER THE STEPS:

אִיתְּמַר

יֵאוּשׁ שֶׁלֹּא מִדַּעַת אַבַּיֵּי אָמַר לֹא הָוֵי יֵאוּשׁ
וְרָבָא אָמַר הָוֵי יֵאוּשׁ בְּדָבָר שֶׁיֵּשׁ בּוֹ סִימָן
כּוּלֵּי עָלְמָא לֹא פְּלִיגֵי דְּלֹא הָוֵי יֵאוּשׁ וְאַף
עַל גַּב דְּשַׁמְעִינֵיהּ דְּמְיָאֵשׁ (א) לְסוֹף לֹא הָוֵי
יֵאוּשׁ דְּכִי אָתָא לְיָדֵיהּ בְּאִיסּוּרָא הוּא דְּאָתָא
לְיָדֵיהּ דִּלְכִי יָדַע דְּנָפַל מִינֵּיהּ לֹא מְיָאֵשׁ
מֵימַר אָמַר סִימָנָא אִית לִי בְּגַוֵּיהּ יָהֲבְנָא
סִימָנָא וְשָׁקִילְנָא לֵיהּ בְּזוּטוֹ שֶׁל יָם וּבִשְׁלוּלִיתוֹ
שֶׁל נָהָר אע"ג דְּאִית בֵּיהּ סִימָן רַחֲמָנָא שַׁרְיֵיהּ
כִּדְבָעֵינָן לְמֵימַר לְקַמָּן כִּי פְּלִיגֵי בְּדָבָר שֶׁאֵין
בּוֹ סִימָן אַבַּיֵּי אָמַר אלֹא הָוֵי יֵאוּשׁ דְּהָא לֹא
יָדַע דְּנָפַל מִינֵּיהּ רָבָא אָמַר הָוֵי יֵאוּשׁ דִּלְכִי
יָדַע דְּנָפַל מִינֵּיהּ מְיָאֵשׁ מֵימַר אָמַר סִימָנָא
לֵית לִי בְּגַוֵּיהּ מֵהַשְׁתָּא הוּא דְּמְיָאֵשׁ (סִימָן
פמג"ש ממקגט"י ככסע"ז) תָּא שְׁמַע פֵּירוֹת
מְפוּזָּרִין הָא לֹא יָדַע דְּנָפַל מִינֵּיהּ הָא אָמַר
רַב עוּקְבָא בַּר חָמָא הָכָא בְּמַכְנִשְׁתָּא (ב) דְּבִיזְרֵי
עָסְקִינָן דַּאֲבֵידָה מִדַּעַת הִיא ת"ש מָעוֹת
מְפוּזָּרוֹת הֲרֵי אֵלּוּ שֶׁלּוֹ אַמַּאי הָא לֹא יָדַע
דְּנָפַל מִינֵּיהּ הָתָם נַמִּי כִּדְרַבִּי *יִצְחָק דְּאָמַר
באָדָם עָשׂוּי לְמַשְׁמֵשׁ בְּכִיסוֹ בְּכָל שָׁעָה
וְשָׁעָה גהָכָא נַמִּי אָדָם עָשׂוּי לְמַשְׁמֵשׁ בְּכִיסוֹ
בְּכָל שָׁעָה וְשָׁעָה ת"ש עִיגּוּלֵי דְּבֵילָה וְכִכָּרוֹת
שֶׁל נַחְתּוֹם הֲרֵי אֵלּוּ שֶׁלּוֹ אַמַּאי וְהָא לֹא יָדַע
דְּנָפַל מִינֵּיהּ הָתָם נַמִּי [א] דאַגַּב דְּיַקִּירֵי מֵידַע
יָדַע בְּהוּ ת"ש וּלְשׁוֹנוֹת שֶׁל אַרְגָּמָן הֲרֵי אֵלּוּ
שֶׁלּוֹ וְאַמַּאי הָא לֹא יָדַע דְּנָפַל מִינֵּיהּ הָתָם
נַמִּי האַגַּב דַּחֲשִׁיבֵי מַשְׁמוּשֵׁי מְמַשְׁמֵשׁ בְּהוּ
וְכִדְרַבִּי יִצְחָק ת"ש והַמּוֹצֵא מָעוֹת בְּבָתֵּי
כְּנֵסִיּוֹת וּבְבָתֵּי מִדְרָשׁוֹת וּבְכָל מָקוֹם שֶׁהָרַבִּים
מְצוּיִין שָׁם הֲרֵי אֵלּוּ שֶׁלּוֹ מִפְּנֵי שֶׁהַבְּעָלִים
מִתְיָאֲשִׁין מֵהֶן וְהָא לֹא יָדַע דְּנָפַל מִינֵּיהּ אָמַר
רַבִּי יִצְחָק אָדָם עָשׂוּי לְמַשְׁמֵשׁ בְּכִיסוֹ בְּכָל
שָׁעָה ת"ש *)זמֵאֵימָתַי כָּל אָדָם מוּתָּרִים
בְּלֶקֶט מִשֶּׁיֵּלְכוּ בָּהּ הַנָּמוּשׁוֹת וְאַמְרִינָן מַאי
נְמוּשׁוֹת וְא"ר יוֹחָנָן סָבֵי דְּאָזְלֵי **)אַתִּיגְרָא
רֵישׁ לָקִישׁ אָמַר לְקוּטֵי בָּתַר לְקוּטֵי וְאַמַּאי
נְהִי דַּעֲנִיִּים דְּהָכָא מְיָאֲשֵׁי אִיכָּא עֲנִיִּים
בְּדוּכְתָּא אַחֲרִיתָא דְּלֹא מְיָאֲשֵׁי אַמְרֵי כֵּיוָן
דְּאִיכָּא עֲנִיִּים הָכָא הַנָּךְ ◦מֵעִיקָּרָא אַיְאוּשֵׁי
מְיָאֵשׁ וְאַמְרֵי עֲנִיִּים דְּהָתָם מְלַקְּטֵי לֵיהּ ת"ש
*חקְצִיעוֹת בַּדֶּרֶךְ וַאֲפִילּוּ בְּצַד שָׂדֶה קְצִיעוֹת
טוְכֵן תְּאֵנָה הַנּוֹטָה לַדֶּרֶךְ וּמָצָא תְּאֵנִים
תַּחְתֶּיהָ מוּתָּרוֹת מִשּׁוּם גָּזֵל וּפְטוּרוֹת מִן
הַמַּעֲשֵׂר בְּזֵיתִים וּבַחֲרוּבִים אָסוּר בִּשְׁלָמָא
רֵישָׁא לְאַבַּיֵּי לֹא קַשְׁיָא אַגַּב דַּחֲשִׁיבֵי
מְמַשְׁמֵשׁ בְּהוּ תְּאֵנָה נַמִּי מֵידַע יְדִיעַ דְּנַתְרָא
אֶלָּא סֵיפָא לְרָבָא קַשְׁיָא דְּקָתָנֵי בְּזֵיתִים
וּבַחֲרוּבִים אָסוּר אָמַר רַבִּי אֲבָהוּ שַׁאנִי זַיִת
הוֹאִיל וְחָזוּתוֹ מוֹכִיחַ עָלָיו וְאע"ג דְּנָתְרִין
זֵיתֵי מֵידַע יְדִיעַ *דּוּכְתָּא דְּאִינִישׁ אִינִישׁ
הוּא אִי הָכִי אֲפִילּוּ רֵישָׁא נַמִּי אָמַר רַב
פָּפָּא תְּאֵנָה עִם נְפִילָתָהּ נִמְאֶסֶת

VOCABULARY REVIEW:

פְּלִיג ____________________

הַשְׁתָּא ____________________

דוּכְתָּא ____________________

מֵעִיקָּרָא ____________________

רֵישָׁא ____________________

סֵיפָא ____________________

בִּשְׁלָמָא ____________________

הוֹאִיל ____________________

חָזֵי ____________________

מַאי אִרְיָא ____________________

LABEL AND SUMMARIZE:

For each step, write what type of step it is and a brief explanation.

שיעור ז
STEP 1 מֵימְרָא
In the case of יֵאוּשׁ שֶׁלֹּא מִדַּעַת, אַבַּיֵי says it is not considered יֵאוּשׁ and רָבָא says it is.

שיעורים ח-יא
STEPS 2-10

TO REVIEW THESE STEPS, PLEASE LOOK BACK TO PAGE 87.

שיעור יב
STEP 11

STEP 12

שיעור יג
STEP 13

STEP 14

שיעור יד-טו
STEP 15

שיעור טו
STEP 16

STEP 17

STEP 18

STEP 19

Come and hear [a proof from a בְּרַיְיתָא]: תָּא שְׁמַע

The גְּמָרָא will now present another רַאֲיָה from a בְּרַיְיתָא. As always, we will first learn the בְּרַיְיתָא independently before working to understand the proof.

Before we learn the בְּרַיְיתָא, there is a bit of background information that is important. The בְּרַיְיתָא will discuss two different types of people who steal things. First, we will learn about a גַּנָּב. A גַּנָּב is someone who steals things secretly. For example, he sneaks into someone's house while everyone is sleeping. He moves around quietly so that no one wakes up. By the time the homeowner wakes up, the גַּנָּב is long gone with whatever he has taken. We will translate the word גַּנָּב as "a thief."

The next type of stealer that the בְּרַיְיתָא will discuss is a גַּזְלָן. A גַּזְלָן steals openly. He might boldly walk up to someone and threaten to hurt him unless he gives up his money (or other valuable possessions). We will translate the word גַּזְלָן as "a robber."

With this information, we are ready to learn the בְּרַיְיתָא:

A thief	**הַגַּנָּב**
that took [something] from this [person]	**שֶׁנָּטַל מִזֶּה**
and gave it to this [other person],	**וְנָתַן לְזֶה**

This means that someone secretly stole something from one person and then left it on the property of another person.

and so too,	**וְכֵן**
a robber	**גַּזְלָן**
that took [something] from this [person] and gave it to this [other person],	**שֶׁנָּטַל מִזֶּה וְנָתַן לָזֶה**
and so too,	**וְכֵן**
the יַרְדֵּן (or any other river)	**יַרְדֵּן**
that took [something] from this [person] and gave it to this [other person],	**שֶׁנָּטַל מִזֶּה וְנָתַן לָזֶה**

The בְּרַיְיתָא discusses three cases. In the first two cases, someone (either a גַּנָּב or a גַּזְלָן) stole something from one person and gave it to another person. In the final case, the current of a river swept something away and the item washed up on another person's property.

Now, the בְּרַיְיתָא will teach us one הֲלָכָה that applies to all three cases:

what it took, it took (the owner cannot get it back),	**מַה שֶּׁנָּטַל נָטַל**
and what it gave, it gave (the one who received it may keep it).	**וּמַה שֶּׁנָּתַן נָתַן**

The בְּרַיְיתָא teaches that in these three cases, the person who received the item (whether from a גַּנָּב, a גַּזְלָן, or a river) may keep them; he does not need to give it back.

Now that we understand the הֲלָכָה that the בְּרַיְיתָא taught, the גְּמָרָא will explain the רַאֲיָה:

It is understandable	**בִּשְׁלָמָא**
[in the cases of] the robber and the יַרְדֵּן	**גַּזְלָן וְיַרְדֵּן**
[the finder can keep it] because [the owner] saw them [being taken]	**דְּקָא חָזֵי לְהוּ**
and was מְיָאֵשׁ.	**וּמְיָאֵשׁ**

In the cases of a גַּזְלָן or river, the owner saw that his item was taken and was מְיָאֵשׁ. For that reason, the receiver of the item may keep it. These are not cases of יֵאוּשׁ שֶׁלֹּא מִדַּעַת. The גְּמָרָא will now explain that the רַאֲיָה is from the case of a גַּנָּב (who steals secretly):

But [in the case of] a thief,	**אֶלָּא גַּנָּב**
did [the owner] see it	**מִי קָא חָזֵי לֵיהּ**
that he [could have been] מְיָאֵשׁ?!	**דִּמְיָאֵשׁ**

Because a גַּנָּב steals secretly, it is very likely that when the item is received by the other person, the owner still does not know that his item was taken out of his possession. Therefore, the case of a גַּנָּב is a case of יֵאוּשׁ שֶׁלֹּא מִדַּעַת.

Since the בְּרַיְיתָא taught that the receiver of the item may keep it, we have a רַאֲיָה that יֵאוּשׁ שֶׁלֹּא מִדַּעַת is considered to be יֵאוּשׁ. This is a רַאֲיָה to the שִׁיטָה of רָבָא.

Again, please identify the object and support of this רַאֲיָה:

STEP SUMMARY

The Object THE THING WHICH WE ARE PROVING	
The Support THE STATEMENT OR LOGIC WHICH PROVES THE OBJECT	

STEP 20

The גְּמָרָא explains that we misunderstood what the בְּרַיְיתָא meant when it used the word גַּנָּב. Although the word גַּנָּב usually means someone who steals secretly, רַב פָּפָּא explains that in this case, the בְּרַיְיתָא used the word גַּנָּב to mean something else:

רַב פָּפָּא interpreted [the case of גַּנָּב]	**תַּרְגְּמָהּ רַב פָּפָּא**
[that it was talking about] an armed bandit.	**בְּלִסְטִים מְזוּיָּן**

We were assuming that when the בְּרַיְיתָא used the word גַּנָּב, it meant someone stealing secretly. However, רַב פָּפָּא teaches us that the בְּרַיְיתָא was actually referring to a לִסְטִים מְזוּיָּן - an armed bandit (someone who uses a weapon when robbing people).* In this case, too, the owner obviously knows that his item has been taken and he is מְיָאֵשׁ. For that reason, the בְּרַיְיתָא teaches that the receiver of the item may keep it. With this understanding, we see that this is not a case of יֵאוּשׁ שֶׁלֹּא מִדַּעַת and is not a רַאֲיָה for רָבָא.

*For a detailed understanding of why the בְּרַיְיתָא used the word גַּנָּב to mean an armed bandit, please see Artscroll Schottenstein Gemara, Bava Metzia 22a note 5.

Again, please identify the הֲוָה אַמִינָא and מַסְקָנָא:

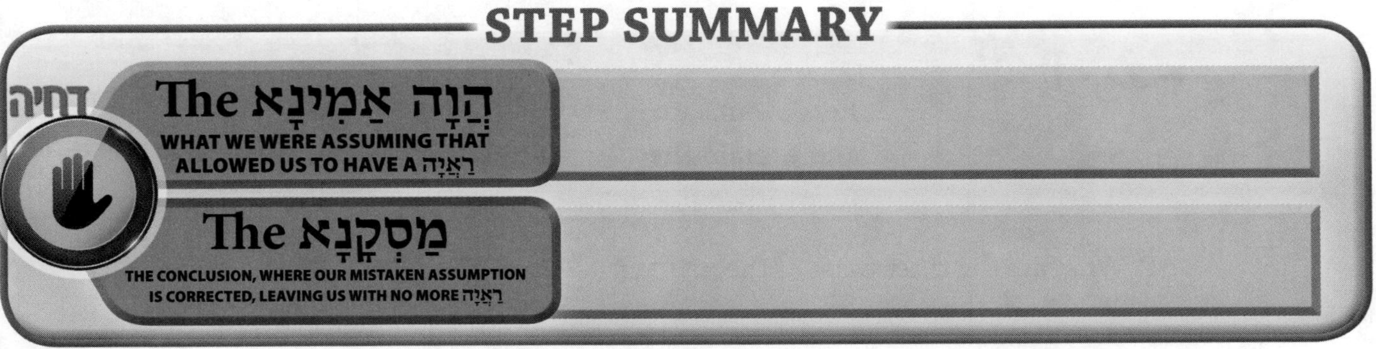

STEP 21

The גְמָרָא questions רַב פָּפָּא's interpretation of the word גַּנָּב in our בְּרַיְיתָא:

If so,	**אִי הָכֵי**
this is the same thing as a robber!?	**הַיְינוּ גַּזְלָן**

The בְּרַיְיתָא listed two cases of someone stealing (a גַּנָּב and a גַּזְלָן). If two cases are listed, then they must be different. רַב פָּפָּא taught us that in our בְּרַיְיתָא, the word גַּנָּב means an armed bandit. However, an armed bandit is a type of גַּזְלָן (a robber who steals openly). It seems that רַב פָּפָּא's interpretation cannot be correct because it would mean that the בְּרַיְיתָא is listing the case of גַּזְלָן twice!?

The target of this קֻשְׁיָא is רַב פָּפָּא's interpretation of the word גַּנָּב. The attack is the fact that an armed bandit is a type of גַּזְלָן.

STEP 22

The גְמָרָא gives a very simple answer to the קֻשְׁיָא:

[There are] two types of robbers.	**תְּרֵי גַּוְונֵי גַּזְלָן**

We were assuming that all גַּזְלָנִים (plural of גַּזְלָן) are the same (whether they use a weapon or not). Therefore, there would be no reason to list the cases of גַּזְלָן and לִסְטִים מְזוּיָּן separately. However, the גְמָרָא corrects that false assumption by teaching us that a לִסְטִים מְזוּיָּן (who robs with a weapon) is different than a regular גַּזְלָן (a robber who uses force but does not have a weapon), and therefore it needed to be listed on its own.

At this point, the גְמָרָא accepts the interpretation of רַב פָּפָּא. We now understand that when the בְּרַיְיתָא used the word גַּנָּב, it was referring to an armed bandit. The בְּרַיְיתָא taught us that if someone steals something openly (whether he uses a weapon or not) and gives it to someone else, the other person may keep it. However, the בְּרַיְיתָא never discussed a case of someone who steals without the owner knowing about it. Therefore, none of the cases of this בְּרַיְיתָא are examples of יֵאוּשׁ שֶׁלֹּא מִדַּעַת and they cannot be used as רַאֲיוֹת in this סוּגְיָא.

שיעור כב Review

PUT IT ALL TOGETHER:

תָּא
שְׁמַע *הַגַּנָּב שֶׁנָּטַל מִזֶּה וְנָתַן לָזֶה וְכֵן גַּזְלָן שֶׁנָּטַל מִזֶּה וְנָתַן לָזֶה
וְכֵן יַרְדֵּן שֶׁנָּטַל מִזֶּה וְנָתַן לָזֶה מַה שֶּׁנָּטַל
נָטַל וּמַה שֶּׁנָּתַן נָתַן בִּשְׁלָמָא גַּזְלָן וְיַרְדֵּן
דְּקָא חָזֵי לְהוּ וּמְיָאֵשׁ אֶלָּא גַּנָּב מִי קָא חָזֵי
לֵיהּ דְּמְיָאֵשׁ תַּרְגְּמָהּ רַב פָּפָּא בְּלִסְטִים
מְזוּיָּן אִי הָכִי הַיְינוּ *גַּזְלָן תְּרֵי גַּוְונֵי גַּזְלָן

1. Read, translate and explain the following גְּמָרָא.

2. What are the three cases of the בְּרַיְיתָא?
 a. ______
 b. ______
 c. ______

3. What is the הֲלָכָה in all three cases? ______

4. Which two cases are not a proof to either opinion (רָבָא or אַבַּיֵי)? ______

5. Why are those two cases not a רַאֲיָה? ______

6. Which case is a proof? ______

7. Which שִׁיטָה does it prove? ______

8. Please explain the רַאֲיָה and דְּחִיָּה that we learned in this שִׁיעוּר:

The Object ______

The Support ______

דחיה

The הֲוָה אַמִינָא ______

The מַסְקָנָא ______

9. Please explain the קֻשְׁיָא (Step 21) and תֵּירוּץ (Step 22) that we learned in this שִׁיעוּר:

The Target ______

The Attack ______

The הֲוָה אַמִינָא ______

The מַסְקָנָא ______

10. AT THE END OF THE שִׁיעוּר - what have we successfully proven? (circle one)
 a. the שִׁיטָה of אַבַּיֵי b. the שִׁיטָה of רָבָא c. nothing

IDENTIFY THE STEPS:

BE SURE TO INCLUDE EVERY WORD.

תָּא
שְׁמַע *הַגַּנָּב שֶׁנָּטַל מִזֶּה וְנָתַן לְזֶה וְכֵן גַּזְלָן שֶׁנָּטַל מִזֶּה וְנָתַן לְזֶה
וְכֵן יַרְדֵּן שֶׁנָּטַל מִזֶּה וְנָתַן לְזֶה מַה שֶּׁנָּטַל
נָטַל וּמַה שֶּׁנָּתַן נָתַן בִּשְׁלָמָא גַּזְלָן וְיַרְדֵּן
דְּקָא חָזֵי לְהוּ וּמְיָאֵשׁ אֶלָּא גַּנָּב מִי קָא חָזֵי
לֵיהּ דְּמְיָאֵשׁ תִּרְגְּמָה רַב פַּפָּא בְּלִסְטִים
מְזוּיָּן אִי הָכֵי הַיְינוּ *גַּזְלָן תְּרֵי גַּוְונֵי גַּזְלָן

Please [bracket] the	Please <u>underline</u> the	Please (parenthesize) the	Please box the
ראיה	דחיה	קשיא	

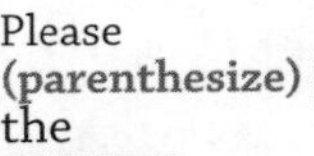

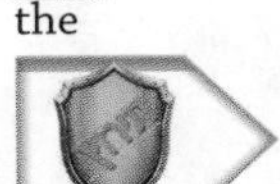

VOCABULARY REVIEW:

עִידְנָא ______________ חָזֵי ______________

אֲלִיבָּא ______________ מַאי אִרְיָא ______________

MATCHING:

(HINT: ONE OF THE CHOICES IS USED TWICE.)

_____ 1. Step 19 of the סוּגְיָא is a _______
_____ 2. Step 20 of the סוּגְיָא is a _______
_____ 3. Step 21 of the סוּגְיָא is a _______
_____ 4. Step 22 of the סוּגְיָא is a _______
_____ 5. The object of the רַאֲיָה
_____ 6. The support of the רַאֲיָה
_____ 7. The הֲוָה אַמִינָא (part of the דְחִיָה)
_____ 8. The מַסְקָנָא (part of the דְחִיָה)
_____ 9. The target of the קֻשְׁיָא
_____ 10. The attack of the קֻשְׁיָא
_____ 11. The הֲוָה אַמִינָא (part of the תֵּירוּץ)
_____ 12. The מַסְקָנָא (part of the תֵּירוּץ)

א. יֵאוּשׁ שֶׁלֹּא מִדַּעַת הֲוֵי יֵאוּשׁ
ב. קֻשְׁיָא
ג. תְּרֵי גַּוְונֵי גַּזְלָן
ד. תֵּירוּץ
ה. The בְּרַיְיתָא meant a לִסְטִים מְזוּיָּן
ו. גַּנָּב... מַה שֶּׁנָּטַל נָטַל וּמַה שֶּׁנָּתַן נָתַן
ז. The בְּרַיְיתָא meant a regular גַּנָּב (who steals secretly)
ח. הַיְינוּ גַּזְלָן
ט. דְחִיָה
י. All גַּזְלָנִים are the same
יא. רַאֲיָה

BEFORE WE BEGIN

There are times when we are told one thing which allows us to figure out something else which was not directly said. Consider the following example:

Your רֶבִּי tells you, "You may go to recess because you finished the assignment." Your friend didn't complete the assignment. He asks you if you think that he will be allowed to go to recess. What would you say?

You would probably tell your friend that you think he will not be allowed to go to recess. Your friend might then ask you why you think so. After all, רֶבִּי never actually said anything about those who didn't finish the assignment. You explain that the fact that רֶבִּי said that you were allowed to go *"because you finished the assignment,"* implies that the inverse (opposite) must also be true. In other words, those who didn't complete it may not go.

In the above scenario, you made a דִּיוּק (an **inference**) in your רֶבִּי's words. In other words, you were מְדַיֵּק (you **inferred**) something based on what your רֶבִּי said. It is as if your רֶבִּי *actually said* that those who did not finish the assignment may not go to recess.

WHAT WAS ACTUALLY SAID	Those who finish the assignment may go to recess.
WHAT WE CAN BE מְדַיֵּק	Those who did not finish the assignment may not go to recess.

Take a minute and try to think of another example of a דִּיוּק that you can make. Please write it below:

WHAT WAS ACTUALLY SAID	
WHAT WE CAN BE מְדַיֵּק	

The גְּמָרָא often uses דִּיוּקִים (plural of דִּיוּק) to prove things. When a מִשְׁנָה, a בְּרַיְיתָא, or an אֲמוֹרָא says something, the גְּמָרָא might be מְדַיֵּק the inverse. When this happens, the גְּמָרָא considers it as if the מִשְׁנָה, the בְּרַיְיתָא, or the אֲמוֹרָא had actually said the inverse as well.

STEP 23

Come and hear [a proof from a בְּרַיְיתָא]:	ת"ש

By now, you know that we will first learn the בְּרַיְיתָא before discussing the רַאֲיָה. This בְּרַיְיתָא will teach us a הֲלָכָה and give a reason for that הֲלָכָה. The reason will be very important to us. So, let's learn the בְּרַיְיתָא and make sure that we are very clear about both the הֲלָכָה and the reason.

First, the הֲלָכָה:

[If an overflowing] river washed away	שָׁטַף נָהָר
[someone's] beams,	קוֹרָיו
his wood,	עֵצָיו
or his stones,	וַאֲבָנָיו
and it put them	וּנְתָנוֹ
into his friend's field,	בְּתוֹךְ שְׂדֵה חֲבֵירוֹ
these are [the finder's to keep],	הֲרֵי אֵלוּ שֶׁלּוֹ

Now, the reason:

because the owner was מְיָאֵשׁ.	מִפְּנֵי שֶׁנִּתְיָאֲשׁוּ הַבְּעָלִים

The בְּרַיְיתָא has taught us that when an overflowing river washes away heavy items like beams, wood, or stones, whoever receives these items may keep them. The בְּרַיְיתָא explains that the reason he may keep them is because we can be quite sure that the owner was מְיָאֵשׁ. After all, when a river flood washes away items, it is a very noteworthy event. Certainly, the owner immediately knew that his items had been washed away. Also, considering the fact that a flooding river carries things very far and very quickly, the owner knew that he had no hope of getting them back.

The בְּרַיְיתָא has taught us a הֲלָכָה and has given us a reason for the הֲלָכָה. The גְּמָרָא will now make a דיוק based on that reason:

The reason [that the finder may keep them]	טַעְמָא
[is] because the owner was מְיָאֵשׁ,	דְּנִתְיָאֲשׁוּ הַבְּעָלִים
but in a regular case (where we don't know whether he was מְיָאֵשׁ or not)	הָא סְתָמָא
[the finder may] not [keep them].	לֹא

The בְּרַיְיתָא taught that the receiver of the items may keep them because, in this case, we know that the owner was מְיָאֵשׁ. Therefore, we can make a דיוק that in other cases (not involving overflowing rivers),

where we don't know whether the owner was מְיָאֵשׁ or not (because he may not have known that the object was lost), the receiver would not be allowed to keep the objects.

Because the דִּיּוּק is so clear, we consider it as if the בְּרַיְיתָא actually said this. It is as if the בְּרַיְיתָא said that in a case when we don't know whether the owner knew that his object was lost, the receiver may not keep the items. This proves that אַבַּיֵּי is correct that יֵאוּשׁ שֶׁלֹּא מִדַּעַת is not considered to be יֵאוּשׁ. This שִׁיטָה of אַבַּיֵּי is the object of the רַאֲיָה. The support of the רַאֲיָה is a bit trickier to identify. The support is the fact that the בְּרַיְיתָא gave the reason of "מִפְּנֵי שֶׁנִּתְיָאֲשׁוּ הַבְּעָלִים".

STEP 24

In order to have a רַאֲיָה from this בְּרַיְיתָא, we were making the following assumption: In any situation of a flooding river, the owner will have no chance of saving his items, so he is מְיָאֵשׁ. Therefore, when the בְּרַיְיתָא said that the receiver may keep the objects "because the owner has been מְיָאֵשׁ," we made a דִּיּוּק that in **other situations** (not involving overflowing rivers), when the owner may not have been מְיָאֵשׁ, the finder may not keep it.

This assumption (our הֲוָה אַמִינָא) is why we thought that the case of the דִּיּוּק is a case of יֵאוּשׁ שֶׁלֹּא מִדַּעַת and a רַאֲיָה for the שִׁיטָה of אַבַּיֵּי. However, the גְּמָרָא will reject this רַאֲיָה by correcting our הֲוָה אַמִינָא with the following מַסְקָנָא:

With what [case] are we dealing here?	**הָכָא בְּמַאי עָסְקִינַן**
When [the owner] was able to save [them].	**כְּשֶׁיָּכוֹל לְהַצִּיל**

The גְמָרָא explains that the case of the בְּרַיְיתָא is one where the items which were washed away were able to be saved by the owner. The river was not moving fast, so if the owner had tried, he could have saved them. However, he chose not to save his items and was מְיָאֵשׁ. Therefore, the בְּרַיְיתָא tells us that the receiver may keep the items **because the owner was מְיָאֵשׁ.**

With this understanding, we see that the words "מִפְּנֵי שֶׁנִתְיָאֲשׁוּ הַבְּעָלִים" cannot be used to make the דִּיוּק that we tried to make. The בְּרַיְיתָא was not comparing the case of overflowing rivers with other cases. Rather, the בְּרַיְיתָא was teaching us that (in a case of a flooding river) the receiver can keep the items if the owner was מְיָאֵשׁ. The דִּיוּק that we **can** make is that he may not keep the items if the owner was trying to save them.

The case of this new דִּיוּק is not a case of יֵאוּשׁ שֶׁלֹּא מִדַּעַת and cannot be used as a רַאֲיָה in this סוּגְיָא.

Again, please identify the הֲוָה אַמִינָא and מַסְקָנָא:

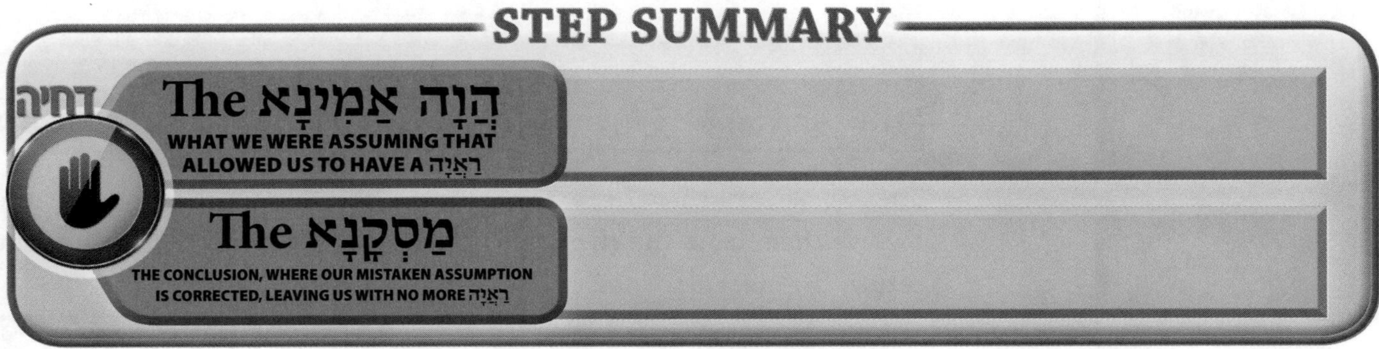

שיעור יז
כב. lines 6-15
Continued

STEP 25

The גְּמָרָא asks a קֻשְׁיָא which challenges the דְּחִיָּה that we just learned:

If so,	**אִי הָכִי**
I will say the end of the בְּרַיְיתָא:	**אֵימָא סֵיפָא**

The גְּמָרָא is telling us that what we learned in the earlier part of this שִׁיעוּר is not the complete בְּרַיְיתָא. There is an ending of the בְּרַיְיתָא that was not yet quoted. Because they are two parts of the same בְּרַיְיתָא, the רֵישָׁא and the סֵיפָא must be discussing the same case. We just explained that the case of the רֵישָׁא of the בְּרַיְיתָא was that the owner was able to save his items. This new explanation needs to also be the case of the סֵיפָא. It would not make sense for two halves of the same בְּרַיְיתָא to be discussing different cases (unless the בְּרַיְיתָא clearly told us so).

The גְּמָרָא will now teach us the ending of the בְּרַיְיתָא. Then, the גְּמָרָא will examine whether the new understanding of the בְּרַיְיתָא fits with the סֵיפָא. As always, we will first learn this part of the בְּרַיְיתָא on its own before we attempt to understand the קֻשְׁיָא:

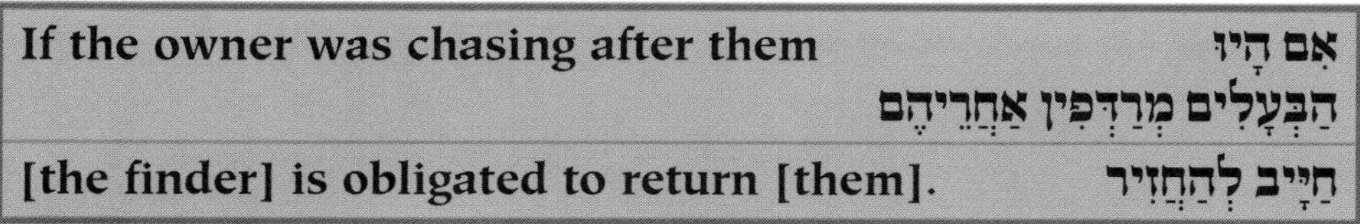

If the owner was chasing after them	**אִם הָיוּ הַבְּעָלִים מְרַדְּפִין אַחֲרֵיהֶם**
[the finder] is obligated to return [them].	**חַיָּיב לְהַחֲזִיר**

The בְּרַיְיתָא says that if the owner of the objects was chasing after them to save them from the river, he is clearly not מְיָאֵשׁ and the receiver must return the objects to him.

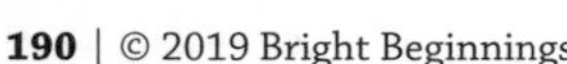

The גְּמָרָא will now ask that our earlier explanation of the בְּרַיְיתָא (that the owner was able to save the items) does not seem to work with the סֵיפָא of the בְּרַיְיתָא:

If [the בְּרַיְיתָא was talking about a case] where he was able to save [them]	אִי בִּיכוֹלִין לְהַצִּיל
why [did it] specifically speak	מַאי אִרְיָא
[about a case where the owner was] chasing,	מְרַדְּפִין
even [if the owner] was not chasing	אֲפִילוּ אֵין מְרַדְּפִין
[the finder should] also [have to return it]!?	נַמִּי

If the בְּרַיְיתָא was discussing a case in which the owner was able to save his items, he would likely not be מְיָאֵשׁ. Therefore, the receiver should have to return the items whether the owner was chasing after them or not. Just because he was not chasing after the items at this moment does not mean that he was מְיָאֵשׁ. Therefore, it seems that our explanation of the בְּרַיְיתָא (that the owner was able to save his items) cannot be correct!?

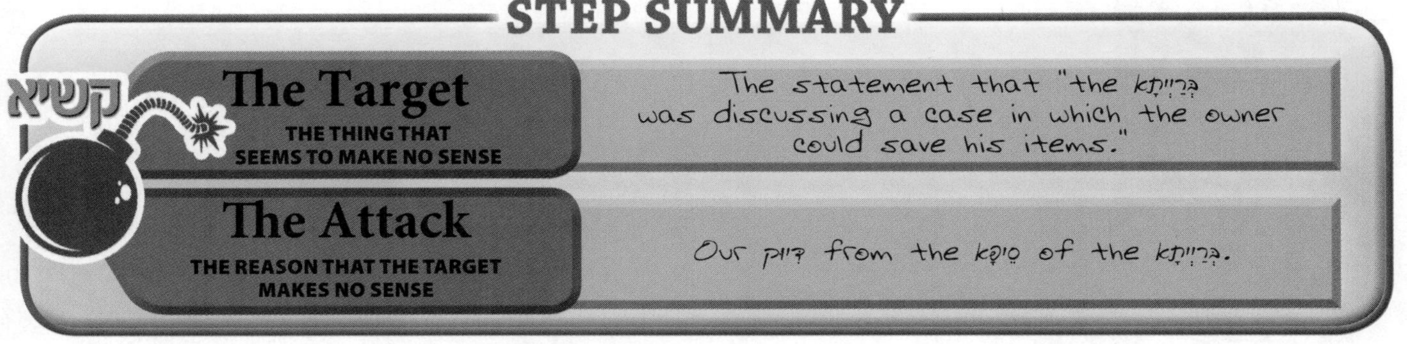

STEP 26

To answer the קֻשְׁיָא, the גְּמָרָא will have to clarify what it meant when it said that the בְּרַיְיתָא was discussing a case in which the owner could save his items. The הֲוָה אַמִינָא was that the גְּמָרָא was saying that the owner could save his items without too much difficulty. Therefore, the גְּמָרָא asked that the receiver of the items should have to return them even if the owner was not chasing after them. Now, the גְּמָרָא will answer the קֻשְׁיָא by correcting the הֲוָה אַמִינָא:

With what [case] are we dealing here?	**הָכָא בְּמַאי עַסְקִינַן**
When [the owner] was able to save them	**בִּיכוֹלִין לְהַצִּיל**
with difficulty.	**עַל יְדֵי הַדְּחָק**
[If the owner was] chasing	**מְרַדְּפִין**
he was not מְיָאֵשׁ,	**לֹא אַיְיאוּשׁ**
[but if] he was not chasing,	**אֵין מְרַדְּפִין**
he was מְיָאֵשׁ.	**אַיְיאוּשֵׁי מְיָאֵשׁ**

The גְּמָרָא explains that when we learned earlier that the בְּרַיְיתָא was discussing a case in which the owner was able to save the items, what the גְּמָרָא really meant was that he could save them with great difficulty. If he would quickly chase the items, he would be able to save them from being washed away. However, if he was to delay in getting back his items, the river would wash them away completely.

With this מַסְקָנָא, the בְּרַיְיתָא is easily understood. The רֵישָׁא taught that when the river washes away someone's items, the owner (who certainly knows what happened) will be מְיָאֵשׁ. We know that he was מְיָאֵשׁ because he is not running after his items and he will not be able to do so later (because the items will be washed away). Therefore, the receiver of the items may keep them. The סֵיפָא of the בְּרַיְיתָא teaches that if, on the other hand, the owner was chasing his items, he has clearly not been מְיָאֵשׁ. Therefore, the receiver must return the items to him.

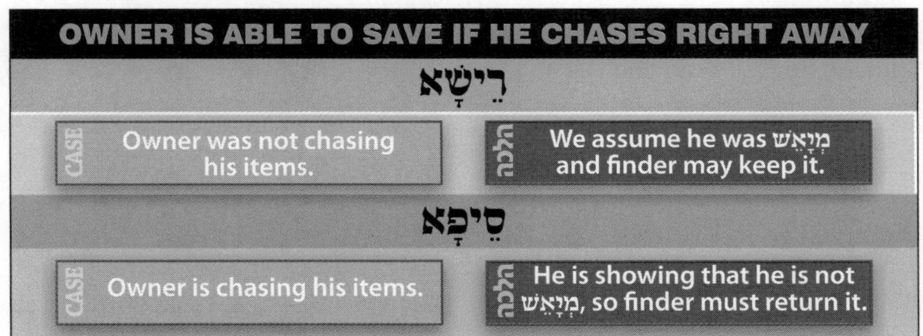

Now that the קַשְׁיָא has been answered, the גְּמָרָא accepts the דְּחִיָּה of the רַאֲיָה. We have successfully explained that the בְּרַיְיתָא was not discussing a case of יֵאוּשׁ שֶׁלֹּא מִדַּעַת. Once again, we are left with no proof to either the שִׁיטָה of אַבַּיֵי or of רָבָא.

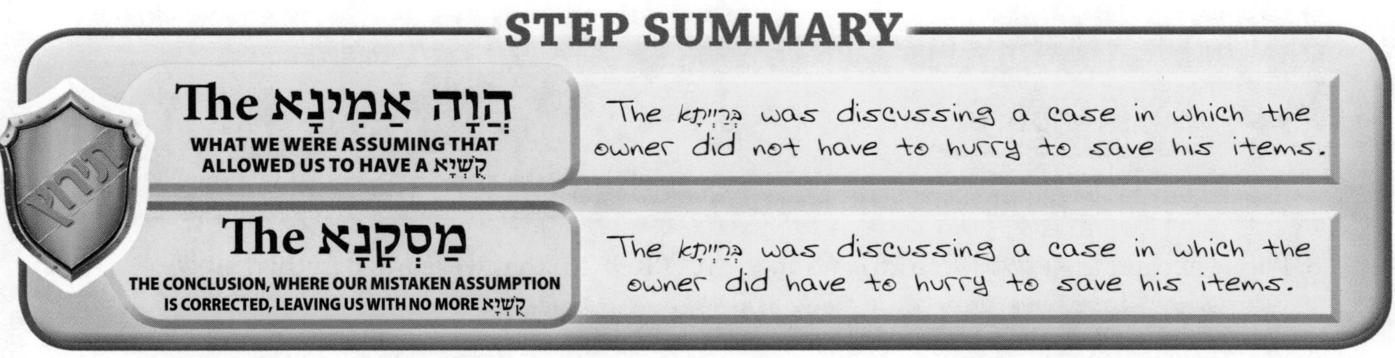

PUT IT ALL TOGETHER:

1. Read, translate and explain the following גְּמָרָא.

ת"ש *אשָׁטַף נָהָר קוֹרָיו עֵצָיו וַאֲבָנָיו וּנְתָנוֹ בְּתוֹךְ שְׂדֵה חֲבֵירוֹ *הֲרֵי אֵלּוּ שֶׁלּוֹ מִפְּנֵי שֶׁנִּתְיָאֲשׁוּ הַבְּעָלִים טַעְמָא דְּנִתְיָאֲשׁוּ הַבְּעָלִים הָא סְתָמָא לֹא הָכָא בְּמַאי עַסְקִינָן כְּשֶׁיָּכוֹל לְהַצִּיל אִי הָכִי אֵימָא סֵיפָא *אִם הָיוּ הַבְּעָלִים מְרַדְּפִין אַחֲרֵיהֶם חַיָּיב לְהַחֲזִיר אִי בִּיכוֹלִין לְהַצִּיל מַאי אִרְיָא מְרַדְּפִין אֲפִילּוּ אֵין מְרַדְּפִין נַמִּי הָכָא בְּמַאי עַסְקִינָן בִּיכוֹלִין לְהַצִּיל עַל יְדֵי הַדְּחָק מְרַדְּפִין לֹא אַיְיאוּשׁ אֵין מְרַדְּפִין אַיְיאוּשֵׁי מְיָאֵשׁ

2. What הֲלָכָה does (the רֵישָׁא of) the בְּרַיְיתָא teach? ______________________

3. What reason does (the רֵישָׁא of) the בְּרַיְיתָא give for the הֲלָכָה? ______________________

4. What is a דִּיוּק? ______________________

5. What דִּיוּק do we make from (the רֵישָׁא of) the בְּרַיְיתָא? ______________________

____

6. Please explain the רַאֲיָה and the דְּחִיָּה that we learned in this שִׁיעוּר:

The Object

The Support

דחיה

The הֲוָה אַמִינָא

The מַסְקָנָא

7. What הֲלָכָה does the סֵיפָא of the בְּרַיְיתָא teach? ______________________

8. Please explain the קֻשְׁיָא (Step 25) and the תֵּירוּץ (Step 26) that we learned in this שִׁיעוּר:

קשיא

The Target

The Attack

The הֲוָה אַמִינָא

The מַסְקָנָא

9. AT THE END OF THE שִׁיעוּר - what have we successfully proven? (circle one)

a. the שִׁיטָה of אַבַּיֵי b. the שִׁיטָה of רָבָא c. nothing

VOCABULARY REVIEW:

מִסְתַּבְּרָא ______________________

אִי סָלְקָא דַעְתָּךְ ________________

עִידָּנָא ______________________

אֲלִיבָּא ______________________

נְהִי ______________________

שְׁאֵלָה ______________________

תְּשׁוּבָה ______________________

IDENTIFY THE STEPS:

BE SURE TO INCLUDE EVERY WORD.

ת"ש *שָׁטַף נָהָר קוֹרָיו עֵצָיו וַאֲבָנָיו וּנְתָנוֹ בְּתוֹךְ שְׂדֵה חֲבֵירוֹ *הֲרֵי אֵלּוּ שֶׁלּוֹ מִפְּנֵי שֶׁנִּתְיָאֲשׁוּ הַבְּעָלִים טַעְמָא דְּנִתְיָאֲשׁוּ הַבְּעָלִים הָא סְתָמָא לֹא הָכָא בְּמַאי עַסְקִינָן כְּשֶׁיָּכוֹל לְהַצִּיל אִי הָכִי אֵימָא סֵיפָא *אִם הָיוּ הַבְּעָלִים מְרַדְּפִין אַחֲרֵיהֶם חַיָּיב לְהַחֲזִיר אִי בִּיכוֹלִין לְהַצִּיל מַאי אִרְיָא מְרַדְּפִין אֲפִילּוּ אֵין מְרַדְּפִין נַמִּי הָכָא בְּמַאי עַסְקִינָן בִּיכוֹלִין לְהַצִּיל עַל יְדֵי הַדְּחָק מְרַדְּפִין לֹא אַיְיאוּשׁ אֵין מְרַדְּפִין אַיְיאוּשֵׁי מְיָאֵשׁ

Please [bracket] the

Please underline the

Please (parenthesize) the

Please box the

MATCHING:

(HINT: ONE OF THE CHOICES IS USED TWICE.)

_____ 1. Step 23 of the סוּגְיָא is a _______

_____ 2. Step 24 of the סוּגְיָא is a _______

_____ 3. Step 25 of the סוּגְיָא is a _______

_____ 4. Step 26 of the סוּגְיָא is a _______

_____ 5. The object of the רַאֲיָה

_____ 6. The support of the רַאֲיָה is from a ______ that we made in the בְּרַיְיתָא

_____ 7. The הֲוָה אַמִינָא (part of the דְּחִיָּה)

_____ 8. The מַסְקָנָא (part of the דְּחִיָּה)

_____ 9. The target of the קֻשְׁיָא

_____ 10. The attack of the קֻשְׁיָא (the part of the בְּרַיְיתָא from which we make a דִּיוּק)

_____ 11. The הֲוָה אַמִינָא (part of the תֵּירוּץ)

_____ 12. The מַסְקָנָא (part of the תֵּירוּץ)

א. אִם הָיוּ הַבְּעָלִים מְרַדְּפִין אַחֲרֵיהֶם חַיָּיב לְהַחֲזִיר

ב. תֵּירוּץ

ג. We meant that he could save the items easily

ד. בִּיכוֹלִין לְהַצִּיל עַל יְדֵי הַדְּחָק

ה. הָכָא בְּמַאי עַסְקִינָן כְּשֶׁיָּכוֹל לְהַצִּיל

ו. The items were not saveable

ז. קֻשְׁיָא

ח. רַאֲיָה

ט. דְּחִיָּה

י. דִּיוּק

יא. יֵאוּשׁ שֶׁלֹּא מִדַּעַת לֹא הָוֵי יֵאוּשׁ

STEP 27

Another רַאֲיָה is attempted:

ראיה #10 EIGHTH PROOF FOR THE שיטה OF רָבָא

Come and hear [a proof from a בְּרַיְיתָא]: תָּא שְׁמַע

This רַאֲיָה is based on a בְּרַיְיתָא. Because this בְּרַיְיתָא is a bit complex, we will learn the בְּרַיְיתָא in this שִׁיעוּר and the explanation of the רַאֲיָה in the next שִׁיעוּר.

The בְּרַיְיתָא that we are going to learn discusses some הֲלָכוֹת about תְּרוּמָה. We will begin with a brief introduction to the מִצְוָה of תְּרוּמָה.

When a farmer grows produce, he has a מִצְוָה to give a portion of it to a כֹּהֵן. This is called תְּרוּמָה. The תּוֹרָה does not require a specific amount that must be given. In fact, according to the תּוֹרָה, the farmer can give just one kernel of wheat as תְּרוּמָה from an entire field. However, the חֲכָמִים established minimum amounts that must be given.

It is important to understand that before the farmer can give the תְּרוּמָה to a כֹּהֵן, it first must be separated from the rest of the produce and designated as תְּרוּמָה.

Basically, we can view the separating and giving of תְּרוּמָה as a two-step process:

The owner separates part of his produce and declares that it is תְּרוּמָה. As soon as he does that, the portion that he separated gets the קְדוּשָּׁה of תְּרוּמָה. After that point, the תְּרוּמָה may be eaten by כֹּהֲנִים (but they cannot share it with non-כֹּהֲנִים, even if they want to). There is no way to remove the קְדוּשָּׁה of תְּרוּמָה. Once the produce becomes תְּרוּמָה, it will be תְּרוּמָה permanently. At this point, the תְּרוּמָה collectively belongs to all of the כֹּהֲנִים in the world. However, the farmer has the right to give it to any כֹּהֵן that he chooses.

The farmer gives the תְּרוּמָה to a כֹּהֵן that he chooses. The תְּרוּמָה is then owned by that כֹּהֵן alone. The כֹּהֵן can eat the תְּרוּמָה or share it with other כֹּהֲנִים (or even sell it to them).

Our בְּרַיְיתָא will be discussing the first step of the process (separating the תְּרוּמָה). Specifically, the בְּרַיְיתָא will discuss the הֲלָכָה if someone separates תְּרוּמָה from someone else's produce, without the owner knowing about it. For example: רְאוּבֵן goes to שִׁמְעוֹן's silo, separates a portion of שִׁמְעוֹן's wheat and declares it to be תְּרוּמָה. While this was happening, שִׁמְעוֹן (the owner) had no idea that it was going on.

The חֲכָמִים taught a הֲלָכָה which was well-known, but the details were not well-understood. They taught that sometimes what רְאוּבֵן did (separating תְּרוּמָה from שִׁמְעוֹן's produce) counts enough to put the קְדוּשָׁה of תְּרוּמָה on the produce that he separated. However, this הֲלָכָה doesn't apply in all situations. There are some situations when רְאוּבֵן's actions have no effect on שִׁמְעוֹן's produce.

These details were not well-understood and needed to be clarified. This בְּרַיְיתָא will clarify what the חֲכָמִים meant. The בְּרַיְיתָא will teach us when רְאוּבֵן's separation counts and when it doesn't.

In what situation did [the חֲכָמִים] say	**כֵּיצַד אָמְרוּ**
[that] one who separates תְּרוּמָה	**הַתּוֹרֵם**
without the knowledge [of the owner]	**שֶׁלֹּא מִדַּעַת**
his תְּרוּמָה is [considered] תְּרוּמָה?	**תְּרוּמָתוֹ תְּרוּמָה**

We know that the חֲכָמִים said that sometimes it counts and sometimes it doesn't. The בְּרַיְיתָא will now explain what the חֲכָמִים meant:

If someone went down	הֲרֵי שֶׁיָּרַד
into his friend's field	לְתוֹךְ שְׂדֵה חֲבֵירוֹ
and picked [produce] and separated תְּרוּמָה	וְלִיקֵּט וְתָרַם
without permission [of the owner],	שֶׁלֹּא בִּרְשׁוּת
if [the owner] objects [to the תְּרוּמָה separation]	אִם חוֹשֵׁשׁ
because it was robbery,	מִשּׁוּם גֶּזֶל
his תְּרוּמָה is not [considered] תְּרוּמָה.	אֵין תְּרוּמָתוֹ תְּרוּמָה
And if [the owner does] not [object],	וְאִם לָאו
his תְּרוּמָה is [considered] תְּרוּמָה.	תְּרוּמָתוֹ תְּרוּמָה

The בְּרַיְיתָא teaches us that if the owner is upset by what his friend did and considers his friend to have stolen from him, then the תְּרוּמָה separation does not count. However, if the owner seems okay with what his friend did, then the תְּרוּמָה separation does count. This seems easy enough to understand. Since it is only the owner who has the right to choose the portion of his produce that will become תְּרוּמָה, he has to agree to what was done in order for it to count.

What we still don't know is how we can judge whether the owner is really okay with what was done. After all, he won't necessarily clearly say whether he was okay with it or not. Also, if he agrees to it at first, he can't change his mind later (remember, once the קְדוּשָּׁה of תְּרוּמָה comes onto the produce, it can't be removed). Therefore, it is important to have a way of judging the owner's reaction to see if he agrees or not. The בְּרַיְיתָא will now teach us how we can determine this:

And how does he know	וּמִנַּיִן הוּא יוֹדֵעַ
if [the owner] objects [to the תְּרוּמָה separation]	אִם חוֹשֵׁשׁ
because it was robbery,	מִשּׁוּם גֶּזֶל
or if [he does] not [object]?	וְאִם לָאו
If the homeowner comes	הֲרֵי שֶׁבָּא בַּעַל הַבַּיִת
and finds him and says to him,	וּמְצָאוֹ וְאָמַר לוֹ
"You should have gone to the better ones [to take תְּרוּמָה],"	כְּלַךְ אֵצֶל יָפוֹת

if better ones are found	אִם נִמְצְאוּ יָפוֹת מֵהֶן
his תְּרוּמָה is [considered] תְּרוּמָה,	תְּרוּמָתוֹ תְּרוּמָה
and if [better ones are] not [found],	וְאִם לַאו
his תְּרוּמָה is not [considered] תְּרוּמָה.	אֵין תְּרוּמָתוֹ תְּרוּמָה

If the owner tells his friend that he "should have taken תְּרוּמָה from the better ones," we can understand what he said in two ways. One possibility is that he was being sincere. He was telling his friend that in the future, he should take תְּרוּמָה from even better produce. If that is what he meant, he is clearly okay with his friend separating the תְּרוּמָה. (Otherwise, he wouldn't be telling him how to do it better in the future.) If the owner actually has better produce, we will assume that this is what he meant.

The other possibility is that the owner was being sarcastic. He was annoyed by what his friend did and bitterly told him, "Why didn't you even take (steal) from better ones?!" If the owner doesn't really have better ones, we will assume that this is what he meant. After all, he couldn't have meant it sincerely because he didn't have better produce.

We now know how to judge the owner's intention based on his words. The בְּרַיְיתָא will now teach us that there is something that the owner can do which shows us his intention:

[If] the owner picks [more produce]	לִיקְטוּ הַבְּעָלִים
and adds [it] to [what was already separated],	וְהוֹסִיפוּ עֲלֵיהֶן
either way (whether better ones were found or not)	בֵּין כָּךְ וּבֵין כָּךְ
his תְּרוּמָה is [considered] תְּרוּמָה.	תְּרוּמָתוֹ תְּרוּמָה

If the owner adds to the תְּרוּמָה that his friend separated, he is clearly okay with what his friend did, regardless of whether there was better produce or not.

Now that we understand this בְּרַיְיתָא, we are ready to learn the proof in the next שִׁיעוּר.

PUT IT ALL TOGETHER:

ת"ש *כֵּיצַד אָמְרוּ הַתּוֹרֵם שֶׁלֹּא
מִדַּעַת תְּרוּמָתוֹ תְּרוּמָה [א]הֲרֵי שֶׁיָּרַד לְתוֹךְ
שְׂדֵה חֲבֵירוֹ וְלִיקֵּט וְתָרַם שֶׁלֹּא בִּרְשׁוּת אִם
חוֹשֵׁשׁ מִשּׁוּם גֶּזֶל אֵין תְּרוּמָתוֹ תְּרוּמָה וְאִם
לַאו תְּרוּמָתוֹ תְּרוּמָה וּמִנַּיִן הוּא יוֹדֵעַ אִם
חוֹשֵׁשׁ מִשּׁוּם גֶּזֶל וְאִם לַאו [ג]הֲרֵי שֶׁבָּא בַּעַל
הַבַּיִת וּמְצָאוֹ וְאָמַר לוֹ *כְּלַךְ אֵצֶל יָפוֹת
אִם נִמְצְאוּ יָפוֹת מֵהֶן תְּרוּמָתוֹ תְּרוּמָה וְאִם
לַאו אֵין תְּרוּמָתוֹ תְּרוּמָה [ד]לִיקְּטוּ הַבְּעָלִים
וְהוֹסִיפוּ עֲלֵיהֶן בֵּין כָּךְ וּבֵין כָּךְ תְּרוּמָתוֹ
תְּרוּמָה

1. Read, translate and explain the following גְּמָרָא.

2. The גְּמָרָא will be bringing a proof from a ______________________________.

3. In this שִׁיעוּר, why was it important for us to not learn the actual proof yet? ______________________________

4. Which מִצְוָה is the topic of the בְּרַיְיתָא? ______________________________

5. Briefly describe this מִצְוָה: A farmer gives some of his __________ to a ______________.

6. In this שִׁיעוּר, we described this מִצְוָה as a two-step process:

   a. The owner _________ some of his __________ and declares that it is ____________. After he does this, that part belongs to ______________________.

   b. The owner gives that part to a _____. After he does this, that part belongs to __________ .

7. The בְּרַיְיתָא will be focusing on Step #_______ of the process.

8. The בְּרַיְיתָא discusses the הֲלָכָה if someone ______________ from someone else's ________.

9. The חֲכָמִים taught that in this case, sometimes ______________________________ and sometimes ______________.

10. The בְּרַיְיתָא taught the following rule: If the owner considers the other person's actions to be ______________, then ______________________ . However, if the owner doesn't consider the other person's actions to be ____________, then ______________ ____________.

11. The בְּרַיְיתָא tells us that we can figure out what the owner thinks, if the owner said "_______ ______________________." If there were ______________ then the owner meant ______________ and the הֲלָכָה is that ______________. However, if there were not ______________ then the owner meant ______________ and the הֲלָכָה is that ______________.

12. The final thing that the בְּרַיְיתָא teaches is that if the owner went and ______________, then the הֲלָכָה is ______________________.

IDENTIFY THE STEPS:
BE SURE TO INCLUDE EVERY WORD.

ת"ש *כֵּיצַד אָמְרוּ הַתּוֹרֵם שֶׁלֹּא
מְדַעַת תְּרוּמָתוֹ תְּרוּמָה [ב]הֲרֵי שֶׁיָּרַד לְתוֹךְ
שְׂדֵה חֲבֵירוֹ וְלִיקֵּט וְתָרַם שֶׁלֹּא בִּרְשׁוּת אִם
חוֹשֵׁשׁ מִשּׁוּם גֶּזֶל אֵין תְּרוּמָתוֹ תְּרוּמָה וְאִם
לַאו תְּרוּמָתוֹ תְּרוּמָה וּמִנַּיִן הוּא יוֹדֵעַ אִם
חוֹשֵׁשׁ מִשּׁוּם גֶּזֶל וְאִם לַאו [ג]הֲרֵי שֶׁבָּא בַּעַל
הַבַּיִת וּמְצָאוֹ וְאָמַר לוֹ *כְּלַךְ אֵצֶל יָפוֹת
אִם נִמְצְאוּ יָפוֹת מֵהֶן תְּרוּמָתוֹ תְּרוּמָה וְאִם
לַאו אֵין תְּרוּמָתוֹ תְּרוּמָה [ד]לִיקְּטוּ הַבְּעָלִים
וְהוֹסִיפוּ עֲלֵיהֶן בֵּין כָּךְ וּבֵין כָּךְ תְּרוּמָתוֹ
תְּרוּמָה

This שִׁיעוּר is part of what type of step? ________

VOCABULARY REVIEW:

אַשְׁכַּח ____________________

מַר ____________________

מִסְתַּבְּרָא ____________________

אִי סָלְקָא דַעְתָּךְ ____________________

קַשְׁיָא ____________________

תֵּירוּץ ____________________

בְּרַיְיתָא ____________________

הֵיכָא ____________________

MATCHING:

_____	1. Step 27 of the סוּגְיָא is a _______	א. תְּרוּמָתוֹ תְּרוּמָה
_____	2. In this שִׁיעוּר we are only trying to understand the ________	ב. כְּלַךְ אֵצֶל יָפוֹת
_____	3. The case of the בְּרַיְיתָא	ג. הַתּוֹרֵם שֶׁלֹּא מְדַעַת
_____	4. The הֲלָכָה that the חֲכָמִים said (which applies sometimes)	ד. אִם נִמְצְאוּ יָפוֹת מֵהֶן
_____	5. The תְּרוּמָה will not count if the owner is ________	ה. לִיקְּטוּ הַבְּעָלִים וְהוֹסִיפוּ עֲלֵיהֶן
_____	6. A statement that the owner might make	ו. בֵּין כָּךְ וּבֵין כָּךְ
_____	7. Situation which makes us think that the owner was serious	ז. רַאֲיָה
_____	8. Situation which makes us think that the owner was sarcastic	ח. חוֹשֵׁשׁ מִשּׁוּם גֶּזֶל
_____	9. What the owner can do that shows us what he thinks	ט. בְּרַיְיתָא
_____	10. "Whether better ones were found or not"	י. אִם לֹא נִמְצְאוּ יָפוֹת מֵהֶן

STEP 27 continued

Now that we know the בְּרַיְיתָא (from שִׁיעוּר י״ח), we are ready to learn how it can be used as a proof in our סוּגְיָא.

In the בְּרַיְיתָא, we learned that when the בַּעַל הַבַּיִת says "כְּלָךְ אֵצֶל יָפוֹת", if better produce is found, then the תְּרוּמָה that was separated is considered to be תְּרוּמָה. The גְּמָרָא will now question this הֲלָכָה in order to prove its point. Although it will sound as if we are asking a question, this step is still considered a רְאָיָה. Remember, any קַשְׁיָא on one שִׁיטָה is also a proof for the other שִׁיטָה.

The גְּמָרָא introduces the רְאָיָה with a statement of disbelief. This statement can only really be understood if it is read with the correct tone. To understand the way this should be read, please read the following example:

רֶבִּי: *Yankie, where's your homework?*

YANKIE: *A dog ate it.*

רֶבִּי: *A dog ate it?!*

If you read this example incorrectly, it will sound like the רֶבִּי is merely repeating Yankie's words. However, when read with the proper tone, it is clear that the רֶבִּי is in disbelief about what Yankie said.

The same is true about the phrase that the גְּמָרָא will use to introduce the רְאָיָה. If you just read the words, it can sound like the גְּמָרָא is simply repeating what we said in the בְּרַיְיתָא. However, when read with the proper tone, these words show that the גְּמָרָא is challenging that which we said. It is therefore very important to read them with the proper tone. This tone is called "בִּתְמִיָה".

And when better ones are found	**וְכִי נִמְצְאוּ יָפוֹת מֵהֶן**
his תְּרוּמָה is [considered] תְּרוּמָה?!	**תְּרוּמָתוֹ תְּרוּמָה**

Now the גְּמָרָא will explain why the above statement of the בְּרַיְיתָא seems not to be correct:

Why [is that so]?	**אַמַּאי**
At the time	**בְּעִידָּנָא**
that [the friend] separated the תְּרוּמָה	**דְּתָרַם**
[the owner] did not know?!	**הָא לָא הֲוָה יָדַע**

The גְּמָרָא asks that the הֲלָכָה in the בְּרַיְיתָא seems illogical. How can תְּרוּמָה be separated from a person's produce without his knowledge (even if later we see that he was okay with it)? The answer to this question will be a proof

for the שִׁיטָה of רָבָא. However, the גְּמָרָא doesn't directly tell us the answer. Instead, the גְּמָרָא assumes that we can figure out the answer on our own. It seems to be the following:

While the friend was separating תְּרוּמָה, the owner **would have agreed** to what his friend was doing, **if he would have known** about it. Therefore, **we consider it as if he agreed to it when it actually happened**.

We can now apply this logic to יֵאוּשׁ. It seems that the בְּרַיְיתָא would tell us that in a case where the owner **would have been מְיָאֵשׁ if he would have known** that his object was lost (יֵאוּשׁ שֶׁלֹּא מִדַּעַת), **it is considered that he was מְיָאֵשׁ before**.

OWNER WALKED AWAY, LEAVING OBJECT BEHIND.
HE WOULD HAVE BEEN מְיָאֵשׁ IF HE KNEW IT WAS LOST.
יֵאוּשׁ IS CONSIDERED FROM THIS POINT

12:00 PM
1:00 PM
2:00 PM
3:00 PM
4:00 PM
5:00 PM

OWNER WAS ACTUALLY מְיָאֵשׁ

Finder MAY keep it, because we consider it as if יֵאוּשׁ has already happened.

שִׁיטָה שֶׁל רָבָא

STEP SUMMARY

ראיה	
The Object THE THING WHICH WE ARE PROVING	The שיטה of ________ יאוש שלא מדעת ________
The Support THE STATEMENT OR LOGIC WHICH PROVES THE OBJECT	The words of the ברייתא ____ת ____ת ____א ____י ____ו ____א

STEP 28

In this step, the גְּמָרָא will reject the רְאָיָה by teaching us what we were incorrectly assuming. However, we will also see a little bit of the greatness of the אֲמוֹרָאִים.

Often, when people argue, their main goal is to be right and win the argument. They might not be as concerned about finding the actual truth of the matter. They just want to win. It is possible that someone might mistakenly think that this is the way the חֲכָמִים argued. However, in this step we will clearly see that it was not so. The גְּמָרָא taught a proof for the שִׁיטָה of רָבָא, which was a קַשְׁיָא for the שִׁיטָה of אַבַּיֵי. However, רָבָא realized that the proof was based on an assumption, so he himself taught everyone that the proof was not good. Clearly, his main goal was to uncover the truth, and not just to win the argument.

Now let's learn what רָבָא said:

רָבָא explained that we were making an assumption. Our הֲוָה אַמִינָא was that in the case of the בְּרַיְיתָא, the owner had no idea that his friend was separating תְּרוּמָה from his produce. However, רָבָא explains that אַבַּיֵי can explain the בְּרַיְיתָא differently:

רָבָא interpreted [the case]	**תַּרְגְּמָהּ רָבָא**
according to [the שִׁיטָה of] אַבַּיֵי,	**אַלִּיבָּא דְאַבַּיֵי**
that he appointed him as a שָׁלִיחַ (an agent).	**דְּשַׁוְיֵהּ שָׁלִיחַ**

רָבָא provides the מַסְקָנָא which corrects the הֲוָה אַמִינָא. He explains that the owner appointed his friend as a שָׁלִיחַ. A שָׁלִיחַ is someone who is appointed to do something for someone else. When a שָׁלִיחַ does something, it is considered as if the person who appointed him had done the action. As the חֲכָמִים teach us, "שְׁלוּחוֹ שֶׁל אָדָם כְּמוֹתוֹ - the שָׁלִיחַ of a person is like [the person] himself." *

*In English, a שָׁלִיחַ is called "an agent." Nowadays, besides for doing מִצְוֹת, people send agents for many other tasks, such as making deals and signing contracts.

We were assuming that in the case of the בְּרַיְיתָא, the owner didn't know that his friend was separating תְּרוּמָה. רָבָא teaches us that this is not so; the owner appointed his friend to separate תְּרוּמָה and obviously knew that he was going to do it. Therefore, this case cannot be compared to a case of יֵאוּשׁ שֶׁלֹּא מִדַּעַת (because nothing happened without the owner's knowledge), and is not a רַאֲיָה for either שִׁיטָה.

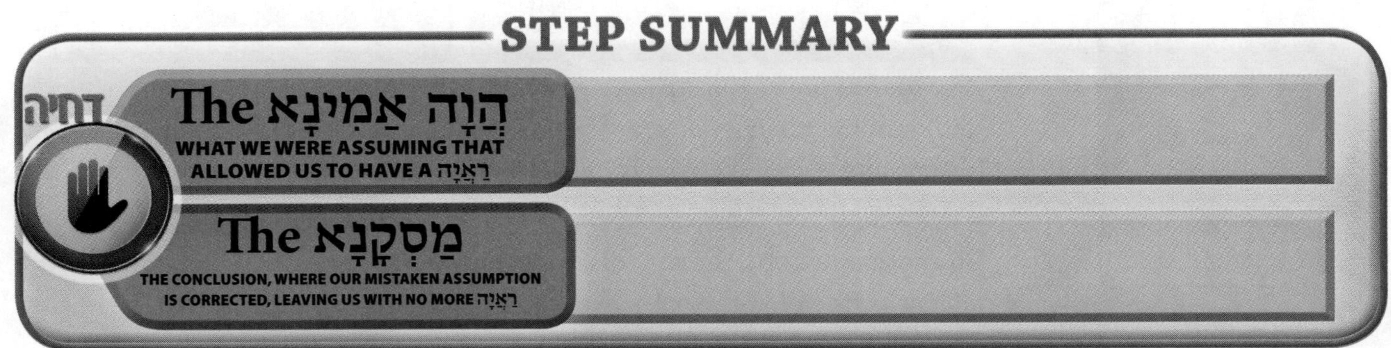

STEP 29

This step is a רְאָיָה. However, it is not the next רְאָיָה to either of the שִׁיטוֹת in the סוּגְיָא of יֵאוּשׁ שֶׁלֹּא מִדַּעַת. It does not prove the שִׁיטָה of רָבָא or the שִׁיטָה of אַבַּיֵי. Rather, it proves what we said in the דְּחִיָּה (Step 28). In that step, רָבָא said that אַבַּיֵי could explain that the בְּרַיְיתָא was discussing a case where the בַּעַל הַבַּיִת made the other person a שָׁלִיחַ. In this step, we will prove that the בְּרַיְיתָא was definitely discussing such a case. The גְּמָרָא introduces the proof:

It is also logical [to say] so,	**ה"נ (הָכִי נַמִּי) מִסְתַּבְּרָא**

It is logical to say that the בְּרַיְיתָא was discussing a case in which the owner appointed his friend to be a שָׁלִיחַ to separate תְּרוּמָה.

because if you will think	**דְּאִי ס"ד (סָלְקָא דַעְתָּךְ)**
that [it is a case where] he did not appoint him as a שָׁלִיחַ,	**דְּלֹא שַׁוְּיֵהּ שָׁלִיחַ**
would it be	**מִי הַוְיָא**
[that] his תְּרוּמָה is [considered] תְּרוּמָה?!	**תְּרוּמָתוֹ תְּרוּמָה**

Sometimes, in order to prove something, the גְּמָרָא will prove that the opposite of that thing cannot be true. If there are only two possibilities, and one of them cannot be true, the other one must be true. In the case of our בְּרַיְיתָא, there are only two possibilities. Either the owner appointed his friend as a שָׁלִיחַ to separate תְּרוּמָה or he did not appoint him as a שָׁלִיחַ.

POSSIBILITY 1

POSSIBILITY 2

In order to prove that the בְּרַיְיתָא was discussing a case in which the owner did appoint his friend as a שָׁלִיחַ, we will prove that the בְּרַיְיתָא cannot be discussing a case in which he didn't. However, before we can learn the proof, we need to learn a bit of background information.

In another מַסֶּכְתָּא*, the גְּמָרָא discusses how we know that a person can appoint a שָׁלִיחַ. After all, if the תּוֹרָה gives me a מִצְוָה to do something (like separating תְּרוּמָה), what right do I have to appoint someone else to do it for me?

*קִידּוּשִׁין מא:

In order to understand this, let's review what we learned all the way back in *Introduction to* גְּמָרָא, Lesson 1:

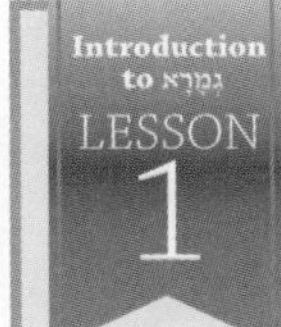

However, for some of the הֲלָכוֹת*, Hashem instructed* מֹשֶׁה *to only write a hint in the* תּוֹרָה שֶׁבִּכְתָב *(such as an extra letter or word). For these* הֲלָכוֹת*, the actual* הֲלָכָה *would be part of* תּוֹרָה שֶׁבְּעַל פֶּה *(Torah that was taught orally).*

The הֲלָכָה that someone can appoint a שָׁלִיחַ to do a מִצְוָה for him is taught with a hint in תּוֹרָה שֶׁבִּכְתָב. First, let's learn a פָּסוּק. The פָּסוּק is teaching about the מִצְוָה of תְּרוּמָה**. The פָּסוּק says the following:

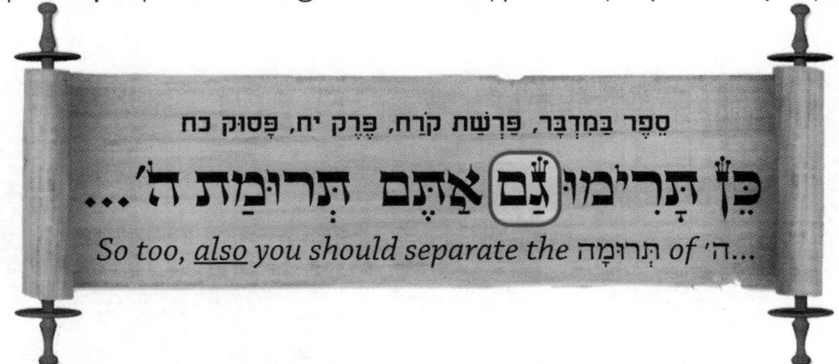

The חֲכָמִים explain that the word "גַם - also" seems extra. After all, the פָּסוּק would make perfect sense if it had just said "כֵּן תָּרִימוּ אַתֶּם תְּרוּמַת ה' - So too, you should separate the תְּרוּמָה of ה'." Therefore, the extra word "גַם" must be hinting to an additional הֲלָכָה. The additional הֲלָכָה is that someone may also appoint a שָׁלִיחַ to separate תְּרוּמָה for him.

It is important to realize that a שָׁלִיחַ's ability to separate תְּרוּמָה is connected to the בַּעַל הַבַּיִת's ability to separate תְּרוּמָה. In other words, whatever the owner can do, his שָׁלִיחַ can "also" do.

Now, the גְּמָרָא will explain:

But,	**וְהָא**
[the תּוֹרָה could have said] "אַתֶּם"	**אַתֶּם**
[however,] the תּוֹרָה said "גַם אַתֶּם"	**גַם אַתֶּם אָמַר רַחֲמָנָא**
[in order] to include your שָׁלִיחַ.	**לְרַבּוֹת שְׁלוּחֲכֶם**

Now that we have learned how the תּוֹרָה teaches us that a person can appoint a שָׁלִיחַ, the גְּמָרָא explains that there is a limit to what a שָׁלִיחַ can do:

Just like you	**מַה אַתֶּם**
[separate תְּרוּמָה] with your knowledge,	**לְדַעְתְּכֶם**
so too, your שָׁלִיחַ	**אַף שְׁלוּחֲכֶם**
[can only separate תְּרוּמָה] with your knowledge.	**לְדַעְתְּכֶם**

**This פָּסוּק is actually discussing a specific type of תְּרוּמָה called תְּרוּמַת מַעֲשֵׂר. This was תְּרוּמָה which a לֵוִי had to give to a כֹּהֵן from the מַעֲשֵׂר that he himself had received from a יִשְׂרָאֵל. However, the הֲלָכוֹת learned out from the hint in this פָּסוּק apply to all kinds of תְּרוּמָה and other מִצְוֹת as well.

The שָׁלִיחַ is "also" able to separate תְּרוּמָה. This means that he can only do what the owner can do. The owner can (obviously) only separate תְּרוּמָה when he knows that the תְּרוּמָה is being separated. Therefore, a שָׁלִיחַ can "also" separate תְּרוּמָה as long as the owner knows about it.

In the case of our בְּרַיְיתָא, if the owner did not appoint his friend as a שָׁלִיחַ (and didn't know what his friend was doing), the תְּרוּמָה that was separated wouldn't be considered תְּרוּמָה. However, the בְּרַיְיתָא said that it is considered תְּרוּמָה. Therefore, the only way that the בְּרַיְיתָא can make sense is if it was discussing a case in which the owner did appoint his friend as a שָׁלִיחַ (and knew about the תְּרוּמָה that was being separated). Because he knew about it, the תְּרוּמָה that was separated is considered תְּרוּמָה.

In this רְאָיָה, the object is רָבָא's interpretation of the בְּרַיְיתָא that the case is "דְּשַׁוְּיֵהּ שָׁלִיחַ". The support is the דְּרָשָׁה which teaches us that a שָׁלִיחַ can only separate תְּרוּמָה with the knowledge of the בַּעַל הַבַּיִת.

STEP 30

Although this step is a מַסְקָנָא, it is not the conclusion of the סוּגְיָא. Rather, it is only the conclusion of our discussion of the case of the בְּרַיְיתָא.

Rather,	**אֶלָּא**
with what [case] are we dealing here?	**הָכָא בְּמַאי עַסְקִינַן**
With a case	**כְּגוֹן**
that he appointed him as a שָׁלִיחַ,	**דְּשַׁוְּיֵהּ שָׁלִיחַ**

As part of the מַסְקָנָא, the גְּמָרָא will continue to teach the final, accepted explanation of the הֲלָכוֹת in the בְּרַיְיתָא*:

and [the homeowner] said to [the שָׁלִיחַ],	וְא״ל (וְאָמַר לֵיהּ)
"Go separate תְּרוּמָה,"	זִיל תְּרוֹם
and he did not say to him	וְלֹא א״ל (אָמַר לֵיהּ)
"Separate תְּרוּמָה from these [specific ones],"	תְּרוֹם מֵהַנֵּי
and the regular [way] of the homeowner [is]	וּסְתָמֵיהּ דְּבַעַל הַבַּיִת
when he separates תְּרוּמָה	כִּי תָּרוֹם
he separates from the average [quality produce],	מִבֵּינוֹנִית הוּא תָּרוֹם
and he (the שָׁלִיחַ) went	וְאָזַל אִיהוּ
and separated תְּרוּמָה from the better ones,	וְתָרַם מִיָּפוֹת
and the homeowner came	וּבָא בַּעַל הַבַּיִת
and found him (the שָׁלִיחַ)	וּמְצָאוֹ
and said to him,	וְא״ל (וְאָמַר לֵיהּ)
"You should have gone to the better ones [to take תְּרוּמָה]."	כְּלַךְ אֵצֶל יָפוֹת
If better ones are found,	אִם נִמְצְאוּ יָפוֹת מֵהֶן
his תְּרוּמָה is [considered] תְּרוּמָה,	תְּרוּמָתוֹ תְּרוּמָה
and if [better ones are] not [found],	וְאִם לָאו
his תְּרוּמָה is not [considered] תְּרוּמָה.	אֵין תְּרוּמָתוֹ תְּרוּמָה

Although the שָׁלִיחַ was appointed to separate תְּרוּמָה, the בַּעַל הַבַּיִת did not tell him which produce to separate. When the שָׁלִיחַ separated the תְּרוּמָה, he didn't do it the way that the בַּעַל הַבַּיִת normally separates his own תְּרוּמָה. This בַּעַל הַבַּיִת would usually separate תְּרוּמָה from his average-quality produce and the שָׁלִיחַ separated from the high-quality produce. That is what the בְּרַיְיתָא meant when it said (in the last שִׁיעוּר) that he separated "שֶׁלֹּא מִדַּעַת - without the owner's knowledge." The בְּרַיְיתָא didn't mean that the owner did not know that his friend was separating תְּרוּמָה; of course he knew - he had appointed him as a שָׁלִיחַ! Rather, the בְּרַיְיתָא meant that the owner did not know that he would separate from the high-quality produce. For that reason, the בְּרַיְיתָא tells us that we have to determine if the בַּעַל הַבַּיִת was okay with what the שָׁלִיחַ did. If he was okay with it, the תְּרוּמָה separation counts. On the other hand, if he was not okay with it, the produce that was separated is not considered תְּרוּמָה.

At this point, we have proven that the בְּרַיְיתָא is not discussing a case that can be compared to יֵאוּשׁ שֶׁלֹּא מִדַּעַת. Therefore, we have no רְאָיָה to either שִׁיטָה.

*Typically, a מַסְקָנָא is a brief final decision/conclusion about something that we discussed. However, in this case, the מַסְקָנָא also provides the final, accepted explanation.

PUT IT ALL TOGETHER:

1. Read, translate and explain the following גְּמָרָא.

ת״ש *כֵּיצַד אָמְרוּ הַתּוֹרֵם שֶׁלֹּא
מִדַּעַת תְּרוּמָתוֹ תְּרוּמָה ב׳הֲרֵי שֶׁיָּרַד לְתוֹךְ
שְׂדֵה חֲבֵירוֹ וְלִיקֵּט וְתָרַם שֶׁלֹּא בִּרְשׁוּת אִם
חוֹשֵׁשׁ מִשּׁוּם גֶּזֶל אֵין תְּרוּמָתוֹ תְּרוּמָה וְאִם
לָאו תְּרוּמָתוֹ תְּרוּמָה וּמִנַּיִן הוּא יוֹדֵעַ אִם
חוֹשֵׁשׁ מִשּׁוּם גֶּזֶל וְאִם לָאו ג׳הֲרֵי שֶׁבָּא בַּעַל
הַבַּיִת וּמְצָאוֹ וְאָמַר לוֹ *כְּלַךְ אֵצֶל יָפוֹת
אִם נִמְצְאוּ יָפוֹת מֵהֶן תְּרוּמָתוֹ תְּרוּמָה וְאִם
לָאו אֵין תְּרוּמָתוֹ תְּרוּמָה ד׳לִיקְּטוּ הַבְּעָלִים
וְהוֹסִיפוּ עֲלֵיהֶן בֵּין כָּךְ וּבֵין כָּךְ תְּרוּמָתוֹ
תְּרוּמָה וְכִי נִמְצְאוּ יָפוֹת מֵהֶן תְּרוּמָתוֹ תְּרוּמָה
אַמַּאי בְּעִידְנָא דְּתָרַם הָא לָא הֲוָה יָדַע
*תִּרְגְּמָהּ רָבָא אַלִּיבָּא דְּאַבַּיֵּי °דְּשַׁוְּיֵהּ שָׁלִיחַ
[א]ה״נ מִסְתַּבְּרָא דְּאִי ס״ד דְּלָא שַׁוְּיֵהּ שָׁלִיחַ מִי
הַוְיָא תְּרוּמָתוֹ תְּרוּמָה וְהָא אַתֶּם °גַּם אַתֶּם
אָמַר רַחֲמָנָא *ה׳לְרַבּוֹת שְׁלוּחֲכֶם מָה אַתֶּם
לְדַעְתְּכֶם אַף שְׁלוּחֲכֶם לְדַעְתְּכֶם אֶלָּא הָכָא
בְּמַאי עַסְקִינָן כְּגוֹן דְּשַׁוְּיֵהּ שָׁלִיחַ וְא״ל זִיל
תְּרוֹם וְלָא א״ל תְּרוֹם מֵהַנֵּי וּסְתָמֵיהּ דְּבַעַל
הַבַּיִת כִּי תָּרוּם מִבֵּינוֹנִית הוּא תָּרוּם וְאָזַל
אִיהוּ וְתָרַם מִיָּפוֹת וּבָא בַּעַל הַבַּיִת וּמְצָאוֹ
וְא״ל כְּלַךְ אֵצֶל יָפוֹת אִם נִמְצְאוּ יָפוֹת מֵהֶן
תְּרוּמָתוֹ תְּרוּמָה וְאִם לָאו אֵין תְּרוּמָתוֹ תְּרוּמָה

2. In the last שִׁיעוּר, we learned a בְּרַיְיתָא. The בְּרַיְיתָא discusses the הֲלָכָה if someone ____________________ from someone else's _______________. The חֲכָמִים taught that in this case, sometimes _______________ and sometimes ___________. The בְּרַיְיתָא taught the following rule: If the owner considers the other person's actions to be __________, then ________________. However, if the owner doesn't consider the other person's actions to be _________, then __________________. The בְּרַיְיתָא tells us that we can figure out what the owner thinks, if the owner said "______________________." If there were ____________________ then the owner meant it ___________ and the הֲלָכָה is that _________________. However, if there were not __________________ then the owner meant it _______________ and the הֲלָכָה is that ______________________.

3. How does the גְּמָרָא compare a הֲלָכָה in this בְּרַיְיתָא to the case of יֵאוּשׁ שֶׁלֹּא מִדַּעַת?

____

____

4. Please fill in the chart based on the רַאֲיָה (Step 27) and דְּחִיָּה of this שִׁיעוּר.

ראיה	The Object	
	The Support	
דחיה	The הֲוָה אַמִינָא	
	The מַסְקָנָא	

5. Which אֲמוֹרָא taught the דְּחִיָּה? ______________________________

6. What do we see from this? ______________________________

7. Step 29 is a רַאֲיָה. What are the object and support of that רַאֲיָה?

ראיה	The Object	
	The Support	

8. Step 30 is a מַסְקָנָא. The גְּמָרָא concludes that ______________________________ .

9. Explain the way we understand the בְּרַיְיתָא at the end of the שִׁיעוּר: The owner told the שָׁלִיחַ to ____________________ but he did not tell him ____________________. The בַּעַל הַבַּיִת would normally separate תְּרוּמָה from ____________________, but the שָׁלִיחַ separated from ____________________. The הֲלָכָה is that if the owner said ____________________, we look and see. If there were ____________________, then ____________________. If there were not ____________________, then ____________________.

10. At the end of the שִׁיעוּר - what have we successfully proven? (circle one)

a. the שִׁיטָה of אַבַּיֵי   b. the שִׁיטָה of רָבָא   c. nothing

VOCABULARY REVIEW:

נִיחָא ______________________________

מִילְּתָא ______________________________

אַשְׁכַּח ______________________________

מַר ______________________________

IDENTIFY THE STEPS:

BE SURE TO INCLUDE EVERY WORD.

ת"ש *כֵּיצַד אָמְרוּ הַתּוֹרֵם שֶׁלֹּא
מִדַּעַת תְּרוּמָתוֹ תְּרוּמָה גהֲרֵי שֶׁיָּרַד לְתוֹךְ
שְׂדֵה חֲבֵירוֹ וְלִיקֵּט וְתָרַם שֶׁלֹּא בִּרְשׁוּת אִם
חוֹשֵׁשׁ מִשּׁוּם גָּזֵל אֵין תְּרוּמָתוֹ תְּרוּמָה וְאִם
לַאו תְּרוּמָתוֹ תְּרוּמָה וּמִנַּיִן הוּא יוֹדֵעַ אִם
חוֹשֵׁשׁ מִשּׁוּם גָּזֵל וְאִם לַאו דהֲרֵי שֶׁבָּא בַּעַל
הַבַּיִת וּמְצָאוֹ וְאָמַר לוֹ *כְּלַךְ אֵצֶל יָפוֹת
אִם נִמְצְאוּ יָפוֹת מֵהֶן תְּרוּמָתוֹ תְּרוּמָה וְאִם
לַאו אֵין תְּרוּמָתוֹ תְּרוּמָה יליִקְּטוּ הַבְּעָלִים
וְהוֹסִיפוּ עֲלֵיהֶן בֵּין כַּךְ וּבֵין כַּךְ תְּרוּמָתוֹ
תְּרוּמָה וְכִי נִמְצְאוּ יָפוֹת מֵהֶן תְּרוּמָתוֹ תְּרוּמָה
אַמַּאי בְּעִידְּנָא דְּתָרַם הָא לֹא הֲוָה יָדַע
*תִּרְגְּמָהּ רָבָא אַלִּיבָּא דְּאַבַּיֵי דְּשַׁוְּיֵהּ שָׁלִיחַ
[א]ה"נ מִסְתַּבְּרָא דְּאִי ס"ד דְּלֹא שַׁוְּיֵהּ שָׁלִיחַ מִי
הַוְיָא תְּרוּמָתוֹ תְּרוּמָה וְהָא אַתֶּם °גַּם אַתֶּם
אָמַר רַחֲמָנָא *הלְרַבּוֹת שְׁלוּחֲכֶם מַה אַתֶּם
לְדַעְתְּכֶם אַף שְׁלוּחֲכֶם לְדַעְתְּכֶם אֶלָּא הָכָא
בְּמַאי עַסְקִינָן כְּגוֹן דְּשַׁוְּיֵהּ שָׁלִיחַ וְא"ל זִיל
תְּרוֹם וְלֹא א"ל תְּרוֹם מֵהַנֵּי וּסְתָמֵיהּ דְּבַעַל
הַבַּיִת כִּי תָּרוּם מִבֵּינוֹנִית הוּא תָּרוּם וְאָזַל
אִיהוּ וְתָרַם מִיָּפוֹת וּבָא בַּעַל הַבַּיִת וּמְצָאוֹ
וְא"ל כְּלַךְ אֵצֶל יָפוֹת אִם נִמְצְאוּ יָפוֹת מֵהֶן
תְּרוּמָתוֹ תְּרוּמָה וְאִם לַאו אֵין תְּרוּמָתוֹ תְּרוּמָה

Please (**parenthesize**) the first רַאֲיָה

Please **underline** the דְחִיָה

Please [**bracket**] the second רַאֲיָה

Please **box** the מַסְקָנָא

 |

MATCHING:

(HINT: ONE CHOICE IS USED THREE TIMES.)

_____ 1. Object of the first רַאֲיָה

_____ 2. Support of the first רַאֲיָה

_____ 3. The הֲוָה אַמִינָא (part of the דְחִיָה)

_____ 4. The מַסְקָנָא (part of the דְחִיָה)

_____ 5. Object of the second רַאֲיָה

_____ 6. Support of the second רַאֲיָה

_____ 7. What the תּוֹרָה could have said

_____ 8. What the תּוֹרָה said

_____ 9. Conclusion of the גְמָרָא

_____ 10. What the owner told the שָׁלִיחַ

_____ 11. What the owner didn't tell the שָׁלִיחַ

_____ 12. Produce that the owner usually separates

_____ 13. Produce that the שָׁלִיחַ separated

_____ 14. He taught the דְחִיָה

א. רָבָא

ב. אַתֶּם

ג. זִיל תְּרוֹם

ד. אִם נִמְצְאוּ יָפוֹת מֵהֶן תְּרוּמָתוֹ תְּרוּמָה

ה. מַה אַתֶּם לְדַעְתְּכֶם אַף שְׁלוּחֲכֶם לְדַעְתְּכֶם

ו. גַּם אַתֶּם

ז. דְשַׁוְיֵה שָׁלִיחַ

ח. יֵאוּשׁ שֶׁלֹּא מִדַּעַת הֲוֵי יֵאוּשׁ

ט. בֵּינוֹנִית

י. תְּרוֹם מֵהַנֵּי

יא. The owner didn't know that תְּרוּמָה was being separated

יב. יָפוֹת

שיעור
כ
כב. lines 37-44

This שִׁיעוּר will not be discussing the topic of יֵאוּשׁ שֶׁלֹּא מִדַּעַת. Instead, the גְּמָרָא gets "sidetracked" by something that we mentioned in שִׁיעוּר י"ט (it is quite common for the גְּמָרָא to do this). But don't worry — we will get back to the exciting debate of יֵאוּשׁ שֶׁלֹּא מִדַּעַת in the next שִׁיעוּר!

STEP 31

The גְּמָרָא tells us a story that happened to some of the אֲמוֹרָאִים:

רַב אַשִׁי and אֲמֵימַר, מַר זוּטְרָא	אֲמֵימַר וּמַר זוּטְרָא וְרַב אַשִׁי
arrived	אִקְלַעוּ
at the orchard of מָרִי בַּר אִיסַק.	לְבוּסְתְּנָא דְמָרִי בַּר אִיסַק
His sharecropper* brought	אַיְיתֵי אֲרִיסֵיהּ
dates and pomegranates	תַּמְרֵי וְרִימּוֹנֵי
and placed [them] before them.	וְשָׁדָא קַמַּיְיהוּ
אֲמֵימַר and רַב אַשִׁי ate [the fruits]	אֲמֵימַר וְרַב אַשִׁי אַכְלֵי
[but] מַר זוּטְרָא did not eat them.	מַר זוּטְרָא לֹא אָכִיל

It seems that מַר זוּטְרָא didn't eat the fruits because the sharecropper did not have מָרִי בַּר אִיסַק's permission to give the fruits to the guests. מַר זוּטְרָא considered these fruits to be stolen from מָרִי בַּר אִיסַק.

The story continues:

Meanwhile,	אַדְּהָכֵי
מָרִי בַּר אִיסַק came	אָתָא מָרִי בַּר אִיסַק
[and] found them	אַשְׁכְּחִינְהוּ
and he said to his sharecropper,	וְא"ל לַאֲרִיסֵיהּ
"Why	אַמַּאי
didn't you bring for the חֲכָמִים [to eat]	לֹא אַיְיתֵית לְהוּ לְרַבָּנָן
from those better ones?"	מֵהַנָךְ שַׁפִּירָתָא

From the fact that מָרִי בַּר אִיסַק said that the sharecropper should have given the חֲכָמִים from "those" better ones, it seems clear that there were

VOCABULARY WORDS

83. שַׁאנִי

84. רָמִי

אלו מציאות
פרק שני
בבא מציעא

*A sharecropper is a worker who is hired to grow crops in someone's field. At the end of the season, the sharecropper and the owner of the field share the crops that grew.

better ones. It seems that מָרִי בַּר אִיסַק sincerely meant that he wished that the sharecropper had given the חֲכָמִים from the better fruits. He was not being sarcastic.

STEP 32

Even after מָרִי בַּר אִיסַק came and said that the sharecropper should have given better fruits, מַר זוּטְרָא still didn't eat the fruits. This was difficult for אֲמֵימַר and רַב אַשִׁי to understand. In fact, מַר זוּטְרָא refusing to eat the fruits is the target of their קַשְׁיָא:

רַב אַשִׁי and אֲמֵימַר said to מַר זוּטְרָא,	**אָמְרוּ לֵיהּ אֲמֵימַר וְרַב אַשִׁי לְמַר זוּטְרָא**
"Now,	**הַשְׁתָּא**
why didn't the master eat [from the fruit]?	**אַמַּאי לֹא אָכִיל מַר**
Didn't the בְּרַיְיתָא teach	**וְהָתַנְיָא**
'If better ones are found	**אִם נִמְצְאוּ יָפוֹת מֵהֶן**
his תְּרוּמָה is [considered] תְּרוּמָה'!?"	**תְּרוּמָתוֹ תְּרוּמָה**

The בְּרַיְיתָא (which we learned in שִׁיעוּר י״ח) teaches that when the owner says "כְּלַךְ אֵצֶל יָפוֹת", if there actually were better fruits available, we assume that the owner was being sincere. Here too, when מָרִי בַּר אִיסַק told the sharecropper that he should have given better fruits, there were better fruits available. Therefore, we can assume that he was being sincere. Certainly, he did not mind that the sharecropper had given the fruits. What reason could מַר זוּטְרָא possibly have for still not eating?

As we said earlier, the target of the קַשְׁיָא is the fact that מַר זוּטְרָא still didn't eat the fruit. The attack is the words in the בְּרַיְיתָא:

STEP 33

מַר זוּטְרָא explains to his friends why he still believed that it was wrong to eat the fruit. The הֲוָה אַמִינָא of אֲמֵימַר and רַב אַשִׁי was that the הֲלָכָה of the בְּרַיְיתָא (which discussed the מִצְוָה of תְּרוּמָה) would also apply in this story. מַר זוּטְרָא corrects this הֲוָה אַמִינָא by explaining that the two cases are not comparable:

שיעור כ

כב. lines 37-44

Continued

He (מַר זוּטְרָא) said to them (רַב אַשִׁי and אֲמֵימַר),	**אָמַר לְהוּ**
So said רָבָא:	**הָכִי אָמַר רָבָא**
"[The חֲכָמִים] didn't say	**לֹא אָמְרוּ**
[the rules of] כְּלַךְ אֵצֶל יָפוֹת,	**כְּלַךְ אֵצֶל יָפוֹת**
except in the case of תְּרוּמָה alone,	**אֶלָּא לְעִנְיַן תְּרוּמָה בִּלְבַד**
because it is a מִצְוָה	**מִשּׁוּם דְּמִצְוָה הוּא**
and it is pleasing for him [to do a מִצְוָה]."	**וְנִיחָא לֵיהּ**
But here (by מָרִי בַּר אִיסַק),	**אֲבָל הָכָא**
it is because of embarrassment	**מִשּׁוּם כְּסִיפוּתָא הוּא**
that he said so.	**דְּאָמַר הָכִי**

מַר זוּטְרָא taught his friends what רָבָא had said. רָבָא explained that we only assume that the owner sincerely wanted to give better fruits when it is a מִצְוָה (like תְּרוּמָה). However, in this story, it is likely that מָרִי בַּר אִיסַק really was upset with his sharecropper for giving fruit. He only told the sharecropper to give better fruits because he would have been too embarrassed to admit that he didn't really want to give the fruit to the חֲכָמִים. In truth, he was being sarcastic. For that reason, מַר זוּטְרָא refused to eat the fruits; he considered them to be stolen from מָרִי בַּר אִיסַק.

VOCABULARY REVIEW:

שַׁאנִי	______	מִילְתָא	______
רָמֵי	______	טוּבָא	______
נִיחָא	______	בָּצִיר	______

PUT IT ALL TOGETHER:

1. Read, translate and explain the following גְּמָרָא.

אֲמֵימַר וּמַר זוּטְרָא וְרַב אַשִׁי
אִקְלַעוּ °לְבוּסְתְּנָא דְּמָרִי בַּר אִיסַק אַיְיתֵי אֲרִיסֵיהּ תַּמְרֵי וְרִימּוֹנֵי וְשָׁדָא קַמַּיְיהוּ
אֲמֵימַר וְרַב אַשִׁי אַכְלֵי מַר זוּטְרָא לֹא אָכִיל אַדְּהָכֵי אָתָא מָרִי בַּר אִיסַק
אַשְׁכְּחִינְהוּ וְא"ל לַאֲרִיסֵיהּ אַמַּאי לֹא אַיְיתֵית לְהוּ לְרַבָּנָן מֵהַנָךְ שַׁפִּירָתָא
אָמְרוּ לֵיהּ אֲמֵימַר וְרַב אַשִׁי לְמַר זוּטְרָא הַשְׁתָּא אַמַּאי לֹא אָכִיל מַר
וְהָתַנְיָא אִם נִמְצְאוּ יָפוֹת מֵהֶן תְּרוּמָתוֹ תְּרוּמָה אָמַר לְהוּ הָכִי אָמַר רָבָא
לֹא אָמְרוּ כְּלַךְ אֵצֶל יָפוֹת אֶלָּא לְעִנְיַן תְּרוּמָה בִּלְבַד מִשּׁוּם דְּמִצְוָה
הוּא וְנִיחָא לֵיהּ אֲבָל הָכָא מִשּׁוּם כְּסִיפוּתָא הוּא דְּאָמַר הָכִי

2. In this שִׁיעוּר, the גְּמָרָא was “sidetracked” and did not discuss the topic of ______.
3. Which three אֲמוֹרָאִים went somewhere? a. ______ b. ______ c. ______
4. Where did they go? ______
5. Who brought out fruit? ______
6. Who ate the fruit? ______
7. Who didn’t eat the fruit? ______
8. What did the owner say when he arrived? ______
9. Please fill in the chart based on the קַשְׁיָא and תֵּירוּץ of this שִׁיעוּר.

The Target	
The Attack	
The הֲוָה אַמִינָא	
The מַסְקָנָא	

IDENTIFY THE STEPS:

BE SURE TO INCLUDE EVERY WORD.

אֲמֵימַר וּמַר זוּטְרָא וְרַב אַשִׁי
אִקְלַעוּ °לְבוּסְתָּנָא דְּמָרִי בַּר אִיסַק אַיְיתֵי אֲרִיסֵיהּ תַּמְרֵי וְרִימּוֹנֵי וְשַׁדָא קַמַּיְיהוּ
אֲמֵימַר וְרַב אַשִׁי אַכְלֵי מַר זוּטְרָא לֹא אָכִיל אַדְּהָכֵי אָתָא מָרִי בַּר אִיסַק
אַשְׁכְּחִינְהוּ וְא״ל לַאֲרִיסֵיהּ אַמַּאי לֹא אַיְיתֵית לְהוּ לְרַבָּנָן מֵהַנָךְ שַׁפִּירָתָא
אָמְרוּ לֵיהּ אֲמֵימַר וְרַב אַשִׁי לְמַר זוּטְרָא הַשְׁתָּא אַמַּאי לֹא אָכִיל מַר
וְהָתַנְיָא אִם נִמְצְאוּ יָפוֹת מֵהֶן תְּרוּמָתוֹ תְּרוּמָה אָמַר לְהוּ הָכִי אָמַר רָבָא
לֹא אָמְרוּ כְּלַךְ אֵצֶל יָפוֹת אֶלָּא לְעִנְיַן תְּרוּמָה בִּלְבַד מִשּׁוּם דְּמִצְוָה
הוּא וְנִיחָא לֵיהּ אֲבָל הָכָא מִשּׁוּם כְּסִיפוּתָא הוּא דְּאָמַר הָכִי

Please (**parenthesize**) the מֵימְרָא

Please <u>**underline**</u> the קֻשְׁיָא

Please [**bracket**] the תֵּירוּץ

MATCHING:

______	1. Target of the קֻשְׁיָא	א. מִשּׁוּם כְּסִיפוּתָא
______	2. Attack of the קֻשְׁיָא	ב. מַר זוּטְרָא לֹא אָכִיל
______	3. The הֲוָה אַמִינָא	ג. אֲמֵימַר וְרַב אַשִׁי
______	4. The מַסְקָנָא (part of the תֵּירוּץ)	ד. אִם נִמְצְאוּ יָפוֹת מֵהֶן תְּרוּמָתוֹ תְּרוּמָה
______	5. כְּלַךְ אֵצֶל יָפוֹת only applies ______	ה. לֹא אָמְרוּ כְּלַךְ אֵצֶל יָפוֹת אֶלָּא לְעִנְיַן תְּרוּמָה בִּלְבַד
______	6. How מַר זוּטְרָא explained why מָרִי בַּר אִיסַק said what he said	ו. לְעִנְיַן תְּרוּמָה בִּלְבַד
______	7. He taught when כְּלַךְ אֵצֶל יָפוֹת applies	ז. כְּלַךְ אֵצֶל יָפוֹת applies in all cases
______	8. He/they ate the fruit	ח. מַר זוּטְרָא
______	9. The other two אֲמוֹרָאִים asked ________ why he didn't eat the fruit	ט. אֲרִיסֵיהּ שֶׁל מָרִי בַּר אִיסַק
______	10. According to מַר זוּטְרָא, __________ was more generous than he should have been	י. רָבָא

כב. line 44-
כב: line 8

STEP 34

The גְּמָרָא attempts yet one more proof:

Come and hear [a proof from a בְּרַיְיתָא]: **תָּא שְׁמַע**

By now, you know that we have to learn the בְּרַיְיתָא and know it well before we can understand the proof. However, in this instance, we cannot even learn the בְּרַיְיתָא until we learn some background information about the topic of the בְּרַיְיתָא.

You may be familiar with the words "טָמֵא" and "טָהוֹר". When something is טָהוֹר we say that it is "spiritually pure." By contrast, when something is טָמֵא, we say that it is "spiritually impure." The הֲלָכוֹת of how someone or something becomes טָמֵא or טָהוֹר are taught in סֵדֶר טְהָרוֹת.

One specific type of טוּמְאָה is the טוּמְאָה that can come to food which has grown from the ground (or a tree). When food is growing from the ground (and is still attached to the plant or tree), it cannot become טָמֵא even if it touches something that is טָמֵא (such as a dead rodent).

VOCABULARY WORDS

85. תִּיוּבְתָּא

86. כַּוָּותֵיהּ

Even after the food is cut from the ground, it is still not able to become טָמֵא. As the תּוֹרָה tells us:

סֵפֶר וַיִּקְרָא, פָּרָשַׁת שְׁמִינִי, פֶּרֶק יא, פָּסוּק לז

וְכִי יִפֹּל מִנִּבְלָתָם עַל כָּל זֶרַע זֵרוּעַ אֲשֶׁר יִזָּרֵעַ טָהוֹר הוּא:

And if the dead body [of a rodent] falls on [food which grew from] a seed which has been planted, it [remains] טָהוֹר.

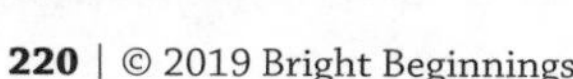

The next פָּסוּק teaches us how a food which has been harvested can be ״הוּכְשַׁר לְקַבֵּל טוּמְאָה״ - "prepared to accept טוּמְאָה":

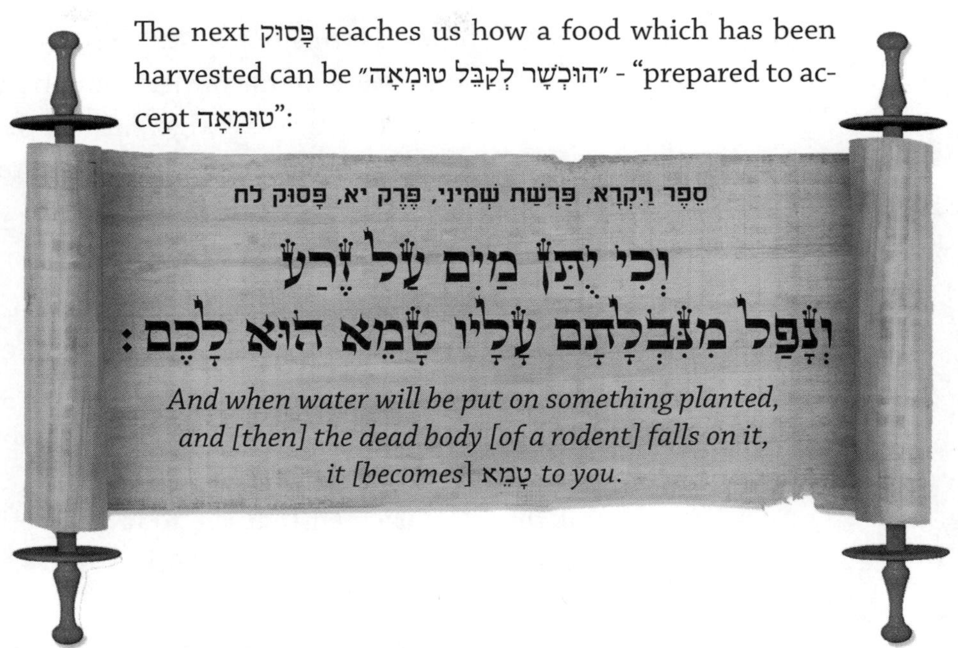

The חֲכָמִים explain this פָּסוּק in the following way:

If the owner of the food intentionally gets it wet, the food will be הוּכְשַׁר לְקַבֵּל טוּמְאָה. In other words, if the owner purposely pours liquid on his food, it becomes "prepared to accept טוּמְאָה" and it will become טָמֵא if it comes in contact with a טָמֵא object.

If, however, the food got wet but the owner did not want it to get wet, the food still cannot become טָמֵא – even if it touches something that is טָמֵא.

The חֲכָמִים refer to this rule as the rule of "כִּי יוּתַּן" (based on the words of the פָּסוּק). If the food becomes wet with the owner's intention, we say that the food is "included in the rule of כִּי יוּתַּן," which means that it is הוּכְשַׁר לְקַבֵּל טוּמְאָה. If, however, the owner did not want the food to get wet, we say that the food is "not included in the rule of כִּי יוּתַּן," which means that it is not הוּכְשַׁר לְקַבֵּל טוּמְאָה.

The בְּרַיְיתָא that we will learn discusses a situation in which the food got wet even though the owner did not intend for it to get wet. However, when the owner saw that the food had gotten wet, he was happy about it. The בְּרַיְיתָא will teach us whether this is considered that the food got wet with the owner's intention and is "included in the rule of כִּי יוּתַּן" (and is הוּכְשַׁר לְקַבֵּל טוּמְאָה), or if this is considered that the food got wet without the owner's intention and is "not included in the rule of כִּי יוּתַּן" (and is not הוּכְשַׁר לְקַבֵּל טוּמְאָה).

If the dew is still on them	**עוֹדֵהוּ הַטַּל עֲלֵיהֶן**
and [the owner] was happy,	**וְשָׂמַח**
this is	**הֲרֵי זֶה**
[included] in [the rule of] כִּי יוּתַּן.	**בְּכִי יוּתַּן**
If they had already dried [before the owner knew that dew had fallen on them],	**נִגְּבוּ**
even though he was happy,	**אַף עַל פִּי שֶׁשָּׂמַח**
they are not [included] in [the rule of] כִּי יוּתַּן.	**אֵינָן בְּכִי יוּתַּן**

The בְּרַיְיתָא has taught us that if the owner is happy that his produce is wet, it is considered as if he had actually made it wet.

However, if he doesn't know that it became wet until after it had already dried off, it doesn't matter if he is happy that it had gotten wet - it will not be הוּכְשַׁר לְקַבֵּל טוּמְאָה.

Now that we have properly learned the בְּרַיְיתָא, we will see how it can be used as a רַאֲיָה in our סוּגְיָא:

What is the reason [that if the owner did not know about the dew until after it had dried, the produce is not included in the rule of כִּי יוּתַּן]?	**טַעְמָא מַאי**
Isn't it	**לַאו**
because we don't say,	**מִשּׁוּם דְּלֹא אַמְרִינַן**
"Since the matter is revealed	**כֵּיוָן דְּאִיגְּלַאי מִילְּתָא**
that now it is pleasing to him,	**דְּהַשְׁתָּא נִיחָא לֵיהּ**
[we consider it as if] also in the beginning (when it got wet)	**מֵעִיקָּרָא נַמִּי**
it was pleasing to him"!?	**נִיחָא לֵיהּ**

When the owner found out that his produce had gotten wet, he was happy about it.

However, we don't say that it is considered as if he was happy about it all along (which would make the produce הוּכְשַׁר לְקַבֵּל טוּמְאָה). Similarly, when someone finds out that he lost an object, even if he is מְיָאֵשׁ immediately, we should not consider it as if he was מְיָאֵשׁ all along.

This is a רְאָיָה to the שִׁיטָה of אַבַּיֵי that יֵאוּשׁ שֶׁלֹּא מִדַּעַת לֹא הָוֵי יֵאוּשׁ.

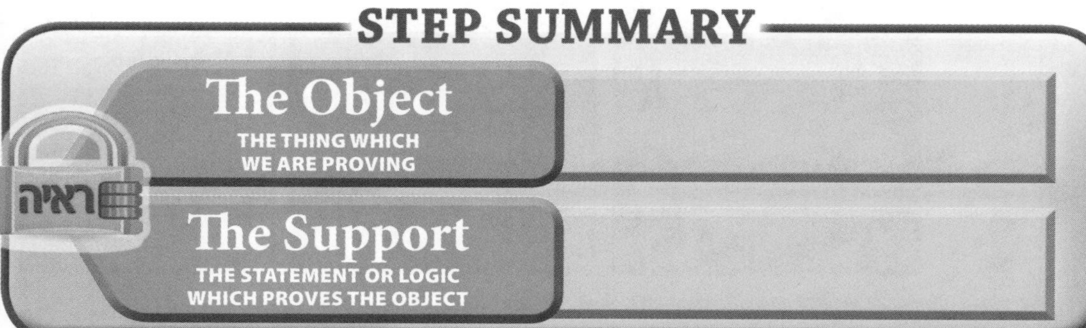

כְּתִיב and קְרִי

Usually, when we read the תּוֹרָה we look at the words that are written and read them. This probably seems obvious. However, it may surprise you to learn that there are times when this is not the case. In certain instances, what is written in the תּוֹרָה is not what we read from the תּוֹרָה.

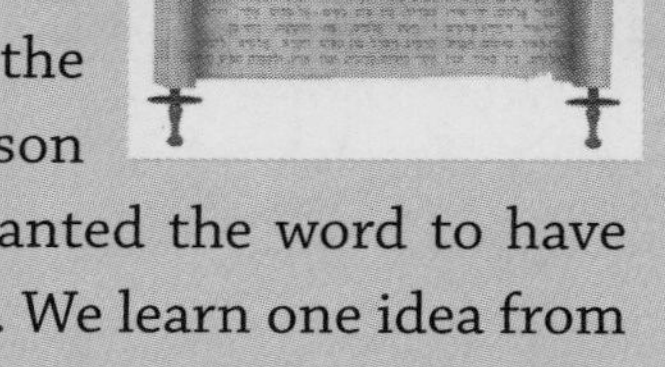

When מֹשֶׁה רַבֵּינוּ was at הַר סִינַי writing the תּוֹרָה, at certain points, ה' instructed him to write a specific word. However, ה' told him to read that word differently from the way he wrote it. The reason for this is because ה' wanted the word to have more than one meaning. We learn one idea from the כְּתִיב – the way the word is written – and another message from the קְרִי – the way the word is read. In this שִׁיעוּר, the גְּמָרָא will have an example of a קְרִי and כְּתִיב and it will explain the message that we learn out of each one.

קְרִי
HOW WE READ THE פָּסוּק

STEP 35

The גְּמָרָא will reject the רַאֲיָה by explaining that we were comparing two things that cannot really be compared. We were assuming (our הֲוָה אַמִינָא) that the owner does not have to actually pour the liquid on the food in order for it to be הוּכְשַׁר לְקַבֵּל טוּמְאָה. We assumed that the owner's "happiness" about the liquid being poured is all that is needed. In other words, what matters is how the owner feels about it. This is similar to יֵאוּשׁ, which is the way the owner feels about his lost object. We assumed that if we don't consider the owner's feeling to have happened earlier in the case of הוּכְשַׁר לְקַבֵּל טוּמְאָה, we will also not consider it to have happened earlier in the case of יֵאוּשׁ.

The גְּמָרָא will now correct that assumption.

In order to understand the תֵּירוּץ, it is important to pay attention to a detail of the פָּסוּק which we discussed earlier - "וְכִי יֻתַּן מַיִם עַל זֶרַע". We translate this פָּסוּק to mean "And when water will be put on something planted..." This makes it sound as if the owner does not have to have anything to do with the liquid being put on the food. Any way in which the liquid gets there is enough to make the food הוּכְשַׁר לְקַבֵּל טוּמְאָה.

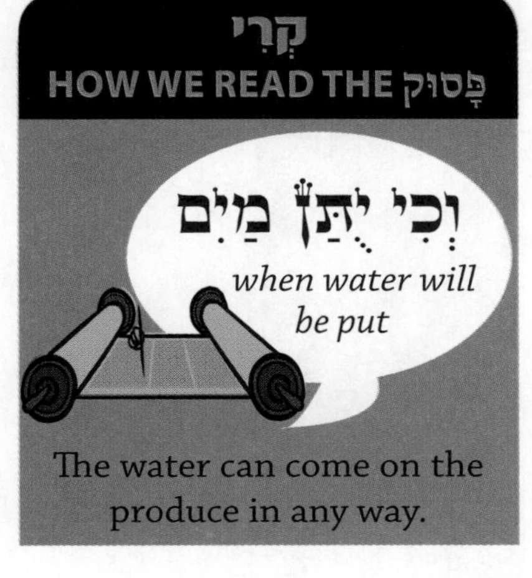

The water can come on the produce in any way.

However, this translation is based only on the קְרִי – the way we read the פָּסוּק. If we look closely at the כְּתִיב – the way the פָּסוּק is written – we notice that the word is not written "יוּתַּן" (with a ו) but rather "יֻתַּן" (without a ו). Based on this spelling, the פָּסוּק can be read as follows: "וְכִי יִתֵּן מַיִם עַל זֶרַע" - "And when he will put water on something planted..." This changes our understanding, as the גְּמָרָא explains:

The owner must pour the water himself.

There it is different,	**שַׁאנִי הָתָם**
because it is WRITTEN [in the פָּסוּק],	**דִּכְתִיב**
"When he will put..."	**כִּי יֻתַּן**
[This teaches us that it will not become הוּכְשַׁר לְקַבֵּל טוּמְאָה] until he [actually] puts [the liquid].	**עַד שֶׁיִּתֵּן**

The גְּמָרָא corrects our assumption (with a מַסְקָנָא) by explaining that it is not enough for the owner to simply be happy that water was poured on his produce. Rather, he needs to put it on himself. The produce can only be הוּכְשַׁר לְקַבֵּל טוּמְאָה because of what the owner does, not the way that he feels. Therefore, this case is not at all similar to the case of יֵאוּשׁ and cannot be used as a רַאֲיָה to either שִׁיטָה in our סוּגְיָא.

STEP 36

The גְּמָרָא asks that what we said in the דְּחִיָּה (which will be the target) doesn't seem to work with what the בְּרַיְיתָא taught us (the attack):

If so,	**אִי הָכִי**
[in] the first case [of the בְּרַיְיתָא] also [it should not be included in the rule of כִּי יוּתַּן]!?	**רֵישָׁא נַמִּי**

How can the גְּמָרָא say that the owner has to actually pour the liquid on the produce? In the first case of the בְּרַיְיתָא, dew fell on the produce without the owner pouring it on. Even so, we learned that if the produce still had dew on it when the owner was happy, it is הוּכְשַׁר לְקַבֵּל טוּמְאָה. It seems that the גְּמָרָא's statement (that the owner has to be the one to pour the liquid) cannot be correct!?

אלו מציאות
פרק שני
בבא מציעא

 |

STEP 37

The גְּמָרָא answers the קֻשְׁיָא by explaining that we were misunderstanding what was meant in the דְחִיָּה. We were assuming that the דְחִיָּה meant that the owner had to be the one to actually pour the liquid on the produce. The correct understanding of the דְחִיָּה is based on the way that רַב פָּפָּא explained the פָּסוּק of כִּי יֻתַּן:

There [the reason is]	הָתָם
like רַב פָּפָּא [taught];	כִּדְרַב פָּפָּא
because רַב פָּפָּא asked a contradiction:	דְּרַב פָּפָּא רָמֵי
It is WRITTEN [in the פָּסוּק] כִּי יִתֵּן – *when he will put,*	כְּתִיב כִּי יִתֵּן
and we READ [the פָּסוּק] כִּי יוּתַּן – *when it will be put?*	וּקְרֵינָן כִּי יוּתַּן
How is this [answered]?	הָא כֵּיצַד
We need "when it was put"	בְּעִינָן כִּי יוּתַּן
[to be] similar to "when he will put."	דּוּמְיָא דְּכִי יִתֵּן
Just like "he will put"	מַה יִתֵּן
[is] with knowledge,	לְדַעַת
so too, "when it was put"	אַף כִּי יוּתַּן
[it] also has to be with [the owner's] knowledge.	נַמִּי לְדַעַת

רַב פָּפָּא explains that the owner does not need to pour the liquid on the produce, but he must know that it has been poured (before it dries up). When the גְּמָרָא said (in the דְחִיָּה) that the owner has to put the liquid, it really meant that the owner has to know that the liquid was poured - the same way he would know about the pouring if he had done it himself.

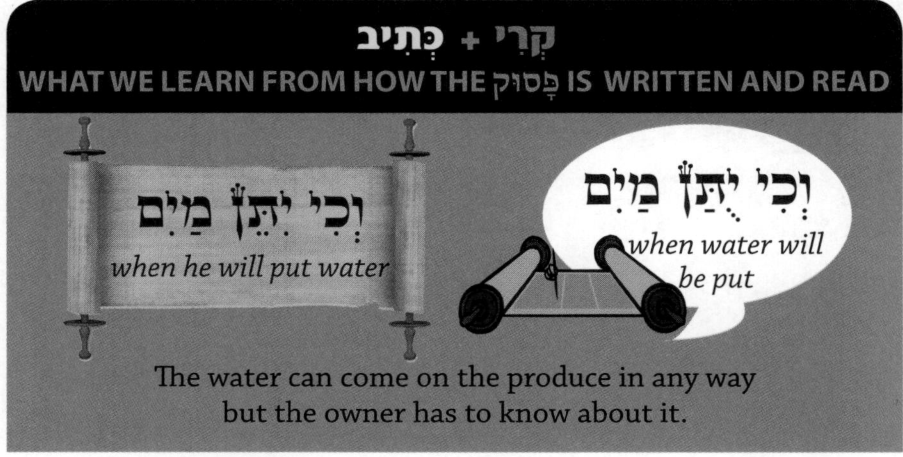

With this new understanding of the דְחִיָּה, we no longer have a קֻשְׁיָא from the first case of the בְּרַיְיתָא. In that case, the owner knew about the dew and was happy. For that reason, it was as if he poured it himself.

שיעור כא Review

PUT IT ALL TOGETHER:

1. Read, translate and explain the following גְּמָרָא.

תָּא שְׁמַע
יעוֹדֵהוּ הַטַּל עֲלֵיהֶן וְשָׂמַח הֲרֵי זֶה °בְּכִי יוּתַּן נִגְּבוּ אַף עַל פִּי שֶׁשָּׂמַח

אֵינָן בְּכִי יוּתַּן טַעְמָא מַאי לַאו מִשּׁוּם דְּלָא
אַמְרִינָן כֵּיוָן דְּאִיגַּלְאִי מִילְּתָא דְּהַשְׁתָּא נִיחָא
לֵיהּ מֵעִיקָּרָא נַמִּי נִיחָא לֵיהּ שַׁאנִי הָתָם
דִּכְתִיב כִּי יִתֵּן עַד שֶׁיִּתֵּן אִי הָכֵי רֵישָׁא
נַמִּי הָתָם *כִּדְרַב פָּפָּא דְּרַב פָּפָּא רָמֵי כְּתִיב
כִּי יִתֵּן וְקָרֵינָן כִּי יוּתַּן הָא כֵּיצַד בְּעֵינָן כִּי
יוּתַּן דּוּמְיָא דְּכִי יִתֵּן מַה יִתֵּן לְדַעַת אַף כִּי
יוּתַּן נַמִּי לְדַעַת

2. What has to happen to produce in order for it to become הוּכְשַׁר לְקַבֵּל טוּמְאָה? ______

____

3. According to the בְּרַיְיתָא, if dew falls on produce and the owner is happy about it, it is הוּכְשַׁר לְקַבֵּל טוּמְאָה if ______________________. However, it is not הוּכְשַׁר לְקַבֵּל טוּמְאָה if ________________.

4. Explain how the גְּמָרָא compares a הֲלָכָה in this בְּרַיְיתָא to the case of יֵאוּשׁ שֶׁלֹּא מִדַּעַת. ______

____

____

5. Please fill in the chart based on the רַאֲיָה (Step 34) and דְּחִיָּה of this שִׁיעוּר.

The Object	
The Support	
The הֲוָה אַמִינָא	
The מַסְקָנָא	

6. Please fill in the chart based on the קֻשְׁיָא and תֵּירוּץ of this שִׁיעוּר.

The Target	
The Attack	
The הֲוָה אַמִינָא	
The מַסְקָנָא	

7. How does רַב פָּפָּא explain why the word is written כִּי יִתֵּן but we read it כִּי יוּתַּן? ______

____

8. AT THE END OF THE שִׁיעוּר - what have we successfully proven? (circle one)
a. the שִׁיטָה of אַבַּיֵי b. the שִׁיטָה of רָבָא c. nothing

VOCABULARY REVIEW:

תְּיוּבְתָּא ______________________

כַּוָּותֵיהּ ______________________

שַׁאנִי ______________________

רָמֵי ______________________

לְהוּ ______________________

לֵיהּ ______________________

IDENTIFY THE STEPS:

BE SURE TO INCLUDE EVERY WORD.

תָּא שְׁמַע
ʾעוֹדֵהוּ הַטַּל עֲלֵיהֶן וְשָׂמַח הֲרֵי זֶה °בְּכִי יוּתַּן נִגְבּוּ אַף עַל פִּי שֶׁשָּׂמַח
אֵינָן בְּכִי יוּתַּן טַעְמָא מַאי לַאו מִשּׁוּם דְּלָא
אַמְרִינַן כֵּיוָן דְּאִיגַּלַּאי מִילְּתָא דְּהַשְׁתָּא נִיחָא
לֵיהּ מֵעִיקָּרָא נַמִּי נִיחָא לֵיהּ שַׁאנִי הָתָם
דִּכְתִיב כִּי יִתֵּן עַד שֶׁיִּתֵּן אִי הָכִי רֵישָׁא
נַמִּי הָתָם *כִּדְרַב פָּפָּא דְּרַב פָּפָּא רָמֵי כְּתִיב
כִּי יִתֵּן וְקָרֵינַן כִּי יוּתַּן הָא כֵּיצַד בְּעֵינָן כִּי
יוּתַּן דּוּמְיָא דְּכִי יִתֵּן ᵃמַה יִתֵּן לְדַעַת אַף כִּי
יוּתַּן נַמִּי לְדַעַת

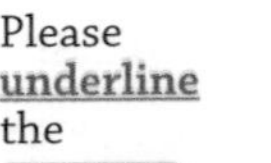
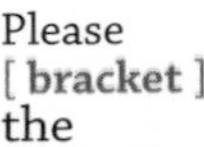

Please (parenthesize) the

Please underline the

Please [bracket] the

Please box the

MATCHING:

_____ 1. Object of the רַאֲיָה

_____ 2. What is written in the פָּסוּק

_____ 3. How we read the פָּסוּק

_____ 4. He asked a סְתִירָה

_____ 5. The case in which dew makes the food ready to accept טוּמְאָה

_____ 6. The case in which dew doesn't make the food ready to accept טוּמְאָה

_____ 7. Step 34 of the סוּגְיָא

_____ 8. Step 35 of the סוּגְיָא

_____ 9. Step 36 of the סוּגְיָא

_____ 10. Step 37 of the סוּגְיָא

א. רַב פָּפָּא

ב. נִגְבּוּ

ג. עוֹדֵהוּ הַטַּל עֲלֵיהֶן וְשָׂמַח

ד. כִּי יִתֵּן

ה. כִּי יוּתַּן

ו. יֵאוּשׁ שֶׁלֹּא מִדַּעַת לָא הֲוֵי יֵאוּשׁ

ז. קֻשְׁיָא

ח. רַאֲיָה

ט. תֵּירוּץ

י. דְחִיָּה

STEP 38

The גְּמָרָא attempts one final proof:

ראיה #12 FOURTH PROOF FOR THE שיטה OF אביי

Come and hear [a proof]:	תָּא שְׁמַע

This proof is not from a בְּרַיְיתָא. Rather, it is from a teaching of רַבִּי יוֹחָנָן, who was one of the very early אֲמוֹרָאִים. Because of his greatness and the fact that he was so close to the time of the תַּנָּאִים, the גְּמָרָא often assumes that אֲמוֹרָאִים of later generations would not argue with him. Therefore, his teachings can be used as a רְאָיָה.

Before we try to understand the proof, we will learn this teaching of רַבִּי יוֹחָנָן and know it well (just like we do when the proof is from a בְּרַיְיתָא).

שיעור ח — כא. lines 2-14

At the beginning of our סוּגְיָא (in שִׁיעוּר ח), we learned the following:

[If the object was swept away] in the high-tide of the sea	בְּזוּטוֹ שֶׁל יָם
or in the overflow of a river,	וּבִשְׁלוּלִיתוֹ שֶׁל נָהָר
even though	אע״ג (אַף עַל גַּב)
it has a סִימָן,	דְּאִית בֵּיהּ סִימָן
the תּוֹרָה has permitted [the finder to keep] it	רַחֲמָנָא שַׁרְיֵיהּ
as we will need to say later on [in our סוּגְיָא].	כְּדִבְעֵינַן לְמֵימַר לְקַמָּן

Now, רַבִּי יוֹחָנָן will finally explain how we see in the תּוֹרָה that an object that has been washed away may be kept by the finder:

Come and hear [a proof]:	ת״ש
That רַבִּי יוֹחָנָן said	דְּא״ר יוֹחָנָן
in the name of רַבִּי יִשְׁמָעֵאל בֶּן יְהוֹצָדָק:	מִשּׁוּם רַבִּי יִשְׁמָעֵאל בֶּן יְהוֹצָדָק
How do we know	מִנַּיִן
that a lost object which was swept away by a river	לַאֲבֵידָה שֶׁשְּׁטָפָהּ נָהָר
that it is permitted [for the finder to keep it]?	שֶׁהִיא מוּתֶּרֶת

רַבִּי יוֹחָנָן will now quote a פָּסוּק and then teach us a דְּרָשָׁה on the פָּסוּק that is the source for this הֲלָכָה.

First, the פָּסוּק:

Because it is written [in the פָּסוּק],	דִּכְתִיב
"And so you should do for his donkey (return it)	וְכֵן תַּעֲשֶׂה לַחֲמוֹרוֹ
and so you should do for his garment (return it)	וְכֵן תַּעֲשֶׂה לְשִׂמְלָתוֹ
and so you should do for any lost object of your brother	וְכֵן תַּעֲשֶׂה לְכָל אֲבֵידַת אָחִיךָ
that was lost from him	אֲשֶׁר תֹּאבַד מִמֶּנּוּ
and you have found it."	וּמְצָאתָהּ

Now, the דְּרָשָׁה (the דְּרָשָׁה is focused on the word מִמֶּנּוּ - from him):

[The only objects that you must return are] the ones that lost from him (the owner)	מִי שֶׁאֲבוּדָה הֵימֶנּוּ
and findable by other people.	וּמְצוּיָה אֵצֶל כָּל אָדָם
This excludes this [case of something swept away by the river]	יָצְאתָה זוֹ
because it is lost from him (the owner)	שֶׁאֲבוּדָה מִמֶּנּוּ
and is not findable by other people.	וְאֵינָהּ מְצוּיָה אֵצֶל כָּל אָדָם

רַבִּי יוֹחָנָן explains that the פָּסוּק teaches us that if an object is lost in such a way that no one can get it (for example, a river washed it away), when someone eventually finds it, he does not have to return it. This applies whether the object had a סִימָן or not.

כב: lines 8-20
Continued

Now, the גְּמָרָא will explain how this proves the הֲלָכָה in a case of יֵאוּשׁ שֶׁלֹּא מִדַּעַת:

And the case in which it is forbidden [to keep it]	וְאִיסוּרָא
[must be] similar to the case in which it is permitted [to keep it].	דּוּמְיָא דְּהֶיתֵּירָא
Just like the case in which it is permitted [to keep it] (because it was lost from all people),	מַה הֶיתֵּירָא
whether it has a סִימָן	בֵּין דְּאִית בָּהּ סִימָן
or whether it doesn't have a סִימָן	וּבֵין דְּלֵית בָּהּ סִימָן
[either way] it is permitted,	שָׁרָא
so too, the case in which it is forbidden [to keep it] (because it was lost only from the owner),	אַף אִיסוּרָא
whether it has a סִימָן	בֵּין דְּאִית בָּהּ סִימָן
or whether it doesn't have a סִימָן	וּבֵין דְּלֵית בָּהּ סִימָן
[either way] it is forbidden.	אֲסוּרָה

The דְּרָשָׁה of רַבִּי יוֹחָנָן makes it clear that the finder may keep it **whether it has a סִימָן or not!**

רַבִּי יוֹחָנָן compared these two cases. We therefore make a דִּיוּק that the finder must return it **whether it has a סִימָן or not!**

אלו מציאות
פרק שני
בבא מציעא

In the case where the finder may keep the object, it doesn't matter if the object had a סִימָן or not. Therefore, it must be true that when the finder must return the object, it also does not matter whether or not the object had a סִימָן.

This seems strange! Why should a finder have to return an object that has no סִימָן? The only logical explanation for this is that even though there was no סִימָן, the owner was not מְיָאֵשׁ because he did not know that he lost his object. In other words, because it was a case of יֵאוּשׁ שֶׁלֹּא מִדַּעַת, the finder may not keep the object. This proves that יֵאוּשׁ שֶׁלֹּא מִדַּעַת is not considered to be יֵאוּשׁ.

The גְּמָרָא concludes the proof by stating:

This is a disproof of רָבָא!	**תְּיוּבְתָּא דְּרָבָא**

STEP 39

The גְּמָרָא concludes the debate:

[Yes,] it is a disproof [of רָבָא and he has been disproven]!	**תְּיוּבְתָּא**

The גְּמָרָא has concluded that רָבָא is disproven and אַבַּיֵי is correct - יֵאוּשׁ שֶׁלֹּא מִדַּעַת לֹא הֲוֵי יֵאוּשׁ!

STEP 40

The גְּמָרָא also concludes by giving us a rule of what the הֲלָכָה is in the many times that רָבָא and אַבַּיֵי argue:

And [in cases in which רָבָא and אַבַּיֵי disagree,] the הֲלָכָה follows אַבַּיֵי	**וְהִלְכְתָא כְּוָותֵיהּ דְּאַבַּיֵי**
in the cases that are abbreviated as יע״ל קג״ם.	**בְּיע״ל קג״ם**

רָבָא and אַבַּיֵי argue many times throughout שַׁ״ס. In most of those arguments, the הֲלָכָה follows the שִׁיטָה of רָבָא. There are only six times when אַבַּיֵי wins the debate and the הֲלָכָה follows his שִׁיטָה. The גְּמָרָא created the acronym (abbreviation) of יע״ל קג״ם to remember those six cases. Many of those cases are long and complicated, so we will not discuss what each one is. But we will list the names of the six times that the הֲלָכָה follows the שִׁיטָה of אַבַּיֵי:

VOCABULARY REVIEW:

נִינְהוּ ____________	כַּוָּותֵיהּ ____________
אַלְמָא ____________	מַאי ____________
תְּיוּבְתָּא ____________	אַמַּאי ____________

PUT IT ALL TOGETHER:

ת"ש *דְּא"ר יוֹחָנָן מִשּׁוּם
*רַבִּי יִשְׁמָעֵאל בֶּן יְהוֹצָדָק ׳מִנַּיִן לַאֲבֵידָה
שֶׁשְּׁטָפָהּ נָהָר שֶׁהִיא מוּתֶּרֶת דִּכְתִיב °וְכֵן
תַּעֲשֶׂה לַחֲמוֹרוֹ וְכֵן תַּעֲשֶׂה לְשִׂמְלָתוֹ וְכֵן
תַּעֲשֶׂה לְכָל אֲבֵידַת אָחִיךָ אֲשֶׁר תֹּאבַד מִמֶּנּוּ
וּמְצָאתָהּ מִי שֶׁאֲבוּדָה הֵימֶנּוּ וּמְצוּיָה אֵצֶל
כָּל אָדָם יָצְאתָה זוֹ שֶׁאֲבוּדָה מִמֶּנּוּ וְאֵינָהּ
מְצוּיָה אֵצֶל כָּל אָדָם וְאִיסּוּרָא דּוּמְיָא דְּהֶיתֵּירָא
מַה הֶיתֵּירָא בֵּין דְּאִית בָּהּ סִימָן וּבֵין דְּלֵית
בָּהּ סִימָן שָׁרָא אַף אִיסּוּרָא בֵּין דְּאִית בָּהּ
סִימָן וּבֵין דְּלֵית בָּהּ סִימָן אֲסוּרָה תְּיוּבְתָּא
דְּרָבָא תְּיוּבְתָּא *וְהִלְכְתָא כַּוָּותֵיהּ דְּאַבַּיֵי
°בְּיע"ל קג"ם

1. Read, translate and explain the following גְּמָרָא.

2. How does the תּוֹרָה teach us that the finder may keep an object which has been swept away by a river? ____________
____
____

3. Please fill in the chart based on the רַאֲיָה of this שִׁיעוּר.

The Object	
The Support	

4. What is the first מַסְקָנָא of the גְּמָרָא (Step 39)? ____________

5. What is the second מַסְקָנָא of the גְּמָרָא (Step 40)? ____________
____

6. At the end of the שִׁיעוּר – what have we successfully proven? (circle one)
a. the שִׁיטָה of אַבַּיֵי b. the שִׁיטָה of רָבָא c. nothing

IDENTIFY THE STEPS:

BE SURE TO INCLUDE EVERY WORD.

Please (parenthesize) the רַאֲיָה

Please underline the first מַסְקָנָא

Please [bracket] the second מַסְקָנָא

ת"ש *דְּא"ר יוֹחָנָן מִשּׁוּם
*רַבִּי יִשְׁמָעֵאל בֶּן יְהוֹצָדָק ג מִנַּיִן לַאֲבֵידָה
שֶׁשְּׁטָפָהּ נָהָר שֶׁהִיא מוּתֶּרֶת דִּכְתִיב °וְכֵן
תַּעֲשֶׂה לַחֲמוֹרוֹ וְכֵן תַּעֲשֶׂה לְשִׂמְלָתוֹ וְכֵן
תַּעֲשֶׂה לְכָל אֲבֵידַת אָחִיךָ אֲשֶׁר תֹּאבַד מִמֶּנּוּ
וּמְצָאתָהּ מִי שֶׁאֲבוּדָה הֵימֶנּוּ וּמְצוּיָה אֵצֶל
כָּל אָדָם יָצְאתָה זוֹ שֶׁאֲבוּדָה מִמֶּנּוּ וְאֵינָהּ
מְצוּיָה אֵצֶל כָּל אָדָם וְאִיסּוּרָא דּוּמְיָא דְּהֶיתֵּירָא
מַה הֶיתֵּירָא בֵּין דְּאִית בָּהּ סִימָן וּבֵין דְּלֵית
בָּהּ סִימָן שָׁרֵא אַף אִיסּוּרָא בֵּין דְּאִית בָּהּ
סִימָן וּבֵין דְּלֵית בָּהּ סִימָן אֲסוּרָה תְּיוּבְתָּא
דְּרָבָא תְּיוּבְתָּא *וְהִלְכְתָא כְּוָותֵיהּ דְּאַבַּיֵי
°בְּיע"ל קג"ם

MATCHING:

______	1. Object of the רַאֲיָה	א. מִמֶּנּוּ
______	2. Support of the רַאֲיָה	ב. רָבָא
______	3. The word that tells us that he can keep a swept-away object	ג. יע"ל קג"ם
______	4. Whom we usually hold like when these אֲמוֹרָאִים argue	ד. יֵאוּשׁ שֶׁלֹּא מִדַּעַת לֹא הָוֵי יֵאוּשׁ
______	5. Whom the הֲלָכָה follows in this מַחֲלוֹקֶת	ה. אַף אִיסּוּרָא בֵּין דְּאִית בָּהּ סִימָן וּבֵין דְּלֵית בָּהּ סִימָן אֲסוּרָה
______	6. When the הֲלָכָה follows the שִׁיטָה of אַבַּיֵי	ו. אַבַּיֵי

STEP 41

Now that it has been settled that יֵאוּשׁ שֶׁלֹּא מִדַּעַת is not considered יֵאוּשׁ, the גְּמָרָא will discuss something that was commonly done by most people.

רַב אַחָא בְּרֵיהּ דְּרָבָא* said to רַב אַשִׁי,	**א"ל רַב אַחָא בְּרֵיהּ דְּרָבָא לְרַב אַשִׁי**
Now that רָבָא has been disproven,	**וְכִי מֵאַחַר דְּאִיתּוֹתַב רָבָא**
these wind-blown dates	**הָנֵי תַּמְרֵי דְּזִיקָא**
how do we eat them [without the owner's permission]?	**הֵיכִי אַכְלִינָן לְהוּ**

It was commonly accepted that when someone would walk by a field and find dates on the ground which had been blown off their trees, he may take them and eat them. However, it seems very unlikely that the owner knew that the dates had fallen. Therefore, we must assume that he was not מְיָאֵשׁ. Now that we have proven that יֵאוּשׁ שֶׁלֹּא מִדַּעַת is not considered יֵאוּשׁ, it seems that the finder should not be allowed to take them!

STEP 42

רַב אַשִׁי explains that the owner was actually מְיָאֵשׁ:

[רַב אַשִׁי] said to [רַב אַחָא בְּרֵיהּ דְּרָבָא],	**אָמַר לֵיהּ**
Since there are disgusting insects and creeping crawlers	**כֵּיוָן דְּאִיכָּא שְׁקָצִים וּרְמָשִׂים**
that eat them,	**דְּקָא אַכְלֵי לְהוּ**
[the owner] is מְיָאֵשׁ on them from the beginning.	**מֵעִיקָּרָא יָאוּשֵׁי מְיָאֵשׁ מִנַּיְיהוּ**

The owner of the field is מְיָאֵשׁ on any dates that will fall from his trees, even before they actually fall. For this reason, the finder may keep them.

*The translation of רַב אַחָא בְּרֵיהּ דְּרָבָא is "רַב אַחָא the son of רָבָא." However, in order for the reading of the גְּמָרָא to flow well, we can simply read it as one long name, the same way we read the names רַבִּי שִׁמְעוֹן בַּר יוֹחַאי or רַבָּן שִׁמְעוֹן בֶּן גַּמְלִיאֵל.

STEP 43

רַב אַחָא בְּרֵיהּ דְּרָבָא now seeks to clarify some details of this הֲלָכָה.

Even though most of the owners may be מְיָאֵשׁ in advance, there may be some owners who cannot be מְיָאֵשׁ in advance.

If the owner of a field dies, his children (the orphans) will inherit the field and become the new owners. If these children are still young, the owners of the field will not yet be בַּר מִצְוָה. The הֲלָכָה is that children who are not yet בַּר מִצְוָה do not have the right to give away what belongs to them. רַב אַחָא בְּרֵיהּ דְּרָבָא wants to know whether we need to be concerned that the owner of the field is an orphan (who is not בַּר מִצְוָה):

[If the owners were] orphans	**יַתְמֵי**
who are not able to give up their rights [to the dates],	**דְּלַאו בְּנֵי מְחִילָה נִינְהוּ**
what [is the הֲלָכָה]?	**מַאי**

STEP 44

רַב אַשִׁי answers:

[רַב אַשִׁי] said to [רַב אַחָא בְּרֵיהּ דְּרָבָא],	**אֲמַר לֵיהּ**
An entire valley	**בַּאגָא**
we don't assume it to be the land of orphans.	**בְּאַרְעָא דְּיַתְמֵי לֹא מַחְזְקִינַן**

רַב אַשִׁי explains that we don't need to be concerned that the owners might be orphans.

STEP 45

רַב אַחָא בְּרֵיהּ דְּרָבָא questions further:

If it is already known [that the land belongs to orphans],	**מוּחְזָק וְעוֹמֵד**
what [is the הֲלָכָה]?	**מַאי**

If we know that the owners of the field are orphans, can we still keep the dates?

STEP 46

Before רַב אַשִׁי has a chance to answer the last question, רַב אַחָא בְּרֵיהּ דְּרָבָא asks one more:

If the dates are surrounded [by stone walls where insects and rodents can't get to them],	**כְּרַכְתָּא**
what [is the הֲלָכָה]?	**מַאי**

If the dates are protected from rodents and insects, can we still assume that the owner was מְיָאֵשׁ on these dates, or must we leave them in case the owner was not מְיָאֵשׁ?

STEP 47

רַב אַשִׁי answers both of the last two שְׁאֵלוֹת:

[רַב אַשִׁי] said to [רַב אַחָא בְּרֵיהּ דְּרָבָא],	**אֲמַר לֵיהּ**
They are forbidden [for someone to take them].	**אֲסִירָן:**

רַב אַשִׁי answers that if we know that the field is owned by orphans or if the dates are protected from rodents and insects, the finder may not take them.

Let's complete the following flow chart of the last nine steps of the סוּגְיָא (starting from the middle of שִׁיעוּר כ״ב).

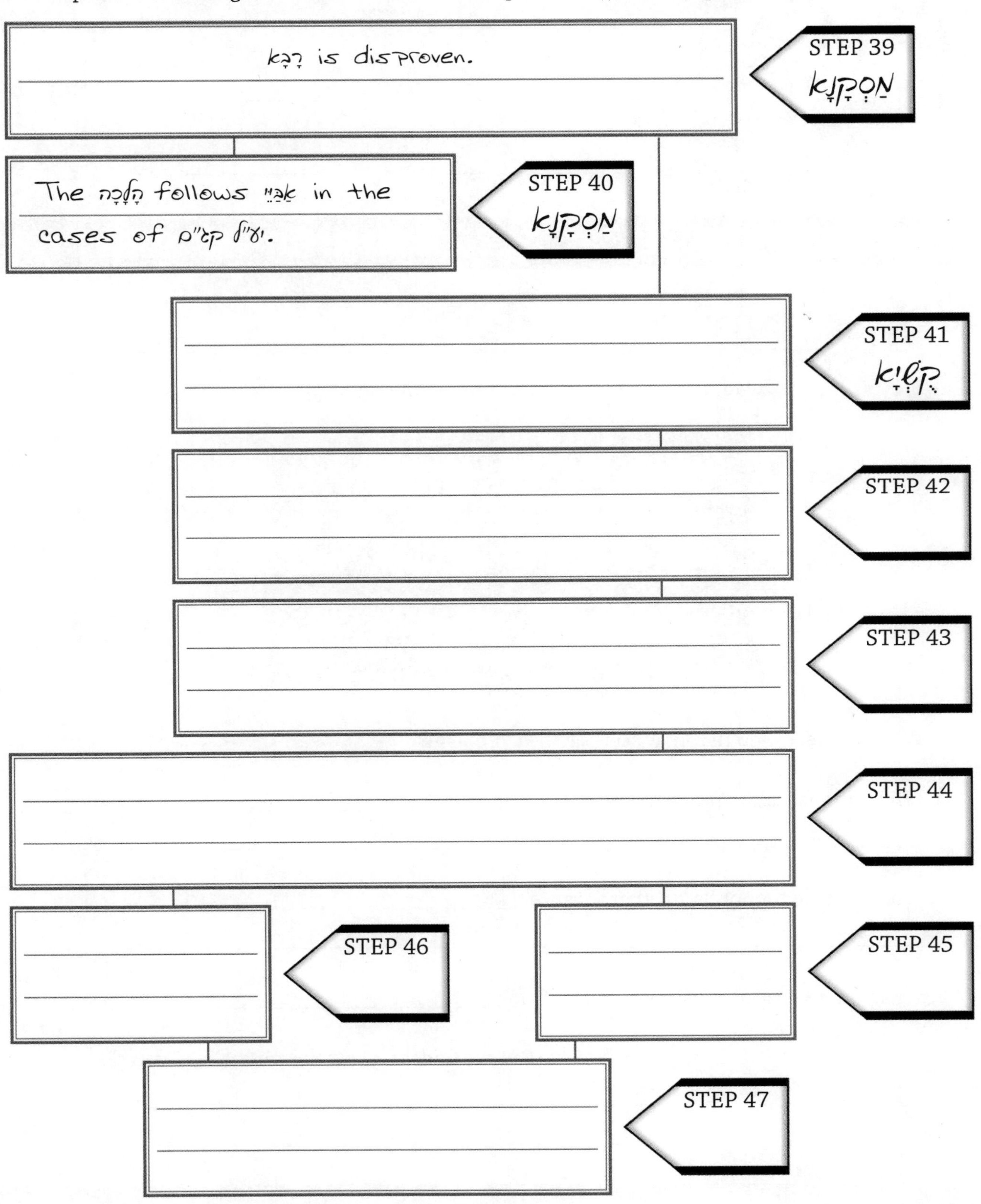

VOCABULARY REVIEW:

סָבַר	____________	אַלְמָא	____________
שְׁמַעְתָּא	____________	עִידְנָא	____________
אִי סָלְקָא דַעְתָּךְ	____________	נִינְהוּ	____________

PUT IT ALL TOGETHER:

1. Read, translate and explain the following גְּמָרָא.

א"ל רַב אַחָא בְּרֵיהּ דְּרָבָא לְרַב
אַשִׁי וְכִי מֵאַחַר דְּאִיתּוֹתַב רָבָא הַנֵּי תַּמְרֵי
דְּזִיקָא הֵיכִי אַכְלִינָן לְהוּ אָמַר לֵיהּ [ג]כֵּיוָן
[א]דְּאִיכָּא שְׁקָצִים וּרְמָשִׂים דְּקָא אַכְלֵי לְהוּ
מֵעִיקָּרָא יֵאוּשֵׁי מְיָאֵשׁ מִנַּיְיהוּ *יַתְמֵי דְּלַאו
בְּנֵי מְחִילָה נִינְהוּ מַאי אָמַר לֵיהּ בַּאֲגָא
בְּאַרְעָא דְּיַתְמֵי לֹא מַחְזְקִינָן מוּחְזָק וְעוֹמֵד
מַאי כְּרַכְתָּא מַאי אָמַר לֵיהּ [י]אֲסִירָן:

2. What did people do that now seems to be a problem? ____________

3. Why is it not really a problem? ____________

____

4. Which people cannot be מְיָאֵשׁ in advance? ____________

____

5. What don't we need to assume about a field? ____________

6. In which two cases may the finder not eat the wind-blown dates?

א. ____________

ב. ____________

IDENTIFY THE STEPS:
BE SURE TO INCLUDE EVERY WORD.

א"ל רַב אַחָא בְּרֵיהּ דְּרָבָא לְרַב
אַשִׁי וְכִי מֵאַחַר דְּאִיתוֹתַב רָבָא הָנֵי תַּמְרֵי
דְּזִיקָא הֵיכִי אַכְלִינָן לְהוּ אָמַר לֵיהּ [ג]כֵּיוָן
[א]דְּאִיכָּא שְׁקָצִים וּרְמָשִׂים דְּקָא אַכְלֵי לְהוּ
מֵעִיקָּרָא יָאוּשֵׁי מְיָאֵשׁ מִנַּיְיהוּ *יַתְמֵי דְּלַאו
בְּנֵי מְחִילָה נִינְהוּ מַאי אָמַר לֵיהּ בַּאגָּא
בְּאַרְעָא דְּיַתְמֵי לֹא מַחְזְקִינָן מוּחְזָק וְעוֹמֵד
מַאי כְּרַכְתָּא מַאי אָמַר לֵיהּ [י]אֲסִירָן:

Please (parenthesize) the קֻשְׁיָא

Please underline the first תֵּירוּץ

Please [bracket] the first שְׁאֵלָה [Step 43]

Please double underline the first תְּשׁוּבָה [Step 44]

Please box the second שְׁאֵלָה [Step 45]

Please circle the third שְׁאֵלָה [Step 46]

Please put "quotes" around the second תְּשׁוּבָה [Step 47]

MATCHING:

_____	1. What seems like a problem	א. דְּלַאו בְּנֵי מְחִילָה נִינְהוּ
_____	2. Why it's not really a problem	ב. בַּאגָּא בְּאַרְעָא דְּיַתְמֵי
_____	3. Why orphans are different	ג. תַּמְרֵי דְּזִיקָא אַכְלִינָן לְהוּ
_____	4. What we don't assume	ד. מוּחְזָק וְעוֹמֵד
_____	5. First case that the dates are forbidden	ה. כְּרַכְתָּא
_____	6. Second case that the dates are forbidden	ו. מֵעִיקָּרָא יָאוּשֵׁי מְיָאֵשׁ מִנַּיְיהוּ

VOCABULARY WORDS

VOCABULARY WORDS

I.T.G. LESSON 1

1	תַּנָּא	חכמים of the משנה (from הלל and שמאי until רבי יהודה הנשיא)
2	אַמוֹרָא	חכמים of the גמרא (from רב and שמואל until רַבִינָא and רַב אַשִׁי)

I.T.G. LESSON 2

3	עַמּוּד	one side of a page
4	דַּף	a page (Both sides)
5	סוּגְיָא	a discussion in the גמרא about a particular topic
6	שַׁקְלָא וְטַרְיָא	the back and forth discussion of the גמרא. (Lit. Give and Take)

I.T.G. LESSON 3

7	מֵימְרָא	a statement
8	רְאָיָה	a proof (usually proves a statement of an אמורא either based on logic or the words of a תנא)
9	דְּחִיָּה	a "disproof" of a ראיה

I.T.G. LESSON 4

10	קֻשְׁיָא	a question that something doesn't make sense
11	תֵּירוּץ	an answer to a קשיא
12	שְׁאֵלָה	a question that asks for information
13	תְּשׁוּבָה	an answer to a שאלה

I.T.G. LESSON 5

14	הֲוָא אַמִינָא	the assumption of the גמרא (Lit. I would have said)
15	מַסְקָנָא	the conclusion of the 1: גמרא. where the הוא אמינא is corrected 2: a step in the גמרא where the גמרא gives a final decision
16	בְּרַיְיתָא	a teaching of a תנא that is not in the משנה
17	סְבָרָא	a logical reason

I.T.G. LESSON 6

18	הֵיכִי	how
19	הָכִי	like this/so
20	הֵיכָא	where
21	הָכָא	here
22	הָתָם	there

I.T.G. LESSON 7

23	דָּמִי	similar/compared
24	הֵיכִי דָּמִי	how was it? (lit. how is it compared)
25	נַמִּי	also

I.T.G. LESSON 8

26	טוּבָא	more
27	בָּצִיר	less
28	דְ	1. because 2. that 3. of

I.T.G. LESSON 9

29	נְפִישׁ	a lot
30	עַסְקִינָן	we are dealing
31	טִירְחָא	bother

I.T.G. LESSON 10

32	הָדַר	return
33	אָתִי	come
34	שָׁקִיל	take

שיעור א

35	לְהוּ	to them/for them
36	לֵיה	to him/for him
37	לָן	to us/for us

שיעור ב

38	בָּעֵי	1. want 2. need 3. ask
39	מַהוּ	what is the דין (law)?
40	טַעֲמָא	reason
41	מַאי	what

שיעור ג

42	מִשּׁוּם	because
43	כֵּיוָן	since
44	דִילְמָא	maybe

שיעור ד

45	כָּל שֶׁכֵּן	certainly
46	טְפֵי	more/extra

שיעור ה

47	תֵּיקוּ	it will stand [as a שְׁאֵלָה]
48	אִיתְּמַר	it was said

שיעור ו

49	הָוֵי	it is
50	כּוּלֵי עַלְמָא	everyone (lit. the whole world)

VOCABULARY WORDS

שיעור ז		
51	פְּלִיג	Argue/divide
52	מִינֵיהּ	from him
53	אִית\אִיתָא\אִיכָּא	there is
54	לֵית\לֵיתָא\לֵיכָּא	there isn't
55	יָהַב	he gave
שיעור ח		
56	רַחֲמָנָא	ה'/the תורה (lit. The Merciful One)
57	שָׁרֵי	permitted (מותר)
58	לְקַמָּן	later on
59	הַשְׁתָּא	now
60	תָּא שְׁמַע	come and hear [a proof]
שיעור ט		
61	אַמַּאי	why
62	אָזִיל	go/continue
שיעור י		
63	בָּתַר	after
64	נְהִי	granted
שיעור יא		
65	הָנֵי	these
66	הָנָךְ	those
שיעור יב		
67	דוּכְתָּא	a place
68	מֵעִיקָּרָא	originally/ in the beginning
שיעור יג		
69	רֵישָׁא	the beginnig
70	סֵיפָא	the end
שיעור יד		
71	בִּשְׁלָמָא	it is understandable
72	הוֹאִיל	since
שיעור טו		
73	חָזִי	see
74	מַאי אִרְיָא	why [specifically] speak [about]

שיעור טז

75	עִידְנָא	a time
76	אַלִיבָּא	according to

שיעור יז

77	מִסְתַּבְרָא	logical
78	אִי סָלְקָא דַעְתָּךְ	if you would think

שיעור יח

79	אַשְׁכַּח	he found
80	מַר	master/sir

שיעור יט

81	נִיחָא	pleasing
82	מִילְתָא	a matter/thing

שיעור כ

83	שַׁאנִי	different
84	רָמִי	asked a contradiction

שיעור כא

85	תְּיוּבְתָּא	a proof against someone
86	כַּוָותֵיהּ	like him

שיעור כב

87	נִינְהוּ	they are
88	אַלְמָא	we see

שיעור כג

89	סָבַר	he held/ he thought/ he reasoned
90	שְׁמַעְתָּא	a סוגיא